Mastercam® 2020

MILL ESSENTIALS TRAINING TUTORIAL

To order more books:

Call 1-800-529-5517 or

Visit www.emastercam.com or

Contact your Mastercam dealer

Mastercam.
CAD/CAM Systems

Home Learning Edition
Demo Software
DOWNLOAD

HOW TO DOWNLOAD:
Mastercam Home Learning Edition (HLE)
Demo Software

Visit www.**eMastercam**.com/**files**

Click on Mastercam Demo Software
from the categories on the right.

Proceed to download!

Mastercam 2020 Mill Essentials Tutorial

Copyright: 1998 - 2020 In-House Solutions Inc. All rights reserved

Software: Mastercam 2020

Authors: Mariana Lendel

ISBN: 978-1-77146-833-6

Date: May 31, 2019

Notice

In-House Solutions Inc. reserves the right to make improvements to this manual at any time and without notice.

Disclaimer Of All Warranties And Liability

Table Of Contents

Mill Essentials Projects

Tutorial	Geometry Functions	Toolpath Creation
#1	Rectangle. Circle Center Point. Chamfer Entities.	Facing Toolpath. Circle Mill Toolpath. Contour Toolpath. Spot Drill Toolpath. Drill Toolpath. 2D Contour (Chamfer Toolpath).
#2	Rectangle. Rectangular Shapes. Polygon. Fillet Entities. Fillet Chains. Line Endpoints. Trim Divide.	Setup 1 Slot Mill Toolpath. 2D HS Dynamic Mill Toolpath. Contour Toolpath. 2D HS Dynamic Contour Toolpath. Setup 2 Facing Toolpaths.
#3	Polar Arcs. Circle Center Point. Line Tangent. Fillet Entities. Mirror. Arc Tangent to 2 Entities. Trim 3 Entities. Ellipse. Offset. Letters. Bounding Box. Translate.	2D High Speed Area Mill Toolpath. 2D HS Dynamic Mill Toolpath. Pocket with Island Toolpath. Pocket Remachine Toolpath.
#4	Circle Center Point. Line Tangent. Mirror. Arc Tangent. Arc Polar. Trim. Fillets. Rotate. Translate. Solids Extrude. Chamfer.	Setup 1 2D High Speed Area Mill Toolpath. 2D HS Dynamic Mill Toolpath. Transform Toolpath. Drill Toolpath. Contour (Chamfer Toolpath). Setup 2 2D HS Dynamic Mill Toolpath.

Tutorial	Geometry Functions	Toolpath Creation
#5	Import a SolidWorks file. Translate 3D.	Setup 1 - Top Tool Planes. 2D HS Area Mill Toolpath. 2D HS Area Mill Rest Toolpath. Setup 2 - Front Tool Plane. Drill Toolpath. Setup 3 - Left Tool Plane. Slot Mill Toolpath.
#6	Rectangle. Circle Center Point. Arc Tangent to 1 Entity. Line Parallel. Chamfer. Line Polar. Trim.	2D HS Dynamic Mill Toolpath. 2D HS Core Mill Toolpath. 2D HS Blend Mill Toolpath. 2D HS Peel Mill Toolpath.
#7	Circle Center Point. Line Tangent. Line Parallel. Rectangular Shapes. Trim. Fillet Chains. Solids Extrude. Solids Chamfer. Solids Fillet.	2D HS Area Mill Toolpath. Feature Based Drilling Toolpath. 2D HS Area Mill Toolpath. Pocket Toolpath. 2D Contour Toolpath.

OBJECTIVES

♦ Starting Mastercam
♦ The student will learn about the Graphical User Interface.
♦ The student will learn how to navigate through Mastercam.

STEP 1: STARTING MASTERCAM

1.1 For Windows 7

♦ Select the **Start** button.
♦ Select **All Programs** and click on Mastercam 2020.

1.2 For Windows 8

♦ Select the **Start** button.
♦ Click on the drop down arrow to open Apps.
♦ Find and click on Mastercam 2020.

1.3 For Windows 10

♦ Select the **Start** button.
♦ Click on the drop down arrow to open Apps.
♦ Find and click on Mastercam 2020.
♦ To start the software, from Desktop, click on the shortcut icon as shown.

STEP 2: GUI - GRAPHICAL USER INTERFACE

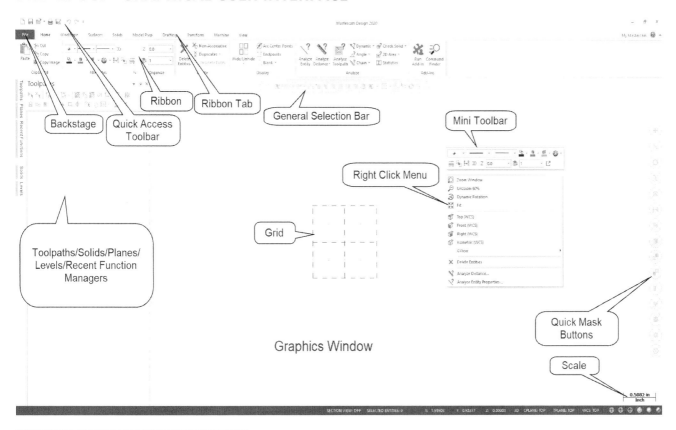

Quick Access Toolbar	**QAT** contains a fully customizable set of functions that can be quickly accessed by the user.
Backstage (File)	Allows you to manage files. You can insert information about files, start a new file, open an existing one or merge files together. You can also save, convert or print files as well as access the help resources.
Tabs	Contains all the functionality within Mastercam.
Ribbon	Displays the commands available for a selected Tab.
Selection Bar	Allows you to set the **AutoCursor** modes and to switch between wireframe or solid selections.
Quick Mask Buttons	Lets you select all entities of a specific type. Clicking on the left side of the button or right side of the button toggles between select all or only.
Right Click Menu	Right click menu allows quick access to functions such as zoom, graphic views or recent functions used. A mini toolbar will also appear that allows you to quickly change the attributes.
Toolpaths/Solids/Planes Manager	Lists the history of the toolpath operations and solids.
Graphics Window	Workspace area in Mastercam where the geometry is displayed.
Scale	Shows you a scale of the object on the screen.
WCS: TOP T/Cplane:	Displays the current **WCS** and **T/Cplane** information.

STEP 3: NAVIGATE THROUGH MASTERCAM

In this step, you will learn how to use the menu functions in Mastercam to create geometry.

3.1 Using the Wireframe tab to select the command to create Line Endpoints

- ♦ Left click on **Wireframe**.
- ♦ Left click on the **Line Endpoints** icon as shown.

- ♦ Once you select Line Endpoints, the Line Endpoints panel appears on the screen as shown.

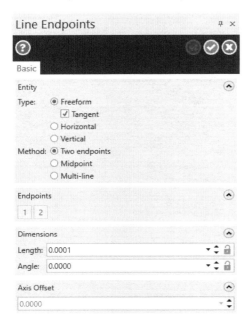

Sketching A Line

- ♦ To sketch a line, left click on two locations on the screen.

Creating A Line Knowing The Endpoint Coordinates

- ♦ To make a line knowing the two endpoint coordinates, select the **AutoCursor Fast Point** icon from the **General Selection** toolbar.

♦ In the coordinates field that opens in the upper left corner enter the coordinates of the first endpoint as shown.

0,1

♦ Press **Enter** to continue.
♦ Select the **AutoCursor Fast Point** icon again and enter in the coordinates of the second endpoint and then press **Enter**.

Creating A Line Knowing An Endpoint, The Length, And The Angle

♦ You can also enter the coordinates of the first endpoint, then enter the **Length** and **Angle** if necessary.
♦ To continue making lines, choose the **OK and Create New Operation** button from the dialog box or press **Enter**.

♦ To exit the current command, select the **OK** button or press the **Esc** button.

♦ To undo the last command, from the **QAT** (**Q**uick **A**ccess **T**oolbar) select the **Undo** button. The Undo button can be used to go back to the beginning of geometry creation or to the last point of the saved file.

Mastercam also has a **Redo** button for your convenience.

Function Prompt

Prompts the user to execute a command.

Example: this prompt is used in the **Line Endpoints** command. Specify the first endpoint

*Note: To find a command, from the **Home** ribbon, select the **Command Finder** icon and type the function name in the field that opens up.*
*For example, to find the **Polygon** command type "polygon" in the text field. From the list, select the desired command.*

STEP 4: SET THE ATTRIBUTES

Mastercam attributes are point style, line style, line thickness, color and levels. Before starting to create geometry, you should set the attributes.

4.1 Attributes Group

Point Style	Displays and sets the system's point style.
Line Style	Displays and sets the system's line style.
Line Width	Displays and sets the current system's line width.
Color	Assigns the current color to wireframe, solid and surface entities. To change the current color, click in the specific color field and select a color from the color pallet. To change an existing geometry color, select the geometry first and then click in the color field and select a color from the color pallet.
Clear Color	When performing a transform function (Xform), Mastercam creates a temporary group from the originals (red) and a result (purple) from the transformed entities. These system groups appear in the Groups dialog box. However, they stay in effect only until you use the Clear Colors function or perform another transform function.
2D / 3D Construction Mode	Toggles between 2D and 3D construction modes. In 2D mode, all geometry is created parallel to the current Cplane at the current system Z depth. In 3D mode, you can work freely in various Z depths, unconstrained by the current system Z depth and Cplane setting.

4.2 Organize Group

Z Depth	Sets the current construction depth. To set this, click the drop down arrow and pick one from the most recently used list or click the Z: label and pick a point in the graphics window to use the Z depth values based on the selected entity.
Level	Sets the main level you want to work with in the graphics window. To change the current working level. Type the level number in the box.

Change The Wireframe Color

♦ Click on the drop down arrow next to the **Wireframe Color** field as shown.
♦ Select the desired color from the dialog box as shown.

Note: Any geometry on your screen will remain in the previous system color. This change will only affect the geometry you create going forward.
To change the color of existing geometry, select the entities first and then click on the drop down arrow next to the Wireframe Color and select the desired color. The same method can be applied for any other attribute that you want to set or change.

STEP 5: MANAGER PANELS

5.1 The Toolpaths Manager

The **Toolpaths Manager** displays all the operations for the current part. You can sort, edit, regenerate, verify and post any operation as shown in Figure: 5.1.1. For more information on the **Toolpaths Manager**, please click on the **Help** icon.

Figure: 5.1.1

♦ The **Toolpaths Manager**, **Solids Manager**, or **Planes Manager** can be hidden to gain more space in the graphics area for creating geometry. Use **Auto Hide** icon to close all **Toolpaths**, **Solids**, **Planes** and **Levels Manager** panels.

◆ The panels will be hidden to the left of the graphics window as shown or at the bottom of the manager as shown previously.

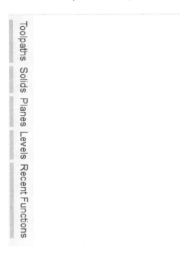

◆ To un-hide them, click on one of the managers to open it and then click again on the Auto Hide icon a shown.

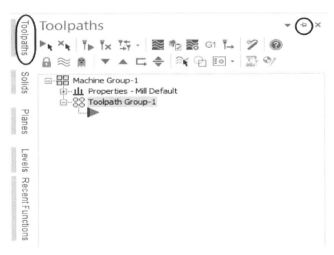

◆ Selecting the **X (Close** icon) instead of the **Auto Hide**, you will close the manager panel. To re-open them, from the **View** tab, select **Toolpaths**, **Solids**, **Planes** or **Levels** as shown.

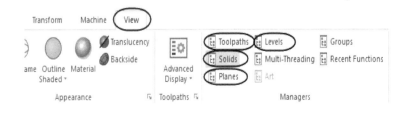

STEP 6: SETTING MASTERCAM TO IMPERIAL

In this step you will learn how to set the imperial system as your default. You will have to select the **Backstage** options and select the system configuration.

6.1 Setting Mastercam to inch for the current session only

Note: You may need to switch Mastercam to run in Inch mode.

File

♦ **Configuration.**
♦ Select the drop down arrow beside **Current** as shown in Figure: 6.1.1 .
♦ Select **mcamxm.config <Inch>** as shown in Figure: 6.1.1.

Figure: 6.1.1

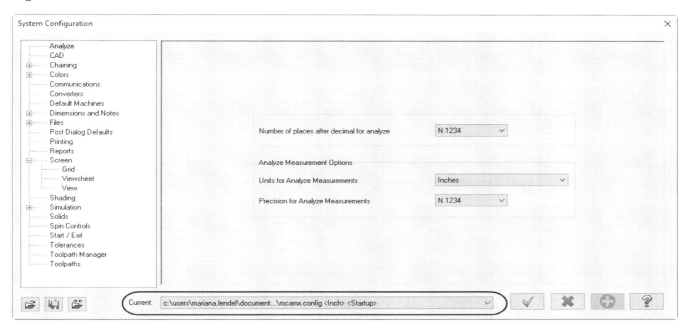

♦ Select the **OK** button to exit the **System Configuration** dialog box.

Note: If you have a drawing on the screen it may ask you to scale the current part to imperial. Choose Yes if you wish to do this.

6.2 Setting Mastercam to imperial as a default

Note: If you wish to always work in Imperial mode, follow these steps to save Imperial as your current configuration file.

File

♦ **Configuration.**
♦ Select **Start/Exit** from the configuration topics.
♦ Select the drop down arrow below **Configuration** in the **Startup** settings area as shown in Figure: 6.2.1
♦ Select **mcamxm.config <Inch>** as shown.

Figure: 6.2.1

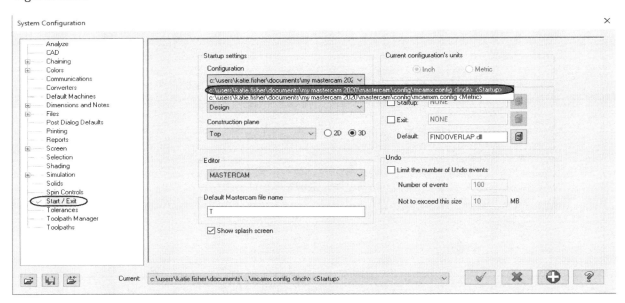

♦ Select the **OK** button to exit the **System Configuration** dialog box.
♦ Mastercam will then prompt you to save these settings to your current configuration file, select **Yes**.

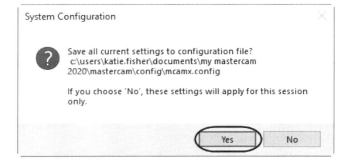

STEP 7: SET THE GRID

Before beginning to create geometry, it is highly recommended to enable the Grid. The grid will show you where the origin is and the orientation of the grid gives you a quick preview of the plane you are working in.

File

♦ **Configuration.**

♦ Select **Screen** from the configuration **Topics**.

♦ Select the plus sign (**+**) beside **Screen** as shown.

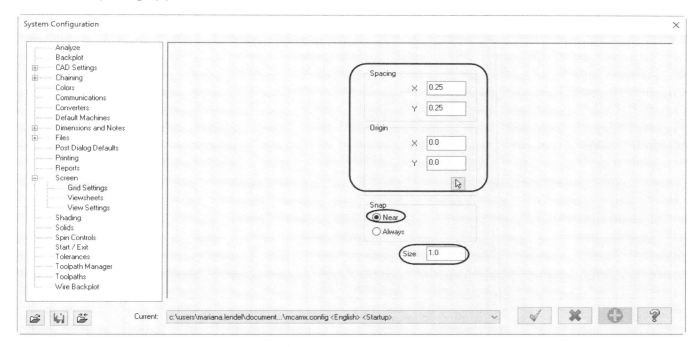

♦ In **Grid Setting**s, change the **Spacing** to **X = 0.25** and **Y = 0.25**.

♦ Set the **Size** to **1.0**.

♦ Choose the **OK** button to exit.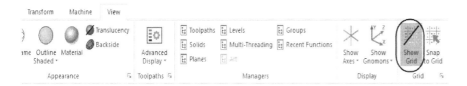

♦ Select the **Yes** button to save the settings in the **System Configuration**.

♦ To see the **Grid** in the graphics window, from the **View** tab, enable **Show Grid** as shown.

♦ The grid should look as shown.

CONVENTIONS USED IN THIS BOOK:

We have attempted to make this manual as uncluttered as possible and provide you with reference information when it is appropriate. It is not intended to be a Reference Guide or all-encompassing user manual.

The Text Styles Used Are The Following:

Standard Text - Represents normal wording needed to provide you the instructions.

STEP 1: STEP TITLES

7.1 Sub step titles

Information about the current step, terms or parameter definitions describing the parameters and description.

Bold Text - Represents menu commands, dialog box settings or other similar items from the screen.

Note: Represents information about the process/step that is important or may require an explanation.

♦ Bulleted text are step by step instructions that are to be followed.

The files used in this book are available for download at http://www.emastercam.com/files/.

MASTERCAM® WORK FLOW

The process to create or import the geometry and to generate a toolpath will be repeated over and over through the tutorials in this book. You will find the process simple and straightforward once you have programmed a few parts. The following is an outline of the process we will follow to create programs:

1. Create or import the part geometry.

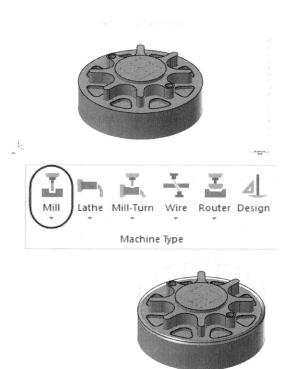

2. Select the Machine type.

3. Define the stock size that your part will be cut from and set tool information.

4. Select a toolpath type such as 2D High Speed Dynamic.

5. Select the geometry of the part you will cut with the different selection options.

6. Fill in the necessary information on the parameter pages that appear for the toolpath type you selected.

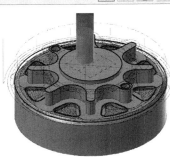

7. Verify the toolpath on your computer screen to confirm the results are as you expected, using Backplot and/or Solid Verify.

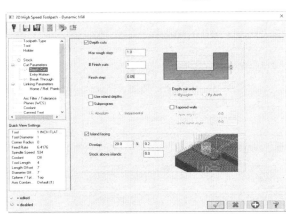

8. Make any changes as required by changing parameters.

9. Regenerate the "Dirty" operation to update the parameter changes.

10. Verify again to make sure the toolpath is correct.

11. Convert the graphical toolpath information into machine code by Post Processing and sending it to the CNC machine.

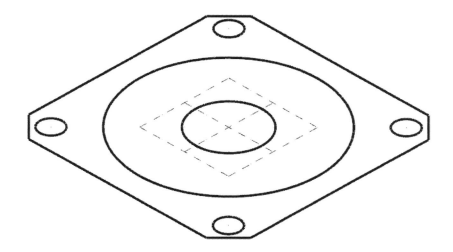

OVERVIEW OF STEPS TAKEN TO CREATE THE PART GEOMETRY:

From Drawing to CAD Model:

◆ The student should examine the drawing on the following page to understand what part is being created in the tutorial.
◆ From the drawing we can decide how to create the geometry in Mastercam.

Create the 2D CAD Model:

◆ The student will create the Top 2D geometry needed to create the toolpaths.
◆ Geometry creation commands such as Rectangle, Circle Center Point, and Chamfer Entities will be used.

TUTORIAL #1 DRAWING

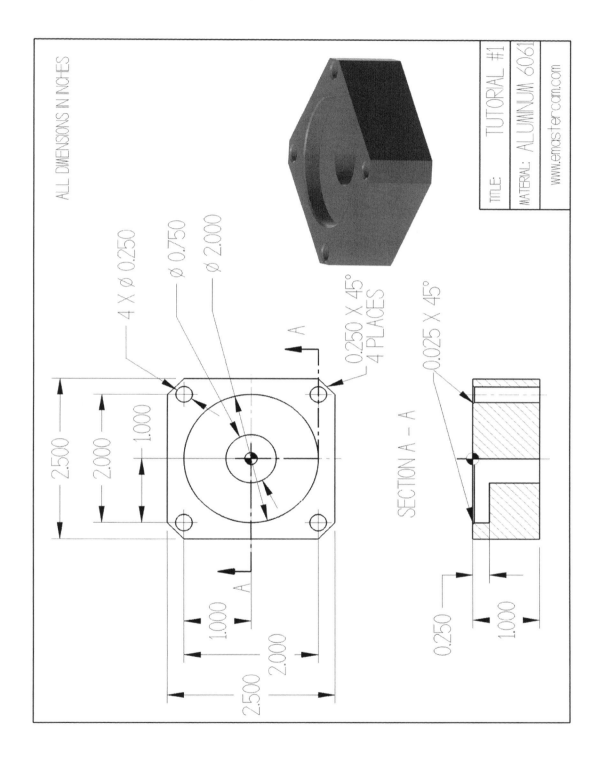

ALL DIMENSIONS IN INCHES

TITLE: TUTORIAL #1
MATERIAL: ALUMINUM 6061
www.emastercam.com

4 X Ø 0.250
Ø 0.750
Ø 2.000

0.250 X 45°
4 PLACES

0.025 X 45°

SECTION A – A

2.500
2.000
1.000

1.000
2.000
2.500

0.250
1.000

STEP 1: SETTING UP THE GRAPHICAL USER INTERFACE

Please refer to the Getting Started section for more info on how to set up the graphical user interface. In this step, you will learn how to hide the manager panels to gain more space in the graphics window.

♦ Use **Auto Hide** icon to hide all **Manager** panels.

♦ The panels will be hidden to the left of the graphics window as shown.

Note: To un-hide them temporally, you can click on one of the Managers to open it as shown.

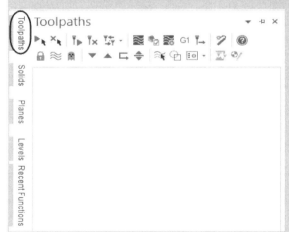

While creating the geometry, keep the Manager panels hidden. This ensures more space in the graphics window for the geometry.

STEP 2: CREATE ONE RECTANGLE

In this step, you will learn how to create a rectangle given the width, the height, and the anchor position. You will create the 2.5" by 2.5" rectangle with the center anchor in the Origin.

Step Preview:

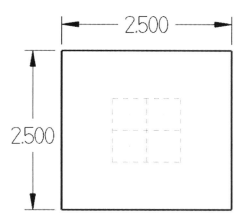

2.1 Create a 2.5" by 2.5" Rectangle

Wireframe

♦ From the **Shapes** group, select **Rectangle**.

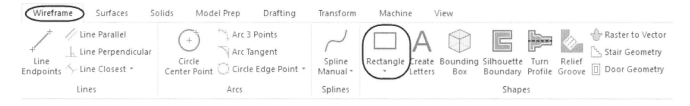

♦ In the **Rectangle** panel, enter the **Width** and **Height** and enable **Anchor to center** as shown.

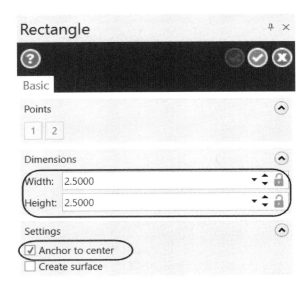

*Note: Make sure that **Create surface** is not selected. **Anchor to center** sets the base point of the rectangle to its center and draws the rectangle outward from the center. **Create surface** creates a surface inside of the rectangle. Surface creation and Surface toolpath are covered in Mill Advanced.*

♦ Select the position of the base point as shown.

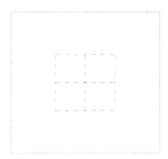

Select the Origin

♦ A preview of the geometry should look as shown.

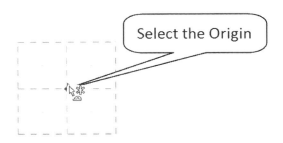

Note: The geometry should appear in cyan blue color which is the color for the live entities. While the rectangle is live, you can adjust the dimensions or select a new base point.

♦ Select the **OK** button to exit the **Rectangle** command.

♦ The geometry should look as shown.

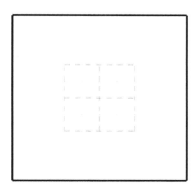

Note: While creating geometry for this tutorial, if you make a mistake, you can undo the last step using the **Undo** icon. You can undo as many steps as needed. If you delete or undo a step by mistake, just use the **Redo** icon. To delete unwanted geometry, select the geometry first and then press **Delete** from the keyboard. To zoom or un-zoom, move the cursor in the center of the geometry and scroll up or down the mouse wheel.

STEP 3: CREATE THE 1/4" DIAMETER CIRCLES

In this step, you will create circles for which you know the diameter and the locations. To use **Circle Center Point**, you need to know the center point and the radius or the diameter of the circle. To complete this step, you will need to know the **Cartesian Coordinate System**. A **Cartesian Coordinate System** is a coordinate system that specifies each point uniquely in a plane by a pair of numerical coordinates, which are the signed distances from the point to two fixed perpendicular directed lines, measured in the same unit of length as shown.

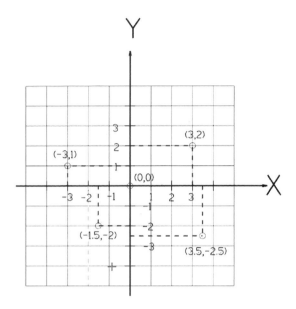

Step Preview:

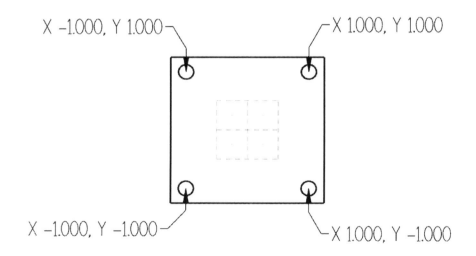

Wireframe

◆ From the **Arcs** group, select **Circle Center Point**.

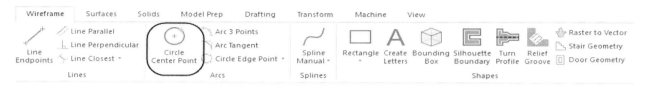

◆ Enter a **Diameter** of **0.25** in the panel as shown.
◆ To create all four circles, click on the locker icon to lock the value.

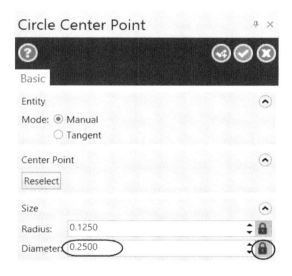

◆ [Enter the center point]: Select the **AutoCursor Fast Point** icon from the **General Selection** toolbar and the field where you can type the coordinates will open at the upper left side of the graphics window as shown.

◆ Type **1, 1** as shown.

*Note: When entering the coordinates for the center point, the first value is the **X** coordinate value, then the **Y** value followed by the **Z** value only if it is different from zero. The coordinate values are separated with commas. You do not need to use the coordinate labels if you enter the values in this order.*

♦ Press **Enter** and the circle will be placed as shown.

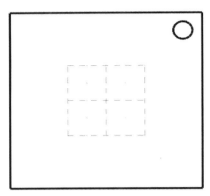

♦ [Enter the center point]: Select the **AutoCursor Fast Point** icon again and enter **1, -1**.
♦ Press **Enter** to place the circle.
♦ [Enter the center point]: Select the **AutoCursor Fast Point** icon again and enter **-1, 1**.
♦ Press **Enter** to place the circle.
♦ [Enter the center point]: Select the **AutoCursor Fast Point** icon again and enter **-1, -1**.
♦ Press **Enter** to place the circle.

♦ Once complete choose the **OK** button to exit the command.
♦ The geometry should look as shown.

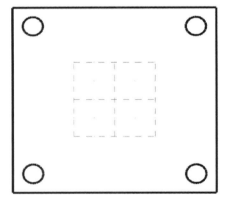

STEP 4: CREATE THE 2.0" AND 0.75" DIAMETER CIRCLES

In this step, you will use the same Circle Center Point to create circles that you know the diameters and the locations.

Step Preview:

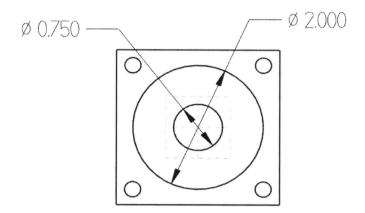

Wireframe

♦ From **Arcs** group, select **Circle Center Point**.

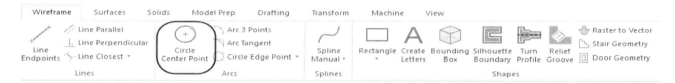

♦ Enter the **Diameter 0.75** in the panel and disable the locker icon as shown.

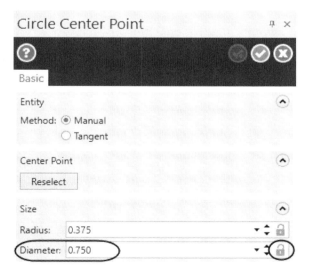

♦ Press **Enter** to see the circle preview.

♦ [Enter the center point]: Move the cursor to the center of the rectangle until the cursor cue tip changes to the Origin as shown.

♦ Click to select the Origin.

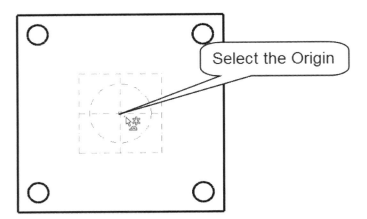

♦ Press **Enter** again to finish the circle.

*Note: While the circle is live, cyan color, the circle diameter and its location can be modified. To avoid this, you need to press **Enter** to finish the circle.*

♦ In the **Diameter** field of the **Circle Center Point** panel, type **2.0** and press **Enter**.
♦ The panel should look as shown.

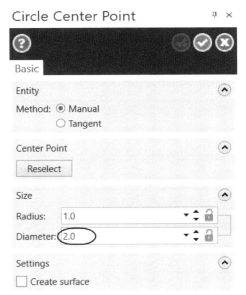

♦ [Enter the center point]: Select the Origin as shown.

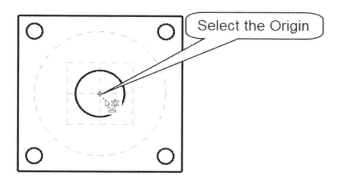

Note: Because the center of the 0.75"
diameter circle is in the Origin, you could also
select the point when the cursor center cue tip
appears as shown.

♦ Once complete, choose the **OK** button to exit the command.
♦ The geometry should look as shown.

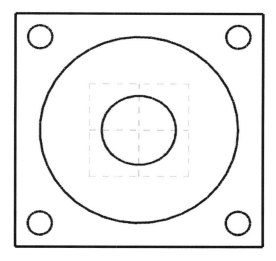

STEP 5: CREATE THE CHAMFERS

In this step, you will create 45 degree chamfers at the corners of the rectangle. You will use the **Chamfer Entities** command.

Step Preview:

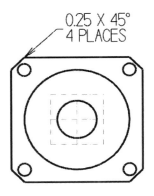

Wireframe

♦ From the **Modify** group, select **Chamfer Entities**.

♦ In the **Chamfer Entities** panel, make sure that **1 Distance** and **Trim entities** are enabled and **Distance 1** is set to **0.25** as shown.

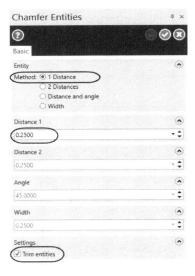

♦ Select the lines as shown.

Note: A preview of the chamfer should appear when you hover the cursor above the second line (Entity B).

♦ The geometry should look as shown.

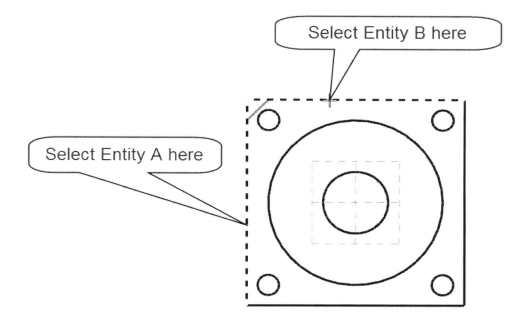

♦ The part will appear as shown.

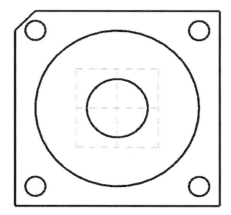

♦ Follow the same steps to chamfer the rest of the corners.
♦ The geometry should look as shown when completed.

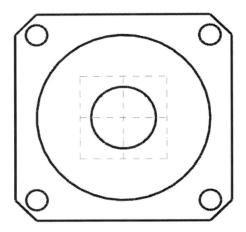

♦ Select the **OK** button to exit the command.

STEP 6: SAVE THE FILE

File

♦ **Save As.**

*Note: You can also click on the **Save As** icon from the **Quick Access Toolbar**.*

♦ Click on the **Browse** icon as shown.
♦ Find a location on the computer to save your file. **File name:** "Your Name_1".

Note: It is highly recommended to save the file from time to time when going through the tutorial.
*Click on the Save icon from the **Quick Access Toolbar** at the upper left corner to save the file.*

TUTORIAL #1 REVIEW EXERCISE

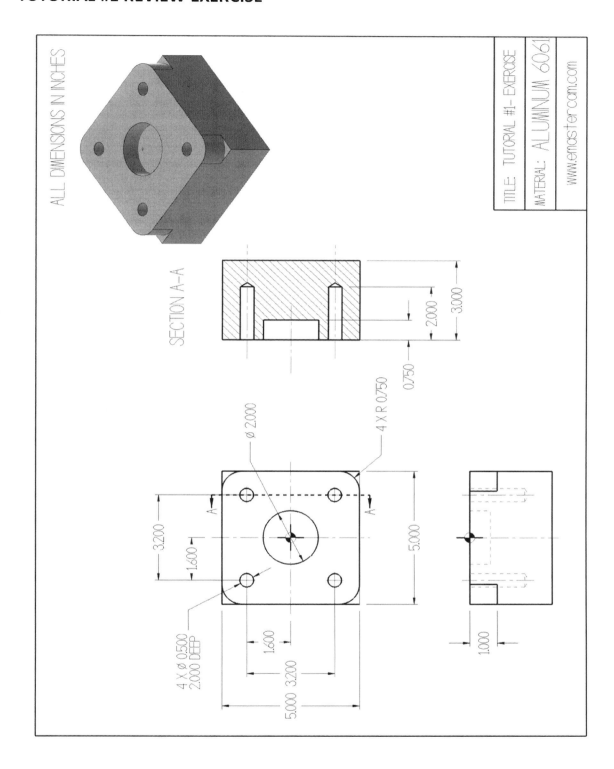

CREATE THE GEOMETRY FOR TUTORIAL #1 EXERCISE

Use these commands from the Wireframe tab to create the geometry.

- ◆ Rectangle.
- ◆ Fillet Entities.
- ◆ Circle Center Point.
- ◆ Trim.

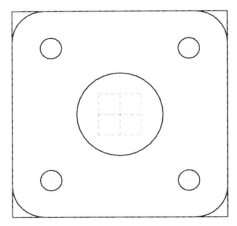

TUTORIAL #1 GEOMETRY CREATION QUIZ

- When creating wireframe geometry, what does the cyan color mean?

- If you make a mistake while creating geometry or delete some geometry by accident, what can you do?

- What is the Cartesian Coordinate System?

OVERVIEW OF STEPS TAKEN TO CREATE THE FINAL PART:

Create the necessary Toolpaths to machine the part:

♦ The student will set up the stock size to be used and the clamping method used.
♦ A Facing toolpath will be created to machine the top of the part.
♦ A Circle Mill toolpath will remove the material inside of the large hole.
♦ A Drilling toolpath will be created to spot drill the four holes.
♦ A Drilling toolpath will be created to machine the through holes.
♦ A Contour toolpath with 2D Chamfer option will be used to chamfer the top of the large hole.
♦ A Contour toolpath will be used to machine the corners.

Backplot and Verify the file:

♦ Backplot will be used to simulate a step-by-step process of the tool's movements.
♦ Verify will be used to watch a tool machine the part out of a solid model.

Post Process the file to generate the G-code:

♦ The student will then post process the file to obtain an NC file containing the necessary code for the machine.

SUGGESTED FIXTURE

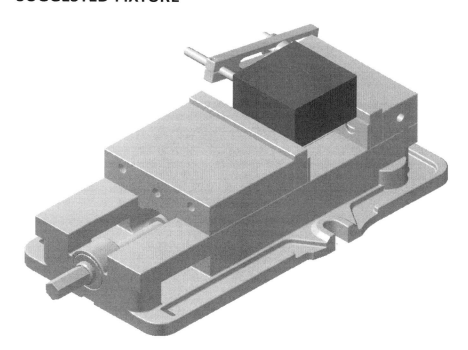

SETUP SHEET

TOOL LIST

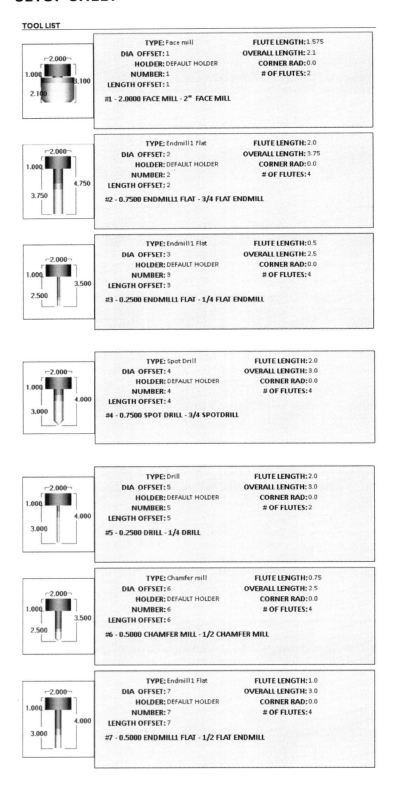

TYPE: Face mill
DIA OFFSET: 1
HOLDER: DEFAULT HOLDER
NUMBER: 1
LENGTH OFFSET: 1
FLUTE LENGTH: 1.575
OVERALL LENGTH: 2.1
CORNER RAD: 0.0
 # OF FLUTES: 2

#1 - 2.0000 FACE MILL - 2" FACE MILL

TYPE: Endmill1 Flat
DIA OFFSET: 2
HOLDER: DEFAULT HOLDER
NUMBER: 2
LENGTH OFFSET: 2
FLUTE LENGTH: 2.0
OVERALL LENGTH: 3.75
CORNER RAD: 0.0
 # OF FLUTES: 4

#2 - 0.7500 ENDMILL1 FLAT - 3/4 FLAT ENDMILL

TYPE: Endmill1 Flat
DIA OFFSET: 3
HOLDER: DEFAULT HOLDER
NUMBER: 3
LENGTH OFFSET: 3
FLUTE LENGTH: 0.5
OVERALL LENGTH: 2.5
CORNER RAD: 0.0
 # OF FLUTES: 4

#3 - 0.2500 ENDMILL1 FLAT - 1/4 FLAT ENDMILL

TYPE: Spot Drill
DIA OFFSET: 4
HOLDER: DEFAULT HOLDER
NUMBER: 4
LENGTH OFFSET: 4
FLUTE LENGTH: 2.0
OVERALL LENGTH: 3.0
CORNER RAD: 0.0
 # OF FLUTES: 4

#4 - 0.7500 SPOT DRILL - 3/4 SPOTDRILL

TYPE: Drill
DIA OFFSET: 5
HOLDER: DEFAULT HOLDER
NUMBER: 5
LENGTH OFFSET: 5
FLUTE LENGTH: 2.0
OVERALL LENGTH: 3.0
CORNER RAD: 0.0
 # OF FLUTES: 2

#5 - 0.2500 DRILL - 1/4 DRILL

TYPE: Chamfer mill
DIA OFFSET: 6
HOLDER: DEFAULT HOLDER
NUMBER: 6
LENGTH OFFSET: 6
FLUTE LENGTH: 0.75
OVERALL LENGTH: 2.5
CORNER RAD: 0.0
 # OF FLUTES: 4

#6 - 0.5000 CHAMFER MILL - 1/2 CHAMFER MILL

TYPE: Endmill1 Flat
DIA OFFSET: 7
HOLDER: DEFAULT HOLDER
NUMBER: 7
LENGTH OFFSET: 7
FLUTE LENGTH: 1.0
OVERALL LENGTH: 3.0
CORNER RAD: 0.0
 # OF FLUTES: 4

#7 - 0.5000 ENDMILL1 FLAT - 1/2 FLAT ENDMILL

STEP 1: SELECT THE MACHINE AND SET UP THE STOCK

In Mastercam, you select a **Machine Definition** before creating any toolpath. The **Machine Definition** is a model of your machine's capabilities and features. It acts like a template for setting up your machine. The machine definition ties together three main components: the schematic model of your machine's components, the control definition that models your control capabilities, and the post processor that will generate the required machine code (G-code). For a Mill Essentials exercise (2D toolpaths), we need just a basic machine definition.

*Note: For the purpose of this tutorial, we will be using the **Default Mill** machine.*

1.1 Unhide the Toolpaths Manager panel

♦ From the left side of the graphics window, click on the **Toolpaths** tab as shown.

♦ Pin the **Toolpaths Manager** by clicking on the **Auto Hide** icon as shown.

1.2 Select the machine

Machine

♦ From the **Machine Type** group, select the drop down arrow below **Mill**. Select the **Default**.

*Note: Once you select the **Mill Default**, the **Ribbon bar** changes to reflect the toolpaths that could be used with **Mill Default**.*

♦ Select the plus sign (**+**) in front of Properties in the **Toolpaths Manager** to expand the **Toolpaths Group Properties**.

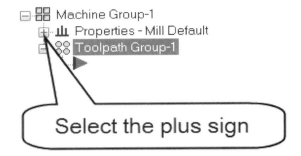

♦ Select **Tool settings** to set the tool parameters.

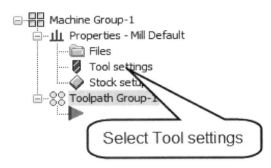

♦ Change the parameters to match the screen shot as shown.

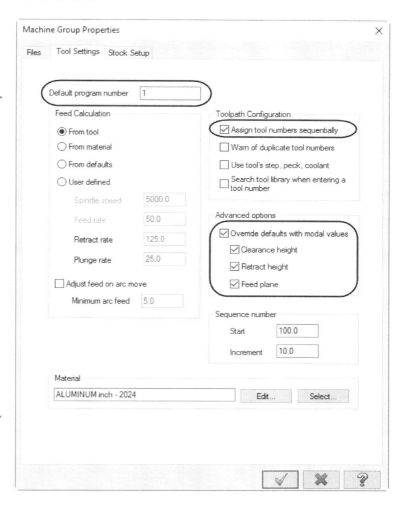

Default program number is used to enter a number if your machine requires a number for a program name.

Assign tool numbers sequentially allows you to overwrite the tool number from the library with the next available tool number. (First operation tool number 1; second operation tool number 2, etc.).

Warn of duplicate tool numbers allows you to get a warning if you enter two tools with the same number.

Override defaults with modal values enables the system to keep the values that you enter.

Feed Calculation set to **From tool** uses feed rate, plunge rate, retract rate, and spindle speed from the tool definition.

- ◆ Select the **Stock Setup** tab to define the stock.
- ◆ Select the **All Entities** button near the bottom of the **Stock Setup** page as shown.
- ◆ In the **Stock Setup**, enter in the **Z** field **1.1** and the **Z Stock Origin 0.1**. Make sure that the rest of the parameters are as shown.

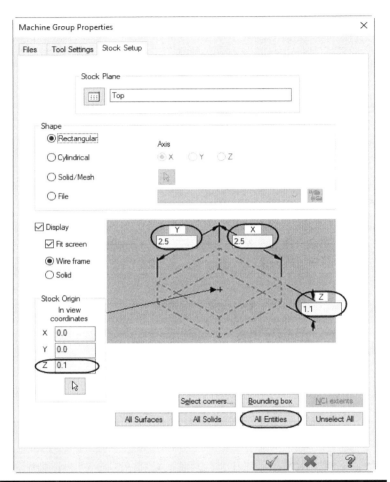

The **X, Y, Z** values in the graphics area are the dimensions of the stock model. They are always positive values.

The **Stock Origin** values adjust the positioning of the stock, ensuring that you have an equal amount of extra stock around the finished part. In the graphics screen, the plus sign (**+**) shows you where the stock origin is. The default position is the middle of the stock.

Display options allow you to set the stock as **Wireframe** and to fit the stock to the screen. (Fit Screen)

Note: The stock model that you create is displayed when viewing the file or the toolpaths, during backplot, and while verifying toolpaths.

- ◆ Select the **OK** button to exit **Machine Group Properties**.

◆ Right mouse click in the graphics window and select the **Isometric** view to see the stock.

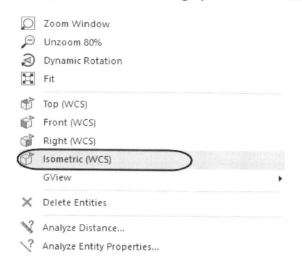

◆ Press **Alt + F1** to fit the drawing to the screen.

◆ The stock model will appear as shown.

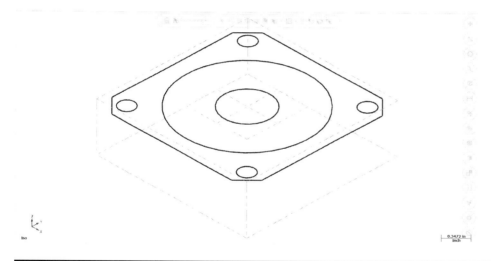

Note: The stock is not geometry and cannot be selected.

◆ Right mouse click in the graphics window and select the **Top** view to see the stock and if needed, press **Alt + F1** to fit the drawing to the screen.

STEP 2: FACE THE PART

A **Facing** toolpath quickly removes material from the top of the part to create an even surface for future operations.

Toolpath Preview:

Toolpaths

♦ From the **2D** group, select **Face** as shown.

♦ When the **Chaining** dialog box appears, choose the **OK** button to use the defined stock and exit the Chaining dialog box.

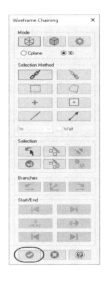

*Note: Mastercam will create the **Facing** toolpath defined from the stock setup.*
*For more information on the **Chaining** button and **Options**, click on the **Help** button.*

♦ In the **Toolpath Type** page, the **Facing** icon will be automatically selected.

Contour   Pocket   Facing   Slot mill   Model Chamfer

*Note: Mastercam updates the pages as you modify them and then marks them, in the **Tree View** list, with a green check mark. Pages that are not enabled are marked with a red circle and slash.*

2.1 Select a 2.0" Face Mill from the library and set the Tool parameters

♦ Select **Tool** from the **Tree View list**.
♦ Click on the **Select library tool** button.

♦ To be able to see all of the tools from the library, disable **Filter Active.**

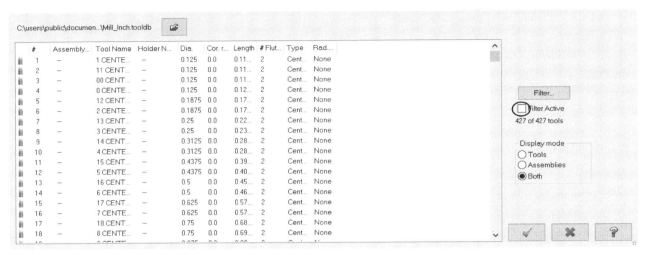

♦ Select the **2" Face Mill (#322)** as shown.

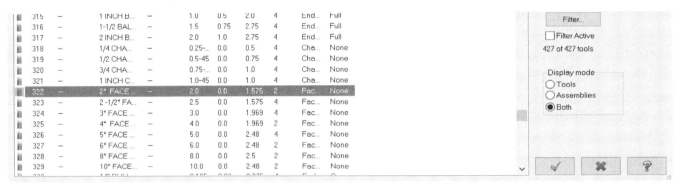

♦ Select the tool in the **Tool Selection** page and then select the **OK** button to exit.

♦ Input a comment and make all the necessary changes, as shown.

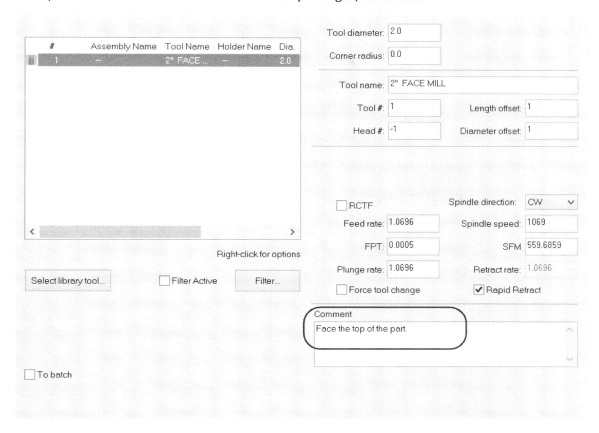

In the **Comment** field, enter a comment to help identify the toolpath in the **Toolpaths Manager** such as the one shown above.

Note: The **Feed rate, Plunge rate, Retract rate**, and **Spindle speed** are based on the tool definition as set in the **Tool Settings**. You may change these values as per your part material and tools.

Note: If by mistake you click the **OK** button, the toolpath will be generated without all the parameters set properly. To return and set the parameters, click on the **Parameters** in the **Toolpaths Manager** as shown below.

♦ Select **Cut Parameters** and make the necessary changes as shown.

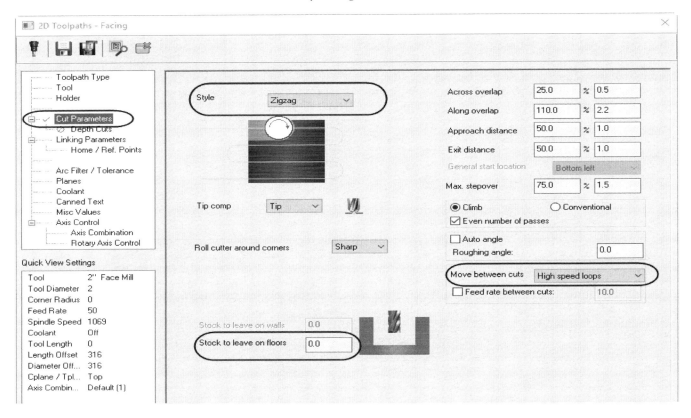

The **Style** (facing cutting method) **Zigzag** creates a back and forth cutting motion.

Move between cuts determines how the tool moves between each cut. This is only available if you select the zigzag cutting method.

High speed loops create 180 degree arcs between each cut.

♦ Select the **Linking Parameters** page and make the necessary changes as shown.

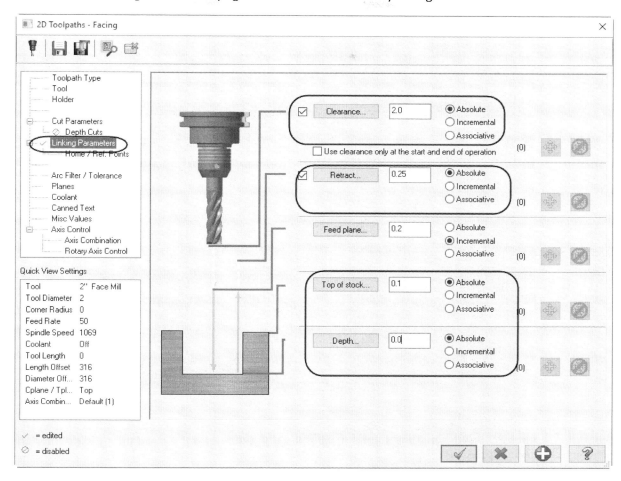

Clearance sets the height at which the tool moves to and from the part.

Retract sets the height that the tool moves up to before the next tool pass.

Feed Plane sets the height that the tool rapids to before changing to the plunge rate to enter the part.

Top of stock sets the height of the material in the Z axis.

Depth determines the final machining depth that the tool descends into the stock.

Note: The **Top of stock** is set to **0.1"** because the **Stock Origin** was set to **0.1"** above the origin. The depth is set to **0.0"** because this is the finish depth. The majority of the values are set to absolute (measured from **Z zero** which is set at the top of the finished part). **Feed plane** set to incremental is measured from the **Top of stock**.

2.2 Preview the Toolpath

◆ To quickly check how the toolpath will be generated, select the **Preview toolpath** icon as shown.

◆ To hide the dialog box, click on the **Hide dialog** icon as shown.
◆ To see the part from an **Isometric** view, right mouse click in the graphics window and select **Isometric** as shown.

    ◻ Zoom Window
    🔎 Unzoom 80%
    ⟳ Dynamic Rotation
    ⛶ Fit

    📦 Top (WCS)
    📦 Front (WCS)
    📦 Right (WCS)
    📦 Isometric (WCS)
       GView   ▸

    ✕ Delete Entities

    ↘? Analyze Distance...
    ↘? Analyze Entity Properties...

◆ The toolpath should look as shown.

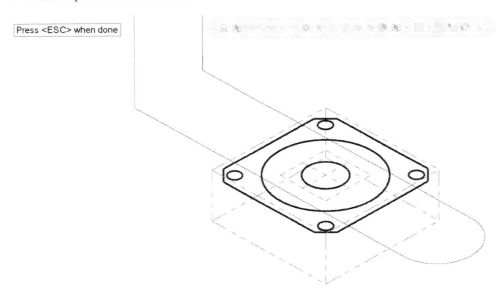

◆ Press **Esc** key to exit the preview.

Note: If the toolpath does not look as shown in the preview, check your parameters again.

♦ Select the **OK** button to exit the **Facing Parameters**.

---

*Note: If you exit the toolpath in the middle of setting the parameters, in the **Toolpaths Manager**, you will have a red **X** on the **Face Toolpath** as shown in. This shows that you modified the toolpath and you need to update it. You will have to select the **Regenerate all dirty operations** icon each time you change something in the toolpath parameters.*

STEP 3: CIRCLE MILL THE LARGE HOLE

Circle Mill Toolpaths remove circular pockets based on a single point. You can select either point entities or center points of arcs. Mastercam will then pocket out a circular area of the diameter to the depth that you specify.

Toolpath Preview:

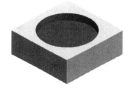

3.1 Drill Point Selection

♦ Press **Alt** + **T** to remove the toolpath display.

Toolpaths

♦ From the **2D** group, click on the drop down arrow until the **Circle Mill** toolpath appears as shown.
♦ Click on the **Circle Mill** icon.

---

*Note: Move the cursor to the center of the graphics window to see the **Toolpath Hole Definition** panel that appears below the **Toolpaths Manager**.*

♦ The **Toolpath Hole Definition** should appear as shown.

♦ Right click and select the **Top** view.

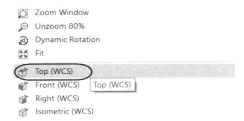

♦ [Select one or more entities to add or remove from the features list]: Select the center of the **2.0"** diameter circle as shown.

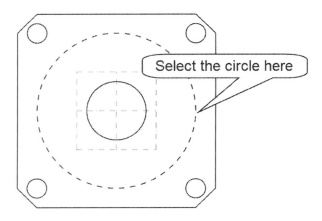

Select the circle here

♦ The Point will be displayed in the **Features** list as shown.

♦ Select the **OK** button to finish the selection and exit **Toolpath Hole Definition**.

♦ In the **Toolpath Type** page, the **Circle Mill** icon will be selected.

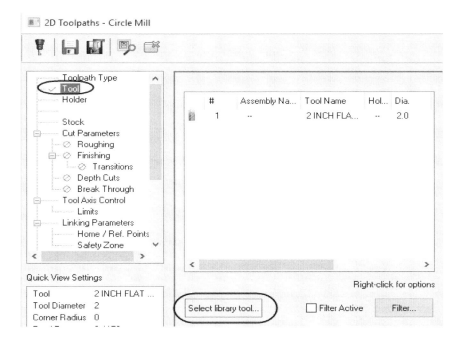

3.2 Select a 3/4" Flat Endmill from the library and set the Tool parameters

♦ Select **Tool** from the **Tree View** list.
♦ Click on **Select library tool** button.

♦ To be able to see all the tools from the library, disable **Filter Active**.

♦ Scroll down and select the **3/4" Flat Endmill (#294** as shown.

289	–	7/16 FLAT ENDMILL	–	0.4375	0.0	0.8	4	End...	None
290	–	1/2 FLAT ENDMILL	–	0.5	0.0	1.0	4	End...	None
291	–	17/32 FLAT ENDMILL	–	0.5312	0.0	1.0	4	End...	None
292	–	5/8 FLAT ENDMILL	–	0.625	0.0	1.5	4	End...	None
293	–	23/32 FLAT ENDMILL	–	0.71...	0.0	1.5	4	End...	None
294	–	3/4 FLAT ENDMILL	–	0.75	0.0	2.0	4	End...	None
295	–	13/16 FLAT ENDMILL	–	0.8125	0.0	2.0	4	End...	None
296	–	7/8 FLAT ENDMILL	–	0.875	0.0	2.0	4	End...	None
297	–	1 INCH FLAT ENDMILL	–	1.0	0.0	2.0	4	End...	None
298	–	1-3/16 FLAT ENDMILL	–	1.1875	0.0	2.0	4	End...	None

♦ Select the tool in the **Tool Selection** page and then select the **OK** button to exit.

♦ Input a comment and make all the necessary changes, as shown.

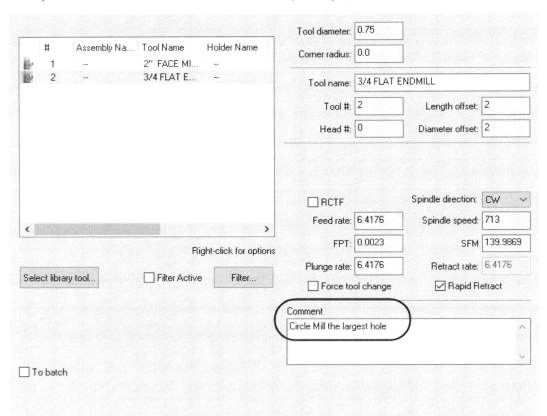

*Note: The **Feed rate, Plunge rate, Retract rate,** and **Spindle speed** are based on the tool definition as set in the **Tool Settings**. You may change these values as per your part material and tools.*

3.3 Cut Parameters

♦ From the **Tree View list**, select **Cut Parameters** and ensure the settings appear as shown.

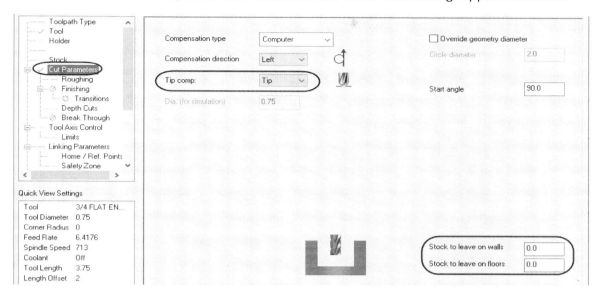

3.4 Roughing

♦ From the **Tree View list**, select **Roughing** and enable it. Set the **Stepover to 50%**, enable **Helical Entry**, and specify the other parameters as shown.

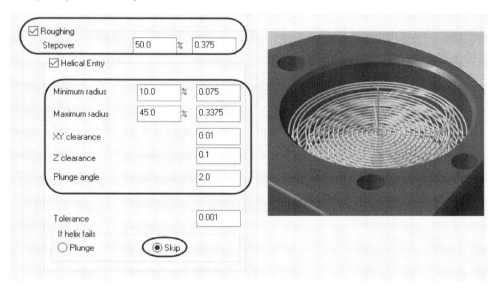

Stepover sets the distance between cutting passes in the **X** and **Y** axes as a percentage of the tool diameter.

Helical Entry creates a helix at the center of the circle to begin the roughing motion. If this option is turned off, the tool plunges to start the toolpath.

Note: The images in the toolpaths change depending on the parameter that you last selected in the page.

3.5 Linking Parameters

♦ Select **Linking Parameters** from the **Tree View list.**
♦ Change the **Top of stock** to **0.0** and set the **Depth** to **-0.25**. Ensure all the values are set the same as shown.

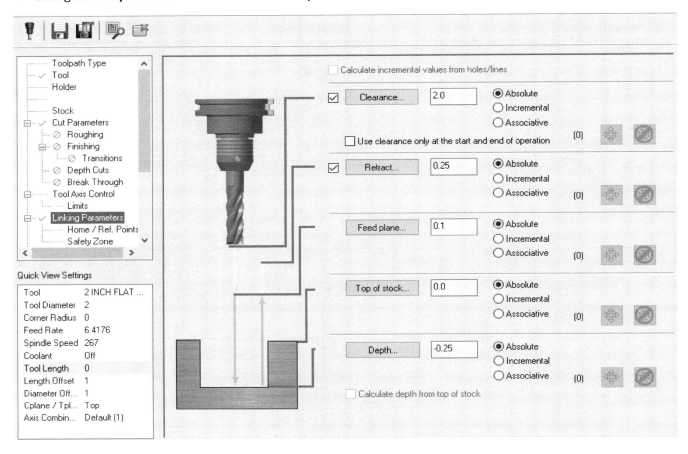

Absolute values are always measured from the origin 0,0,0.

Incremental values are relative to other parameters or chained geometry.

Associative option allows you to select points from the existing geometry from where the values will be measured.

3.6 Preview the Toolpath

♦ To quickly check how the toolpath will be generated, select the **Preview toolpath** icon as shown.

♦ To hide the dialog box, click on the **Hide dialog** icon as shown.

♦ To see the part from an Isometric view, right mouse click in the graphics window and select Isometric as shown.

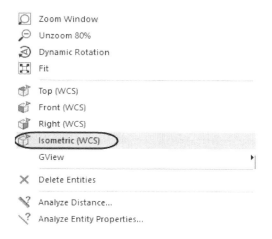

♦ The toolpath should look as shown.

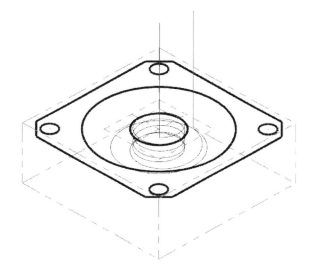

♦ Press **Esc** key to exit the preview.

Note: If the toolpath does not look as shown in the preview, check your parameters again.

♦ Select the **OK** button to exit the **2D Toolpaths - Circle Mill** parameters.

STEP 4: BACKPLOT THE TOOLPATHS

Backplotting shows the path the tools take to cut the part. This display lets you spot errors in the program before you machine the part. As you backplot toolpaths, Mastercam displays additional information such as the X, Y, and Z coordinates, the path length, the minimum and maximum coordinates, and the cycle time.

♦ Make sure that the toolpaths are selected (signified by the green check mark on the folder icon). If both operations are not selected, choose the **Select all operations** icon.

♦ Select the **Backplot selected operations** button.

♦ In the **Backplot** panel, enable **Display with color codes**, **Display tool** and **Display rapid moves** icons as shown.

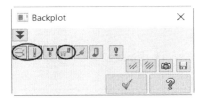

♦ To see the part from an **Isometric** view, right mouse click in the graphics window and select Isometric as shown.

♦ To fit the workpiece to the screen, if needed, right mouse click in the graphics window again and select the Fit.

♦ You can step through the **Backplot** by using the **Step forward** ▶▶ or **Step back** ◀◀ buttons.

♦ You can adjust the speed of the backplot.

♦ Select the **Play** button to run **Backplot**.

♦ The toolpath should look as shown.

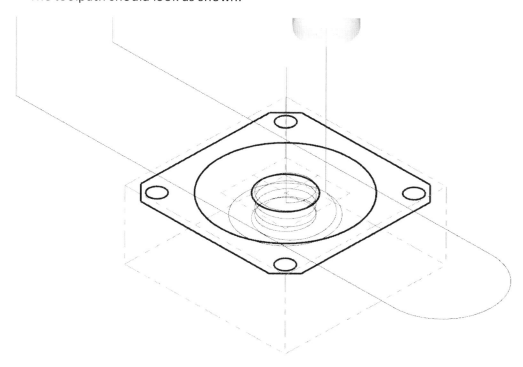

♦ Select the **OK** button to exit **Backplot**.

STEP 5: SIMULATE THE TOOLPATH IN VERIFY

Verify shows the path the tools take to cut the part with material removal. This display lets you spot errors in the program before you machine the part. As you verify toolpaths, Mastercam displays additional information such as the X, Y, and Z coordinates, the path length, the minimum and maximum coordinates, and the cycle time. It also shows any collision between the workpiece and the tool.

♦ From the **Toolpaths Manager**, select **Verify selected operations** icon as shown.

Note: Mastercam launches a new window that allows you to check the part using **Backplot** or **Verify.**

♦ In **Mastercam Simulator**, **Verify** should be enabled and change the settings as shown.

♦ Select the **Play** button to run **Verify**.

♦ The part should appear as shown.

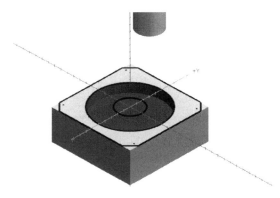

Note: To rotate the part, move the cursor to the center of the part and click and hold the mouse wheel and slowly move it in one direction. To zoom in or out, hold down the mouse wheel and scroll up or down as needed.

♦ Right mouse click in the graphics window and select **Isometric**. Then right mouse click again and select Fit to see the part in the original position.

♦ To check the part step-by-step, click first on the **Start** button.

- Click on the **Step Forward** to see the tool moving one step at a time.
- The part should look as shown after several steps.

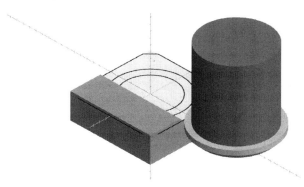

- Click on the **Step Forward** until the toolpath is completed. ▶▶
- To go back to Mastercam window, minimize **Mastercam Simulator** window as shown. ⊖   ▢   ✕

STEP 6: CIRCLE MILL THE INSIDE HOLE

Circle Mill Toolpaths remove circular pockets based on a single point. You can select either point entities or center points of arcs. Mastercam will then pocket out a circular area of the diameter to the depth that you specify.

Toolpath Preview:

6.1 Drill Point Selection

- Hover the cursor in the **Toolpaths Manager** and press **T** or press **Alt + T** to remove the toolpath display.

Toolpaths

- From the **2D** group, click on the **Circle Mill** icon.

♦ The **Toolpath Hole Definition** should appear as shown.

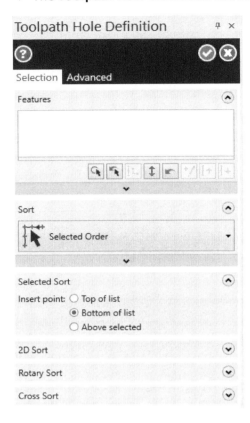

♦ Right click and select the **Top** view.

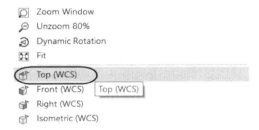

♦ [Select one or more entities to add or remove from the features list]: From the **General Selection Bar**, click on the **AutoCursor** arrow and select **Arc Center** as shown.

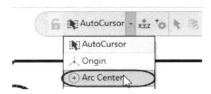

◆ Select the **0.75"** diameter circle as shown.

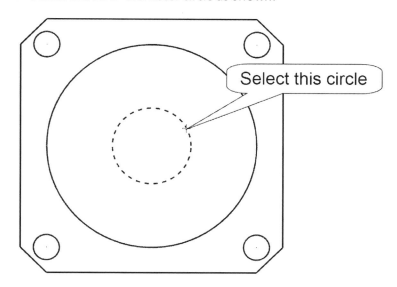

◆ The **Point** will be displayed in the **Features** list as shown.

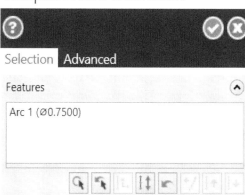

◆ Select the **OK** button to finish the selection and exit **Toolpath Hole Definition**.

◆ In the **Toolpath Type** page, the **Circle Mill** icon will be selected.

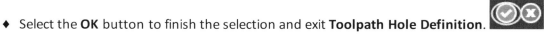

6.2 Select a 1/4" Flat Endmill from the library and set the Tool parameters

♦ Select **Tool** from the **Tree View list**.

♦ Click on **Select library tool** button.

♦ To be able to see all the tools from the library, disable **Filter Active**.

Filter...

☐ Filter Active

427 of 427 tools

♦ Scroll down and select the **1/4" Flat Endmill (#285)** as shown.

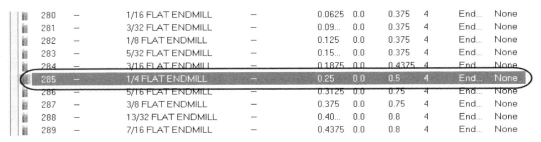

280	—	1/16 FLAT ENDMILL	—	0.0625	0.0	0.375	4	End...	None
281	—	3/32 FLAT ENDMILL	—	0.09...	0.0	0.375	4	End...	None
282	—	1/8 FLAT ENDMILL	—	0.125	0.0	0.375	4	End...	None
283	—	5/32 FLAT ENDMILL	—	0.15...	0.0	0.375	4	End...	None
284	—	3/16 FLAT ENDMILL	—	0.1875	0.0	0.4375	4	End...	None
285	—	1/4 FLAT ENDMILL	—	0.25	0.0	0.5	4	End...	None
286	—	5/16 FLAT ENDMILL	—	0.3125	0.0	0.75	4	End...	None
287	—	3/8 FLAT ENDMILL	—	0.375	0.0	0.75	4	End...	None
288	—	13/32 FLAT ENDMILL	—	0.40...	0.0	0.8	4	End...	None
289	—	7/16 FLAT ENDMILL	—	0.4375	0.0	0.8	4	End...	None

♦ Select the tool in the **Tool Selection** page and then select the **OK** button to exit.

♦ Input a comment and make all the necessary changes, as shown.

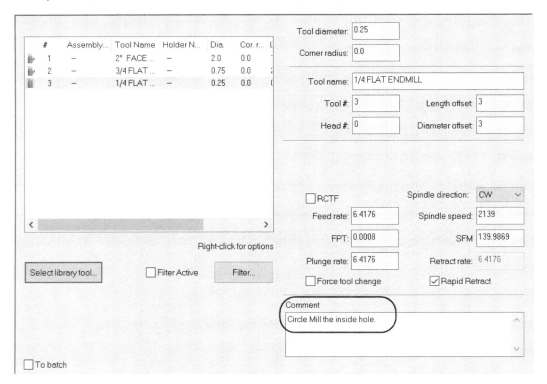

6.3 Cut Parameters

♦ From the **Tree View list**, select **Cut Parameters** and ensure the settings appear as shown.

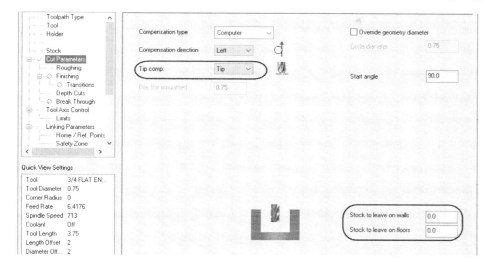

6.4 Roughing

♦ From the **Tree View list**, select **Roughing** and enable it. Set the **Stepover** to **50%**, enable **Helical Entry**, and specify the other parameters as shown.

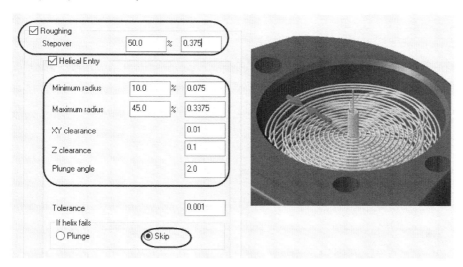

Stepover sets the distance between cutting passes in the X and Y axes as a percentage of the tool diameter.

Helical Entry creates a helix at the center of the circle to begin the roughing motion. If this option is turned off, the tool plunges to start the toolpath.

6.5 Depth Cuts

♦ Make any necessary change as shown.

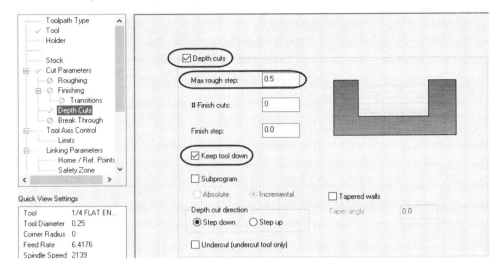

Depth Cuts sets the steps the tool takes along the **Z** axis. Mastercam will take the total depth and divide it into separate depth cuts. Mastercam never performs unequal depth cuts.

Max rough step sets the maximum amount of material removed in the **Z** axis with each rough cut. Mastercam will calculate equal rough cuts no larger than the maximum rough step until it reaches the final Z depth.

Keep tool down determines whether or not to retract the tool between depth cuts.

6.6 Set the Break Through

♦ From the **Tree View list**, select **Break Through** and set the parameters to completely cut through the material by an amount that you specify as shown.

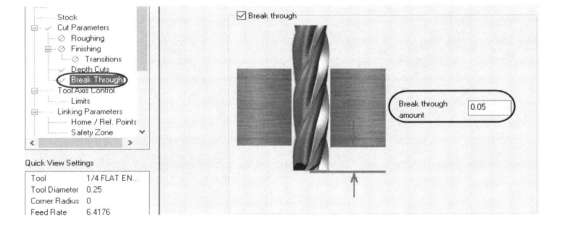

6.7 Linking Parameters

◆ Select **Linking Parameters** from the **Tree View list**.
◆ Change the **Top** of stock to **-0.25** and set the **Depth** to **-1.0**. Ensure all the values are set the same as shown.

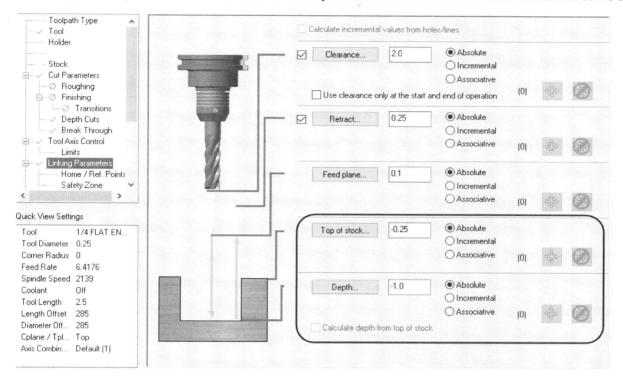

Absolute values are always measured from the origin 0,0,0.

Incremental values are relative to other parameters or chained geometry.

Associative option allows you to select points from the existing geometry from where the values will be measured.

6.8 Preview the Toolpath

♦ Select the **Preview toolpath** icon as shown.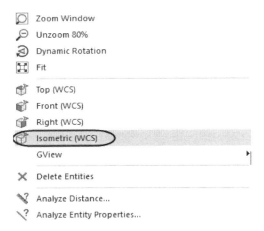

♦ Click on the **Hide dialog** icon as shown.

♦ To see the part from an **Isometric** view, right mouse click in the graphics window and select **Isometric** as shown.

    ◻ Zoom Window

    🔍 Unzoom 80%

    🔄 Dynamic Rotation

    ⊞ Fit

    📦 Top (WCS)

    📦 Front (WCS)

    📦 Right (WCS)

    📦 Isometric (WCS)

       GView ▶

    ✕ Delete Entities

    📐 Analyze Distance...

    📐 Analyze Entity Properties...

♦ The toolpath should look as shown.

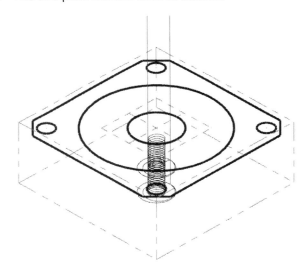

♦ Press **Esc** key to exit the preview.

Note: If the toolpath does not look as shown in the preview, check your parameters again.

♦ Select the **OK** button to exit the **2D Toolpaths - Circle Mill** parameters.

6.9 Verify the Toolpaths

♦ From the **Toolpaths Manager**, click on the **Select all operations** icon.

♦ Click on the **Verify selected operation** icon.

♦ For information on how to set the **Verify** parameters and how to simulate the toolpath, please check **"Simulate the toolpath in Verify" on page 78**.

♦ Disable **Wireframe** as shown.

♦ Select the **Verify** tab, and enable **Color Loop** as shown.

Note: This option will change the material removal color. This can be set based on the operation or on the tool number used to machine the part. This makes it easier to spot if you forget to leave the stock in the finish operations.

♦ Select the **Play** button as shown.

♦ The part will appear as shown.

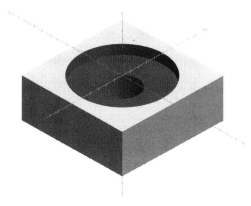

♦ To go back to Mastercam window, minimize **Mastercam Simulator** window as shown.

STEP 7: SPOT DRILL THE 0.25" HOLES

Spot Drilling the holes allows you to start the hole. In this operation, we will use the spot drill to chamfer the hole before drilling it.

Toolpath Preview:

♦ Select all toolpaths and press **T** to remove the toolpath display if needed.

Toolpaths

♦ In the **2D** group, select the **Drill** icon as shown.

♦ In the **Toolpath Hole Definition** panel, choose the option **Mask on Arc**.

*Note: **Mask on Arc** is a tool for selecting arcs whose diameters match the one that you select within a specified tolerance.*

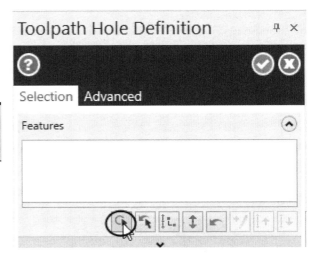

- Hover the cursor above the center of the geometry and scroll down the mouse wheel to unzoom the geometry as shown in Figure: 7.0.1.
- [Select an arc to match]: Select one of the four arcs as shown in Figure: 7.0.1 .
- [Draw a window to select entities]: Left click in the upper left corner of the graphics window, hold the left button down and drag a rectangle to the lower right corner of the part to include all entities, as shown in Figure: 7.0.1.

Figure: 7.0.1

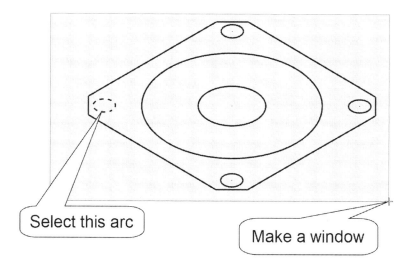

Select this arc

Make a window

- Release the left mouse button and click it again once you have created a window encompassing the entire part.

Note: *Only the four arcs that have the same diameter will be selected. The order in which the holes are selected follows a zigzag pattern as shown.*

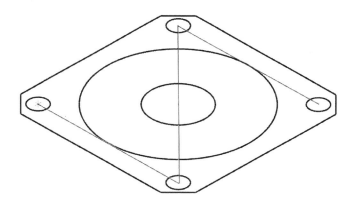

◆ To change the order in which the holes are drilled, in the **Toolpath Hole Definition** click on the **Selected Order** and select the **Point to Point** icon as shown.

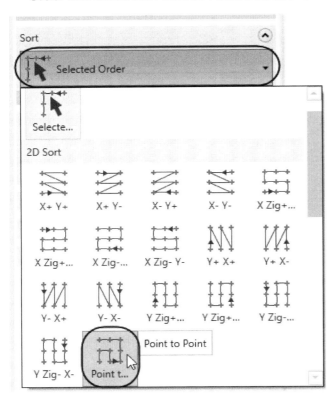

◆ The system will prompt you to select the start point. Reselect the first hole as shown.

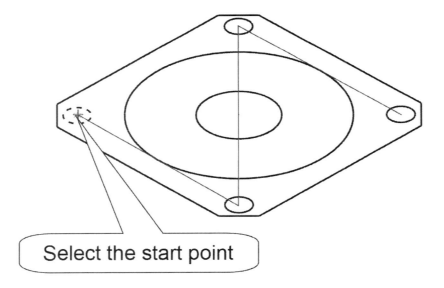

Select the start point

♦ The order in which the holes will be drilled should look as shown.

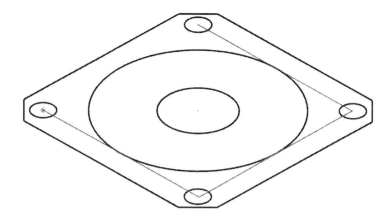

♦ Select the **OK** button in the **Toolpath Hole Definition** panel to accept the 4 center points.
♦ In the **Toolpath Type** page, the **Drill toolpath** should already be selected.

Drill   Circle Mill   Point   Helix Bore   Thread Mill

7.1 Select a 3/4" Spot Drill from the library and set the Tool Parameters

♦ Select **Tool** from the **Tree View list**.

♦ Click on the **Select library tool** button. | Select library tool... |

♦ To view only the spot drill, select the **Filter** button.

♦ Under **Tool Types**, select the **None** button to unselect any unwanted tool.

♦ Hover the cursor over each icon and the tool type will be displayed. Choose the **Spot Drill** icon as shown.

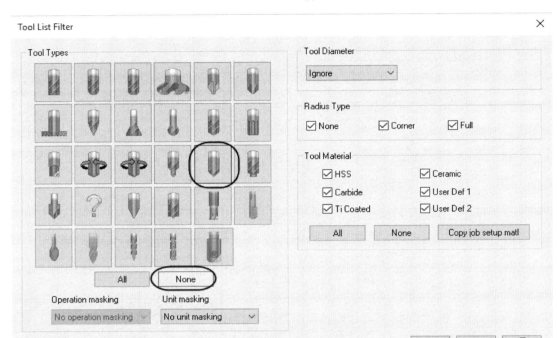

♦ Select the **OK** button to exit the **Tool List Filter** dialog box.
♦ At this point you should only see **Spot Drills**.
♦ From that list select the **3/4" Spot Drill** as shown.

#	Assembly...	Tool Name	Holder N...	Dia.	Cor. r...	Length	# Flut...	Type	Rad...
21	—	1/8 SPOT...	—	0.125	0.0	2.0	2	Spot...	None
22	—	1/4 SPOT...	—	0.25	0.0	2.0	2	Spot...	None
23	—	3/8 SPOT...	—	0.375	0.0	2.0	4	Spot...	None
24	—	1/2 SPOT...	—	0.5	0.0	2.0	2	Spot...	None
25	—	3/4 SPOT...	—	0.75	0.0	2.0	4	Spot...	None
26	—	1. SPOT...	—	1.0	0.0	2.0	4	Spot...	None

♦ Select the tool in the **Tool Selection** page and then select the **OK** button to exit.

♦ Input a comment and make the necessary changes to the **Tool** page as shown.

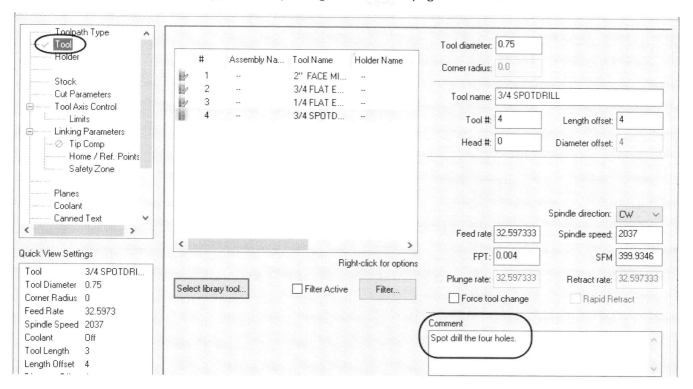

7.2 Set the Cut Parameters

♦ Select **Cut Parameters** and make sure the parameters are set as shown.

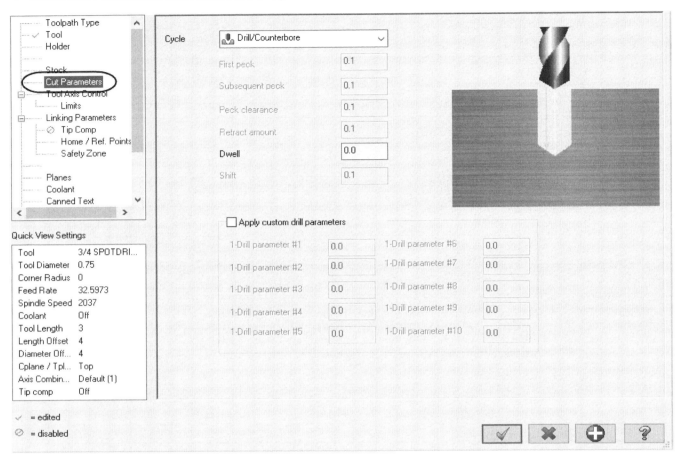

Drill/Counterbore is recommended for drilling holes with depths of less than three times the tool's diameter.

Dwell sets the amount of time in seconds that the tool remains at the bottom of a drilled hole.

7.3 Linking Parameters

◆ Choose **Linking Parameters** and ensure **Clearance** is enabled. Set the **Top of stock** and the **Depth** to **Absolute** and **0.0** as shown.

◆ Select the **Calculator** icon on the right hand side of the **Depth** icon as shown.

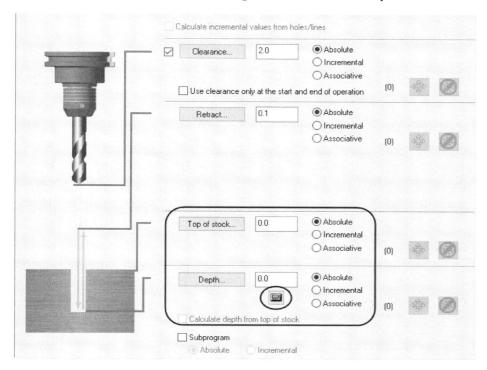

◆ To generate a **0.025** chamfer, input the following equation in the **Finish diameter** area: **0.25 + 0.05** (diameter of the finished hole + 2 X the chamfer size) and hit **Enter** to calculate the **Depth**, as shown. Make sure that **Add to depth** is enabled.

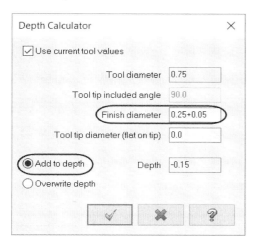

◆ Select the **OK** button to exit the **Depth Calculator**.

♦ You will now see the **Depth** for this spot drilling operation is updated after we specify the finish diameters of the holes including the chamfer. Change the rest of the parameters as shown.

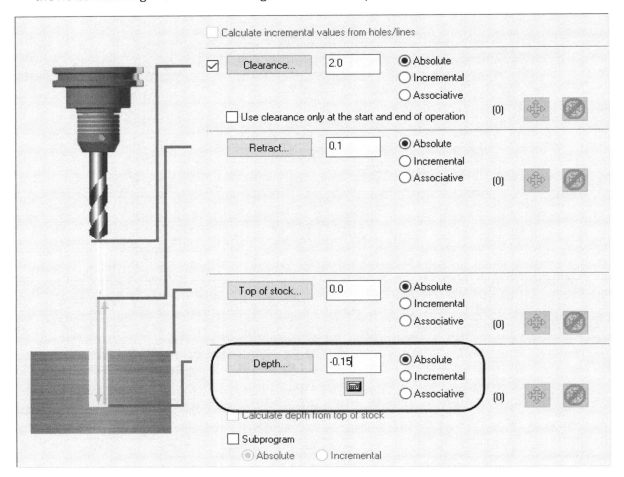

7.4 Preview the Toolpath

◆ To quickly check how the toolpath will be generated, select the **Preview toolpath** icon as shown.

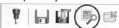

◆ See **"Preview the Toolpath" on page 68** to review the procedure.
◆ The toolpath should look as shown.

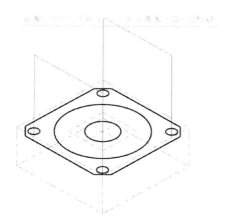

◆ Press **Esc** key to exit the preview.

Note: If the toolpath does not look as shown in the preview, check your parameters again.

◆ Select the **OK** button to exit the **2D Toolpaths - Drill/Circles Simple drill - no peck** parameters.

7.5 Verify the toolpaths

◆ From the **Toolpaths Manager,** click on the **Select all operations** icon.

◆ Click on the **Verify selected operation** icon.

◆ See **"Simulate the toolpath in Verify" on page 78** to review the procedure.

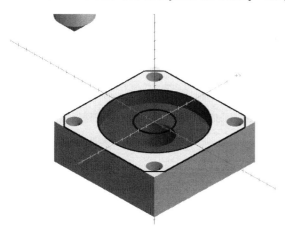

◆ To go back to the Mastercam window, minimize the Mastercam Simulator window as shown.

STEP 8: DRILL THE 0.25" HOLES

In this step, we will drill the holes to a specified depth.

Toolpath Preview:

♦ Move the cursor in the **Toolpaths Manager** and press **Alt + T** until the toolpath display is removed.

Toolpaths

♦ From the **2D** group, select **Drill**.

♦ In the **Toolpath Hole Definition** panel, choose the option **Copy previous points** icon as shown.

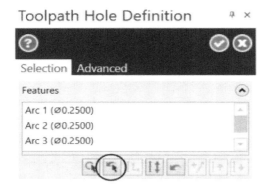

♦ This option will automatically select the 4 holes from the previous drill operation.

♦ Select the **OK** button in the **Toolpath Hole Definition** panel to accept the 4 drill points.

♦ In the **Toolpath Type** page, the **Drill toolpath** will be selected as shown.

Drill   Circle Mill   Point   Helix Bore   Thread Mill

8.1 Select a 1/4" Drill from the library and set the Tool Parameters

♦ Select **Tool** from the **Tree View list**.

♦ Click on the **Select library tool** button. Select library tool...

♦ To view only the drill tools, select the **Filter** button.

Filter...
✔ Filter Active
427 of 427 tools

♦ Under **Tool Types**, select the **None** button and then choose the **Drill** icon. Under the **Tool Diameter** section, select **Equal** and input a value of **0.25**.

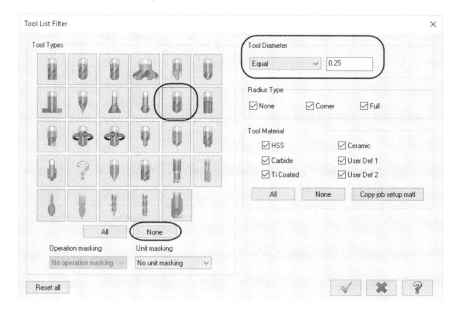

♦ Select the **OK** button to exit the **Tool List Filter** panel.

♦ At this point you should see a **1/4" Drill**.

#	Assembly...	Tool Name	Holder N...	Dia.	Cor. r...	Length	# Flut...	Type	Rad....
124	--	1/4 DRILL	--	0.25	0.0	2.0	2	Drill	None

♦ Select the tool in the **Tool Selection** page and then choose the **OK** button to exit.

♦ Make the necessary changes to the **Tool** page as shown.

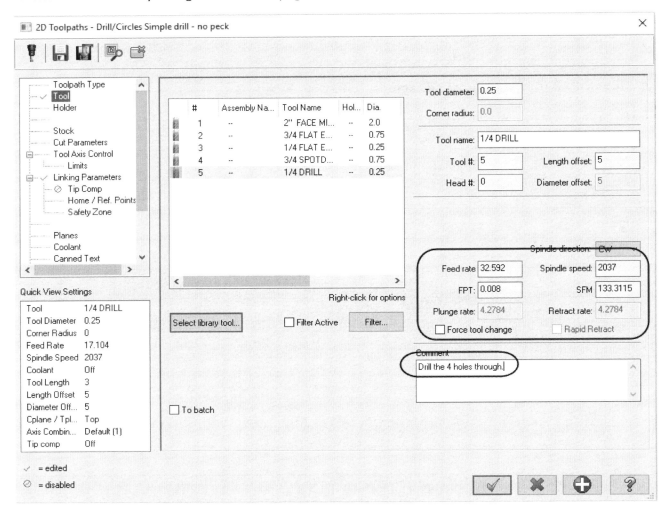

Note: The **Feed rate, Plunge rate, Retract rate,** and **Spindle speed** are based on the tool definition as set in the **Tool Settings**. You may change these values as per your part material and tools.

8.2 Cut Parameters

♦ Select **Cut Parameters** and change the drill **Cycle** to **Peck Drill** as shown.

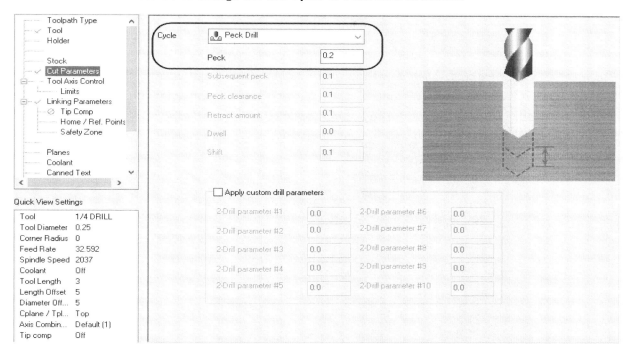

8.3 Linking Parameters

♦ Choose **Linking Parameters** and set the **Top of stock** to **0.0**. Input a **Depth** value of **-1.0** as shown

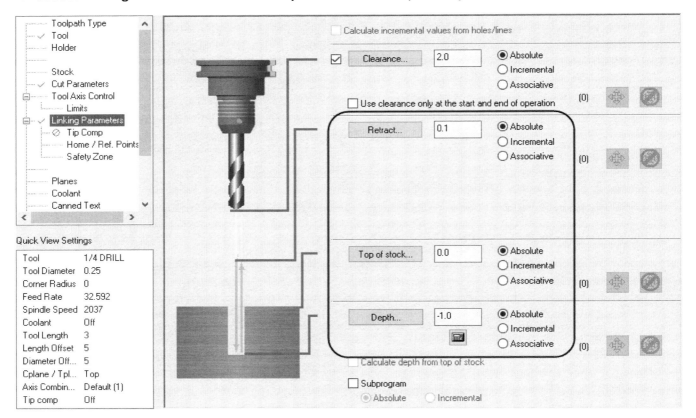

8.4 Set the Tip Compensation

♦ Select **Tip Comp** and enable it.
♦ Set the **Breakthrough amount** to **0.05** as shown.

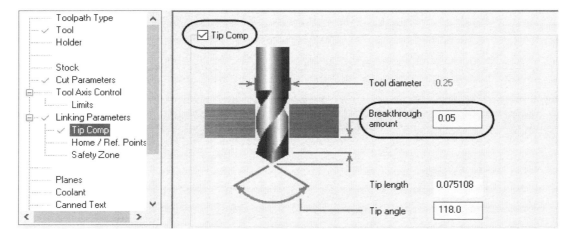

8.5 Preview the Toolpath

♦ To quickly check how the toolpath will be generated, select the **Preview toolpath** icon as shown.

♦ See **"Preview the Toolpath" on page 68** to review the procedure.
♦ Click with the mouse wheel and drag to slightly rotate the part.
♦ The toolpath should look as shown.

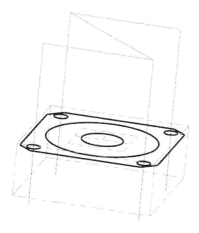

♦ Press **Esc** key to exit the preview.

Note: If the toolpath does not look as shown in the preview, check your parameters again.

♦ Select the **OK** button to exit the **2D Toolpaths - Drill/Circles Peck drill - full retract** parameters.

8.6 Verify the toolpaths

♦ From the **Toolpaths Manager**, click on the **Select all operations** icon.
♦ Click on the **Verify selected operation** icon.
♦ To **Verify** the toolpaths, see **"Simulate the toolpath in Verify" on page 78** to review the procedure.

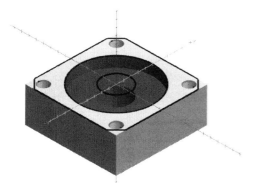

◆ To rotate the part, click in the center of the part with the mouse wheel. Hold down the mouse wheel and slightly drag the cursor to rotate.

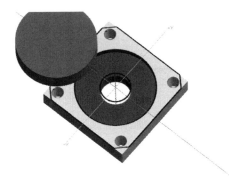

◆ To go back to the Mastercam window, minimize the **Mastercam Simulator** window as shown. ⊖ ⬚ ✕

STEP 9: CHAMFER THE LARGE HOLE

Chamfer Toolpath automatically cuts a chamfer around a contour using a chamfer mill.

Toolpath Preview:

9.1 Chain selection

A **Chain of entities** consists of one or more entities linked together in order and direction. The distance between the endpoints of two consecutive entities of the chain has to be equal or less than the chaining tolerance (0.0001"). In an open chain, the start point is placed at the end of the chain closest to the selection point and the chain direction points to the opposite end of the chain. See **Help** for more information on chaining.

◆ Hover the cursor in the **Toolpaths Managers** and press **Alt + T** to remove the toolpath display.

Toolpaths

- From the **2D** group, click on the upper arrow until the **Contour** toolpath appears as shown.
- Click on the **Contour** icon.

- Leave the default settings in the **Chaining** dialog box as shown.

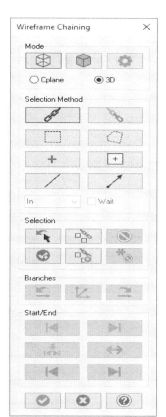

*Note: The **Chain** button is enabled in the **Chaining** dialog box. This lets you chain the entire contour by clicking on one entity.*

♦ Select the chain and ensure the chaining direction is the same as shown.

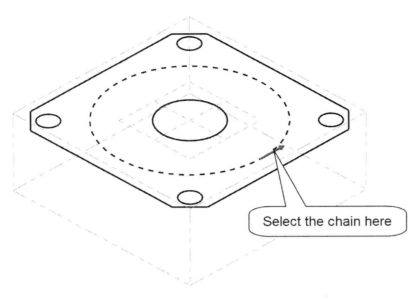

Select the chain here

♦ Select the **OK** button to exit the **Chaining** dialog box.

♦ In the **Toolpath Type** page, the **Contour** toolpath should already be selected.

 Contour   Pocket   Facing   Slot mill   Model Chamfer

9.2 Select a 1/2" Chamfer Mill from the library and set the Tool parameters

♦ Select **Tool** from the **Tree View list**.

♦ Click on the **Select library tool** button. Select library tool...

♦ To be able to see just the spot drill, select the **Filter** button.

♦ Under **Tool Types**, select the **None** button and then choose the **Chamfer mill** icon.

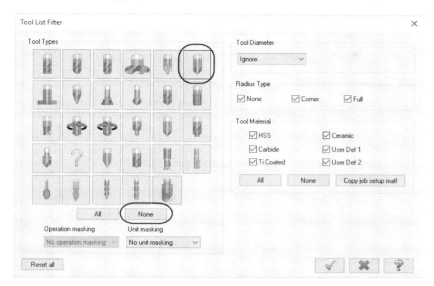

♦ Select the **OK** button to exit the **Tool List Filter** dialog box.
♦ At this point you should only see a list of chamfer mills.
♦ From the **Tool Selection** list, select the **1/2" Chamfer Mill**.

#	Assembly Name	Tool Name	Holder Name	Dia.	Cor. rad.	Length	# Flutes	Type	Ra...
318	—	1/4 CHA...	—	0....	0.0	0.5	4	Ch...	No...
319	—	1/2 CHA...	—	0...	0.0	0.75	4	Ch...	No...
320	—	3/4 CHA...	—	0....	0.0	1.0	4	Ch...	No...
321	—	1 INCH C...	—	1....	0.0	1.0	4	Ch...	No...

♦ In the **Tool Selection** page, choose the **OK** button to exit.
♦ A warning message might appear on the screen telling that the tool selected is not defined as being capable of both roughing and finishing.

Note: The chamfer mill is defined for finish operation only. For chamfer toolpath, we only need a finish operation.

♦ Select the **OK** button to continue.

♦ Input a comment and make the necessary changes as shown.

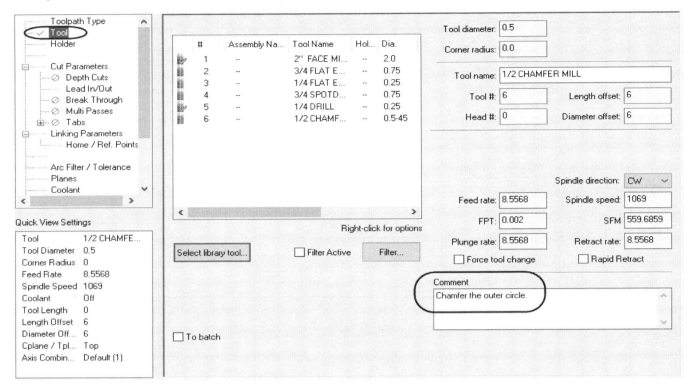

9.3 Cut Parameters

♦ Select the **Cut Parameters** page and change the **Contour type** to **2D chamfer**.
♦ Input a **Chamfer width** of **0.02** and a **Bottom offset** of **0.05** as shown.

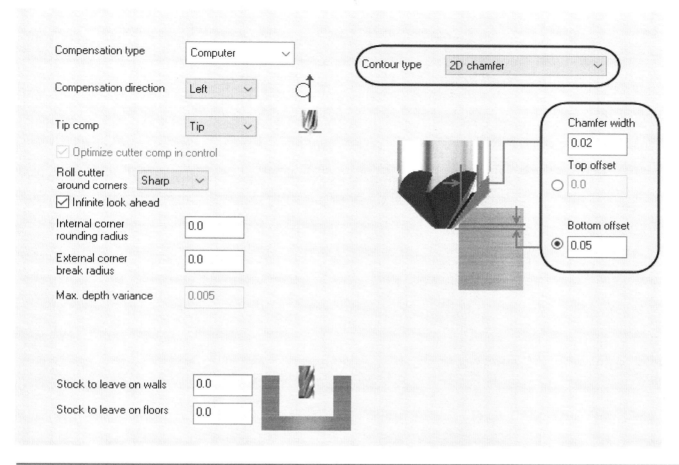

2D chamfer cuts chamfers around a contour.

Chamfer width sets the chamfer width. Mastercam measures the width from the chained geometry adjusted by the cut depths defined on the **Linking Parameters** page.

Bottom offset is an amount to ensure that the tip of the tool clears the bottom of the chamfer.

Roll cutter around corners inserts arc moves around corners in the toolpath.

None guarantees all sharp corners.

Sharp rolls the tool around sharp corners (135 degrees or less).

All rolls the tool around all corners and creates smooth tool movement

9.4 Lead In/Out

♦ From the **Tree View list**, select **Lead In/Out**. Change the **Lead In/Out** parameters and input an **Overlap** value as shown.

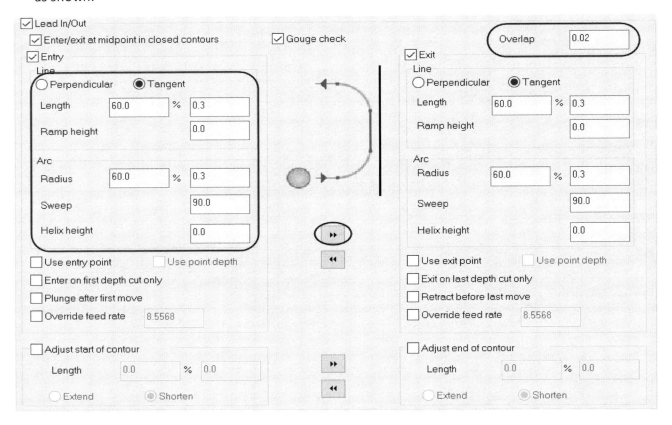

Lead In/Out allows you to select a combination of a Line and an Arc at the beginning and/or end of the contour toolpath for a smooth entry/exit while cutting the part.

Length is set to 60% of the tool diameter to ensure that the linear movement is greater than the tool radius in case **Cutter Compensation** in **Control** was used.

Radius is set to 60% of the tool diameter to ensure that the arc movement is greater than the tool radius to generate an arc output.

Overlap sets how far the tool goes past the end of the toolpath before exiting for a cleaner finish.

9.5 Linking Parameters

♦ Select **Linking Parameters** from the **Tree View list**. Set the **Top of stock** to **0.0** and the **Depth** to **0.0** as shown. Enable **Clearance** if needed, and set it to **2.0**.

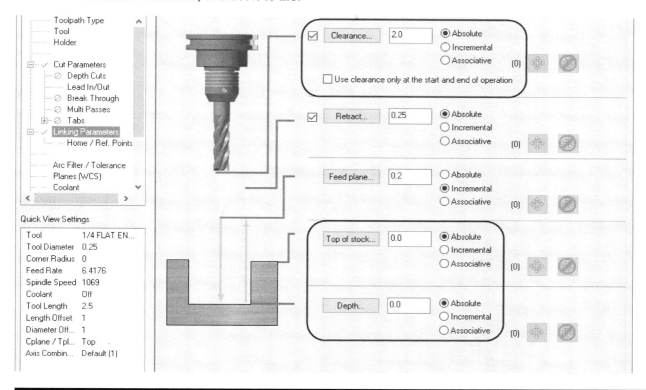

Note: The depth of the chamfer is based on the **Width** and **Tip Offset** set in the **Cut Parameters** page. This is why we set the depth here to zero.

9.6 Preview the Toolpath

♦ To quickly check how the toolpath will be generated, select the **Preview toolpath** icon as shown.

♦ See **"Preview the Toolpath" on page 68** to review the procedure.
♦ The toolpath should look as shown.

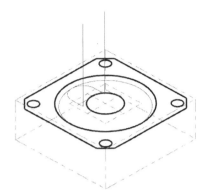

♦ Press **Esc** key to exit the preview.

Note: If the toolpath does not look as shown in the preview, check your parameters again.

♦ Select the **OK** button to exit the **2D Toolpaths - Contour** parameters.

9.7 Verify the Toolpaths

♦ From the **Toolpaths Manager**, click on the **Select all operations** icon.
♦ Click on the **Verify selected operation** icon.
♦ To **Verify** the toolpaths, see **"Simulate the toolpath in Verify" on page 78** to review the procedure.
♦ The part will appear as shown.

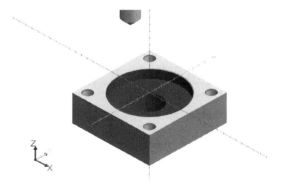

♦ To go back to Mastercam window, minimize **Mastercam Simulator** window as shown.

STEP 10: MACHINE THE CHAMFERS AT THE CORNERS USING CONTOUR TOOLPATH

In this step, you will machine the corners of the part using **Contour Toolpath**.

Toolpath Preview:

♦ To remove the toolpath display, hover the cursor in the **Toolpaths Manager** and press **T** until the toolpaths disappear or press **Alt + T**.

Toolpaths

♦ From the **2D** group, select **Contour** as shown.

♦ To select only one entity at a time, select the **Single** button in the **Chaining** dialog box as shown below.

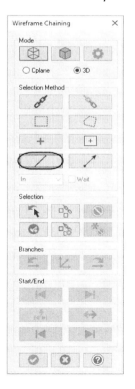

♦ Right mouse click in the graphics window and select the **Top** view as shown.

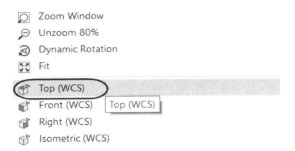

♦ Select the chains and ensure the chaining direction is the same as shown in .

*Note: Select the contour as shown in to ensure that the chaining directions for all four chains are correct. Use the **Reverse** button to flip the chains if needed.* *The green color arrow shows the chain's start location and the red color arrow shows the end of the chain. The chain selection arrows will disappear when you select the next chamfer.*

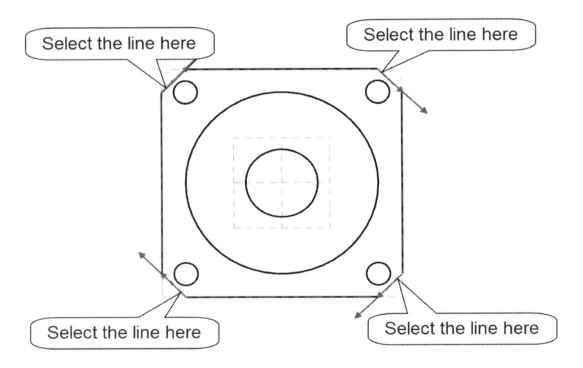

♦ Select the **OK** button to exit the **Chaining** dialog box.

- In the **Toolpath Type** page, the **Contour** toolpath will be selected.

Contour   Pocket   Facing   Slot mill   Model Chamfer

10.1 Select the 1/2" Flat Endmill and set the Tool parameters

- Select **Tool** from the **Tree View list**.

- Click on **Select library tool** button. Select library tool...

- To be able to see all the tools from the library, disable **Filter Active**.

Filter...

Filter Active

280 of 280 tools

- Scroll down and select the **1/2" Flat Endmill (#290)** as shown.

#	Assembly Na...	Tool Name	Holder Name	Dia.	Cor. rad.	Length	# Flutes	Type	Rad. T...
288	--	13/32 FLAT ENDMILL	--	0.406...	0.0	0.8	4	Flat e...	None
289	--	7/16 FLAT ENDMILL	--	0.4375	0.0	0.8	4	Flat e...	None
290	--	1/2 FLAT ENDMILL	--	0.5	0.0	1.0	4	Flat e...	None
291	--	17/32 FLAT ENDMILL	--	0.5312	0.0	1.0	4	Flat e...	None
292	--	5/8 FLAT ENDMILL	--	0.625	0.0	1.5	4	Flat e...	None

- Select the tool in the **Tool Selection** page and then select the **OK** button to exit.

- Make all the necessary changes as shown.

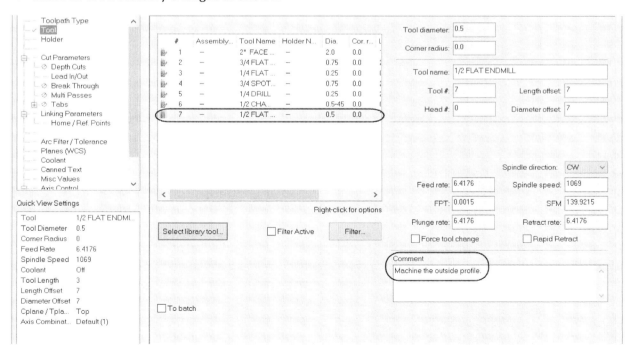

10.2 Cut Parameters

♦ Select the **Cut Parameters** page and change the **Contour type** to **2D** as shown.

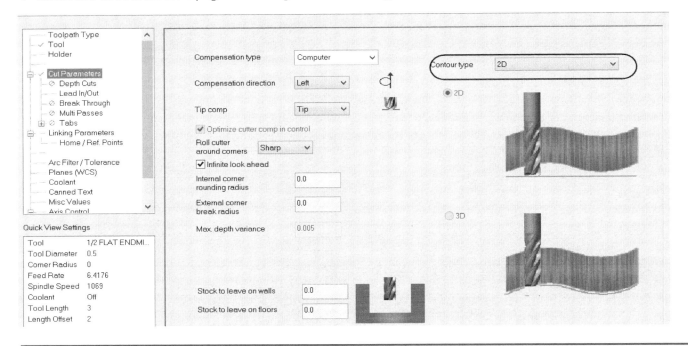

Compensation type allows you to choose the compensation between **Computer**, **Control**, **Wear**, **Reverse wear** or **Off**.

Compensation type set to **Computer** instructs Mastercam to compute the compensated toolpath and does not output control codes for compensation.

Roll cutter around corners inserts arc moves around corners in the toolpath.

Internal corner rounding radius allows you to enter a radius value to create a smoother tool motion in sharp corners. Corner smoothing reduces tool wear and makes your tool motion more efficient.

External corner break radius allows you to enter a radius value to break external sharp corners defined within a chain to create a smooth, rounded corner.

Stock to leave on walls/floors allows you to enter a value to leave material for a finish toolpath.

10.3 Depth Cuts

♦ Select **Depth Cuts** and enable it as shown.
♦ Make sure that the parameters are set as shown.

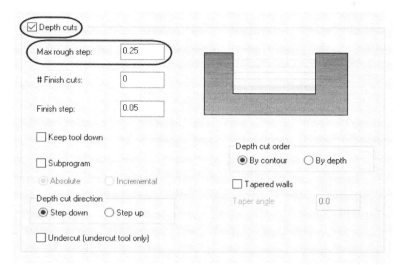

10.4 Lead In/Out

♦ Select **Lead In/Out** from the **Tree View list**. Make sure the parameters are set as shown.

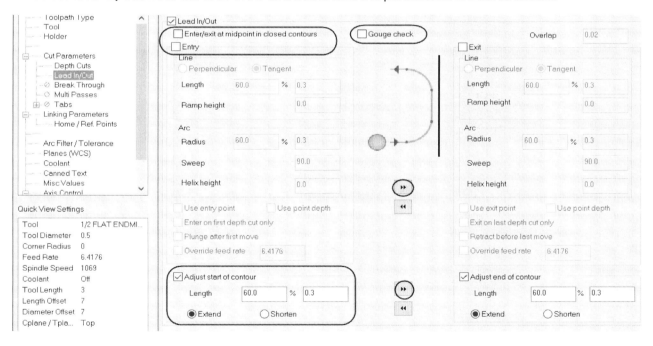

Adjust start/end of contour moves the starting/ending position in open contours by adding (**Extend**) or removing (Shorten) the specified length.

10.5 Linking Parameters

♦ Select **Linking Parameters** from the **Tree View list**. Set the **Top of stock** and the **Depth** as shown.

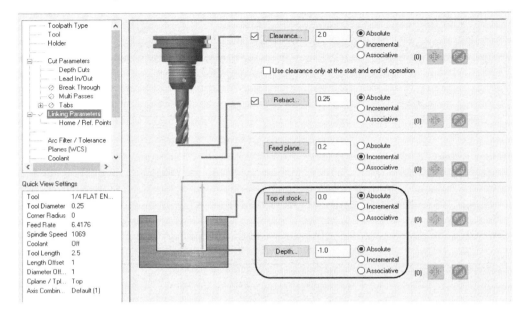

10.6 Preview the Toolpath

♦ To quickly check how the toolpath will be generated, select the **Preview toolpath** icon as shown.

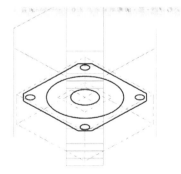

♦ See **"Preview the Toolpath" on page 68** to review the procedure.

♦ The toolpath should look as shown.

♦ Press **Esc** key to exit the preview.

Note: If the toolpath does not look as shown in the preview, check your parameters again.

♦ Select the **OK** button to exit **2D Toolpaths - Contour**.

10.7 Verify the toolpaths

◆ To **Verify** the toolpaths, see **"Simulate the toolpath in Verify" on page 78** to review the procedure.

◆ Ensure all operations are selected; if not, use the button **Select all operations** in the **Toolpaths Manager**.

◆ Right mouse click in the graphics window and select the **Isometric** option.

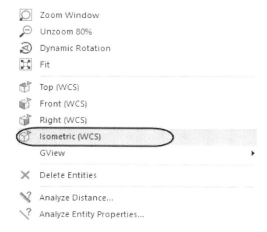

◆ Your part will appear as shown.

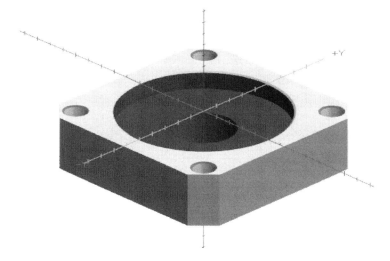

◆ To go back to the Mastercam window, close **Mastercam Simulator** window as shown.

STEP 11: POST THE FILE

- ◆ Ensure all operations are selected. If not, use the button **Select all operations** in the **Toolpaths Manager**.
- ◆ Select the **Post selected operations** icon from the **Toolpaths Manager** as shown.

Note: *The HLE/Demo version of Mastercam does not support post processing. The G1 button does not work and no G-code can be created in the HLE/Demo version.*

- ◆ In the **Post processing** window, make necessary changes as shown.

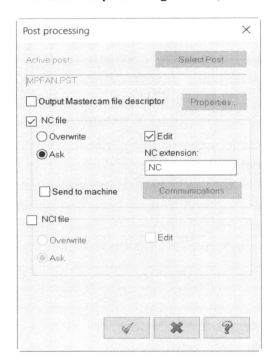

NC file enabled allows you to keep the NC file and to assign the same name as the MCAM file.

Edit enabled allows you to automatically launch the default.

- ◆ Select the **OK** button to continue.
- ◆ Save the **NC** file.

♦ A window with **Mastercam Code Expert** will be launched and the NC program will appear as shown.

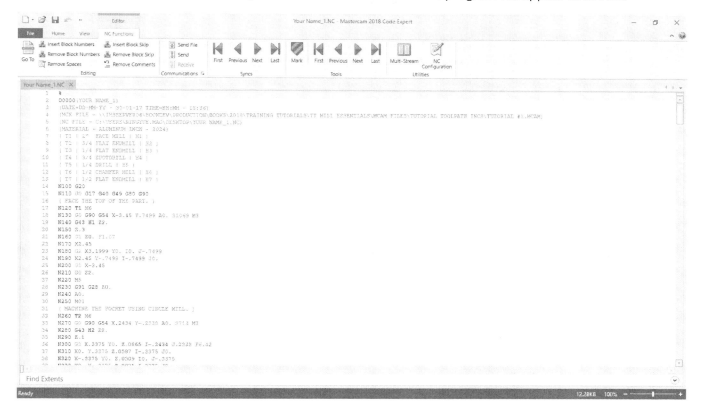

♦ Select the "**X**" box at the upper right corner to exit the editor.

STEP 12: SAVE THE UPDATED MCAM FILE

CREATE THE TOOLPATHS FOR TUTORIAL #1 EXERCISE

Create the Toolpaths for Tutorial #1 Exercise as per the instructions below.

Set the machine properties including the stock.
Remove the material on the outside of the part Contour (2D).

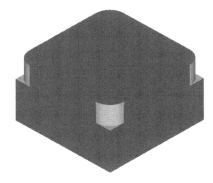

- ◆ Use a **1/2" Flat Endmill**.
- ◆ Based on your chaining direction, ensure the **Compensation** direction is set correctly.
- ◆ Enable **Depth Cuts** and set the **Max rough step** to **0.25"**.
- ◆ In **Lead In/Out**, set **Length** and **Radius** to **60%** with a **90 degree sweep**.
- ◆ No **Break Through**, **Multi Passes**.
- ◆ Set the depth according to the drawing.

Spot drill the holes.

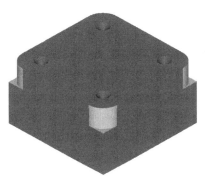

- ◆ Use a **3/4" Spot Drill**.
- ◆ Set the **Cycle** to **Drill/Counterbore** and set a **Dwell** of **1.0 second**.
- ◆ Use the depth calculator to set a **0.05"** chamfer on the hole.

Drill the holes.

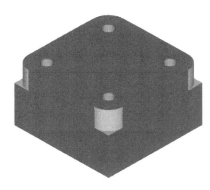

- ◆ Use a **1/2" Drill**.
- ◆ Set the **Cycle** to **Peck Drill** and set your peck values.
- ◆ Set the depth according to the drawing.

Remove the material in the center of the part using Circle Mill toolpath.

- ◆ Use a **1/2" Flat Endmill**.
- ◆ Choose to leave no stock on the walls.
- ◆ Enable **Roughing** and set the parameters.
- ◆ Enable **Depth Cuts** and set the **Max rough step** to **0.5"**and enable and enable **Keep tool down**.
- ◆ Set the depth according to the drawing.

TUTORIAL #1 TOOLPATH CREATION QUIZ

♦ What is a Contour Toolpath used for?

♦ What is a Facing Toolpath used for?

♦ What does a Circle Mill Toolpath allow you to do?

♦ What does Backplot do?

♦ What does Verify allow you to do?

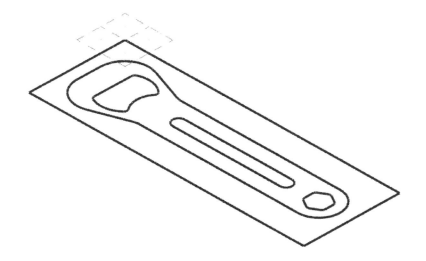

OVERVIEW OF STEPS TAKEN TO CREATE THE PART GEOMETRY:

From Drawing to CAD Model:

♦ The student should examine the drawing on the following page to understand what part is being created in the tutorial.

♦ From the drawing we can decide how to create the geometry in Mastercam.

Create the 2D CAD Model:

♦ The student will create the Top 2D geometry needed to create the toolpaths.

♦ Geometry creation commands such as Rectangle, Polygon, Fillet Entities, Fillet Chain, Circle Center Point, Line Endpoints, Rectangular Shapes, and Trim Break Extend will be used.

TUTORIAL #2 DRAWING

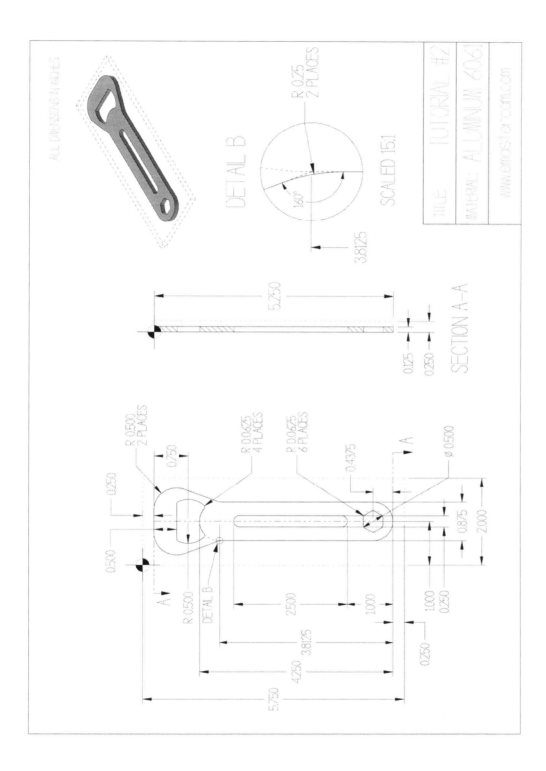

STEP 1: SETTING UP THE GRAPHICAL USER INTERFACE

Please refer to the **Getting Started** section for more info on how to set up the graphical user interface. In this step, you will learn how to hide the manager panels to gain more space in the graphics window.

♦ Use **Auto Hide** icon to hide all **Manager** panels.

♦ The panels will be hidden to the left of the graphics window as shown.

Note: To un-hide them temporally, you can click on one of the Managers to open it as shown.

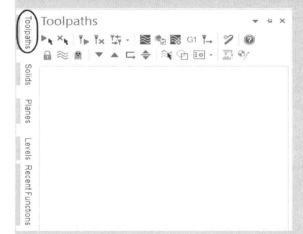

While creating the geometry, keep the Manager panels hidden. This ensures more space in the graphics window for the geometry.

STEP 2: CREATE A RECTANGLE

In this step, you will learn how to create a rectangle given the width, the height, and the anchor position.

Step Preview:

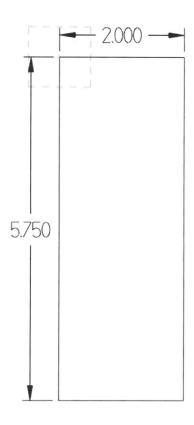

Wireframe

♦ From the **Shapes** group, select **Rectangle**.

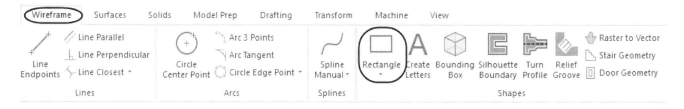

♦ In the **Rectangle** panel, enter the **Width** and **Height** and disable **Anchor to center** as shown.

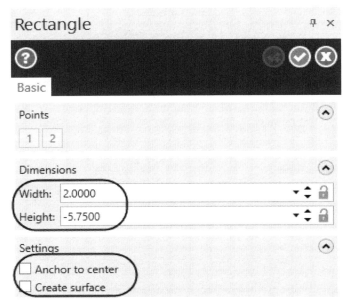

♦ Press **Enter** after typing the values to see a preview of the rectangle.
♦ To select the position of the base point, from the **General Selection** toolbar, click on the drop down arrow next to the **AutoCursor** as shown.

♦ From the fly-out menu, select Origin.

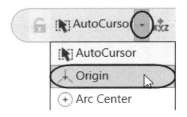

♦ Select the **OK** button to exit the **Rectangle** command.

- Press **Alt + F1** to fit the geometry to the screen.
- The geometry should look as shown.

Note: While creating geometry for this tutorial, if you make a mistake, you can undo the last step using the **Undo** icon. You can undo as many steps as needed. If you delete or undo a step by mistake, just use the **Redo** icon. To delete unwanted geometry, select the geometry first and then press **Delete** from the keyboard. To zoom or un-zoom, move the cursor in the center of the geometry and scroll up or down the mouse wheel.

STEP 3: CREATE TWO OBROUND SHAPES

In this step, you will learn how to create two obround shapes. To create an obround, you need to specify the width and height of the obround, as well as radius of the fillet and any rotation angles if applicable.

Step Preview:

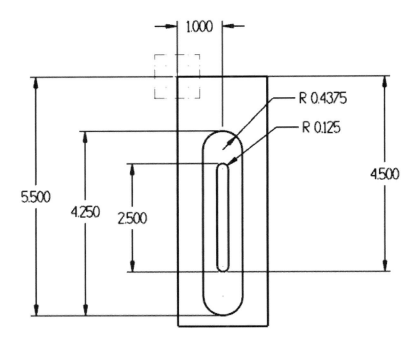

3.1 Create the large obround

Wireframe

♦ From the **Shapes** group, click on the drop down arrow below **Rectangle** and select **Rectangular Shapes** as shown.

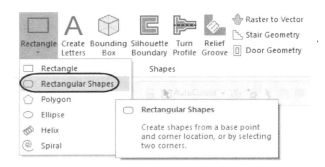

♦ [Select position of base point]: Select **AutoCursor Fast Point** icon from the **General Selection** toolbar.

♦ Enter the coordinates as shown. Press **Enter**.

1,-5.5

---

*Note: When entering the coordinates for the center point, the first value is the **X** coordinate value, then the **Y** value follow by the **Z** value only if it is different from zero. The coordinate values are separated by a comma. You do not need to use the coordinate labels if you enter the values in this order.*

♦ [Enter width and height or select position of corner]: Choose the **Obround** option for the **Type**, and select the lower middle radio button under **Origin**.

♦ Change the settings in the **Rectangular Shapes** panel to create an obround with the width **0.875** and height **4.25** as shown.

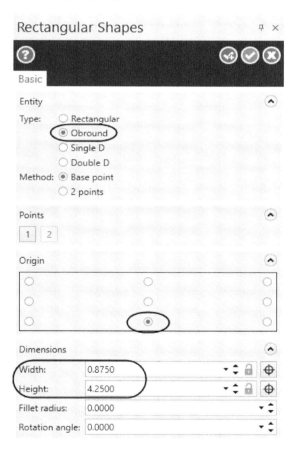

♦ Press **Enter** to see the correctly dimensioned shape created in the graphics window as shown.

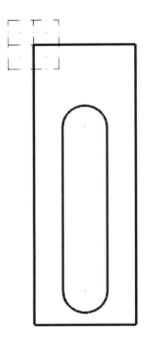

♦ Press Enter or select the **OK and Create New Operation** button to continue with the same command.

3.2 Create the small obround

♦ [Select position of base point]: Select **AutoCursor Fast Point** icon  and enter the coordinates as shown.

1,-4.5

♦ Press **Enter**.
♦ [Enter width and height or select position of corner]: Enter the width **0.25** and the height **2.5** into the appropriate fields as shown.

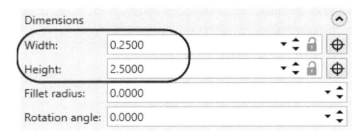

♦ Press Enter to see the correctly dimensioned shape created in the graphics window as shown.

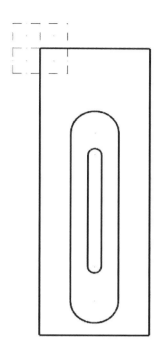

♦ Select the **OK** button to exit the command.

STEP 4: CREATE A CIRCLE

In this step, you will learn how to create a circle using the **Circle Center Point** function. **Circle Center Point** allows you to make a circle given the center point and radius or diameter.

Step Preview:

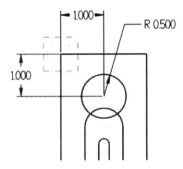

Wireframe

♦ From **Arcs** group, select **Circle Center Point** as shown.

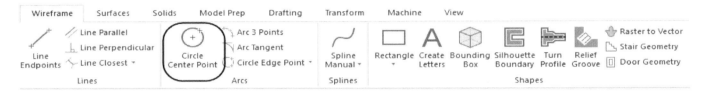

♦ Enter the **Radius 0.5** in the panel as shown. Press **Enter**.

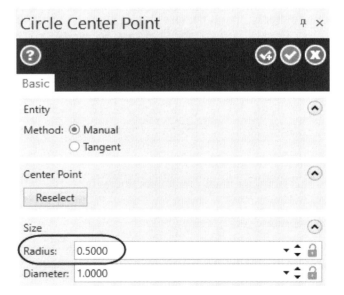

♦ [Enter the center point]: Select the **AutoCursor Fast Point** icon  from the **General Selection** toolbar and enter the coordinates as shown.

♦ Type **1, -1** as shown.

1,-1

♦ Select the **OK** button to exit the command.

♦ The geometry should look as shown.

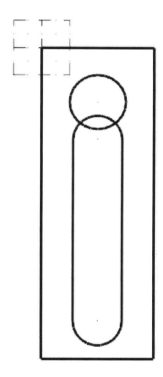

STEP 5: USE TRIM DIVIDE TO CLEAN THE CIRCLE

In this step, you will learn how to trim the geometry using the Divide option. Divide allows you to trim an entity into two disjointed segments by removing the segment that lies between two dividing intersections. It also allows you to delete entities based on the nearest intersection. Always select the segment in the area that should be removed.

Step Preview:

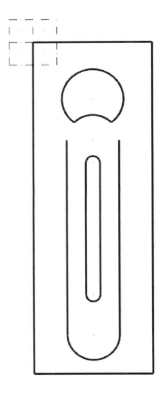

Wireframe

♦ From the **Modify** group, select **Divide** as shown.

♦ Make sure the **Type** is set to **Trim** as shown.

♦ [Select the curve to divide/delete]: Select the arcs as shown in Figure: 5.0.1. You may need to zoom in by placing the cursor over the area you wish to zoom, and then scrolling the mouse wheel up.

Figure: 5.0.1

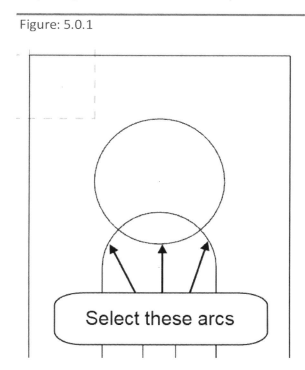

Select these arcs

Note: When hovering above the line, you will notice that the line changes to a hidden line style. This is a preview of what is going to be deleted and lets you select another segment of the line if necessary.

♦ Click the **OK** button in the panel to exit the command.

◆ The geometry should look as shown.

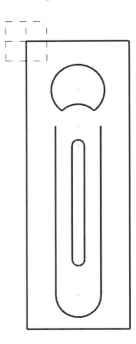

◆ Press **Alt + F1** to fit the geometry to the screen.

STEP 6: CREATE PARALLEL LINES

In this step, you will use the **Line Parallel** command to create two more horizontal lines at different distance.

Step Preview:

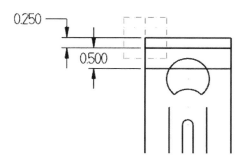

Wireframe

♦ From the **Lines** group, select the **Line Parallel** icon as shown.

♦ [Select a line]: Select the horizontal top line of the rectangle as shown.

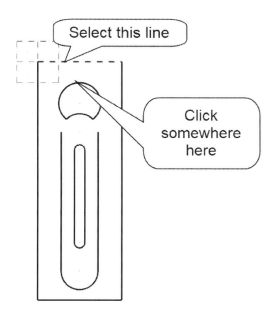

♦ [Select the point to place a parallel line through]: Click anywhere below the selected line.

♦ In the **Line Parallel** panel, enter the **Offset Distance 0.25** and hit **Enter**. Make sure that the **Selected side** is chosen for the **Direction as shown**.

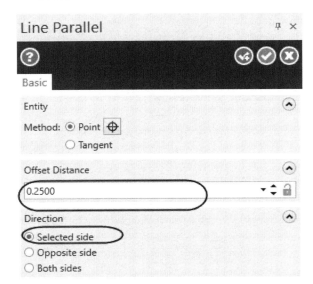

♦ Click the **OK and Create New Operation** button in the panel to continue in the same command.

♦ [Select a line]: Select the line that you just created as shown.

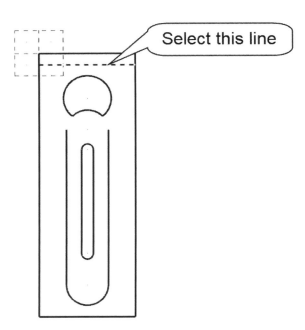

Select this line

♦ [Select the point to place a parallel line through]: Click anywhere below the selected line.

◆ In the **Line Parallel** panel, enter the **Offset Distance 0.5** and hit **Enter**. Make sure that the **Selected side** is chosen for the **Direction as shown**.

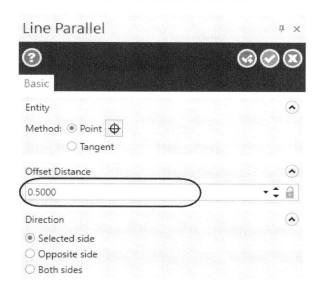

◆ Click the **OK** button in the panel to exit the command.
◆ The geometry should look as shown.

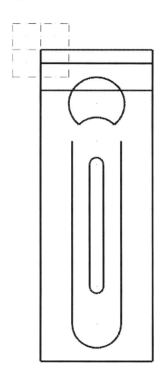

STEP 7: USE TRIM DIVIDE DELETE TO CLEAN UP THE GEOMETRY

In this step, you will divide/delete the unwanted intersections of the circle and the line that passes through it.

Step Preview:

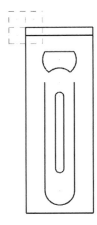

Wireframe

◆ From the **Modify** group, select **Divide** as shown.

◆ Make sure the **Type** is set to **Trim** as shown.

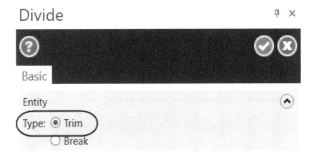

♦ [Select the curve to divide/delete]: Select the lines as shown. You may use the mouse wheel to zoom in if needed.

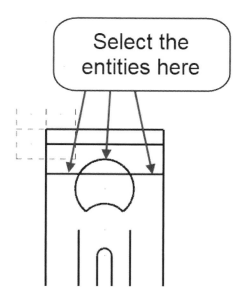

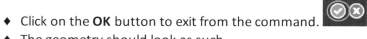

♦ Click on the **OK** button to exit from the command.
♦ The geometry should look as such.

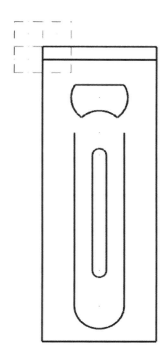

STEP 8: CREATE ANGULAR LINES

Step Preview:

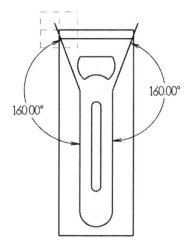

Wireframe

♦ From the **Lines** group, select **Line Endpoints**.
♦ Ensure the **Type** is set to **Freeform**, and set **Length** to **2.0** and Angle to **270-160** as shown. Hit **Enter**.

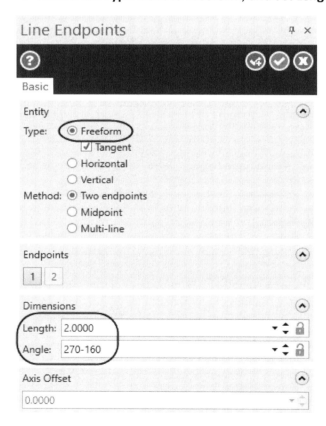

♦ [Specify the first endpoint]: Select the line Endpoint as shown.

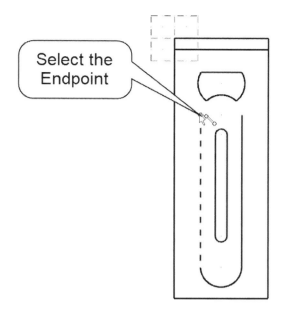

Select the
Endpoint

♦ Click on the **OK** and **Create New Operation** or press **Enter** to stay within the command.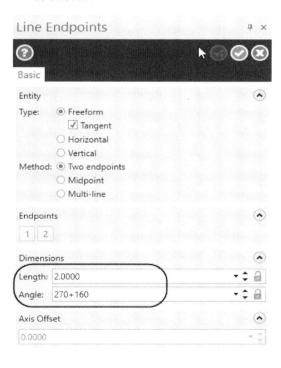
♦ Enter again the **Length** and change the value of the angle to **270+160** while keeping all other settings the same as shown.

♦ Select the line Endpoint as shown.

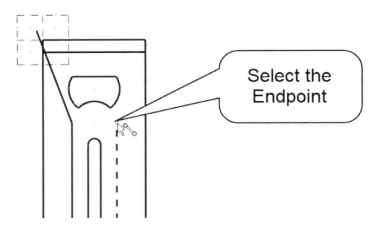

Select the
Endpoint

♦ Select the **OK** icon to exit the command.

♦ The geometry should look as shown.

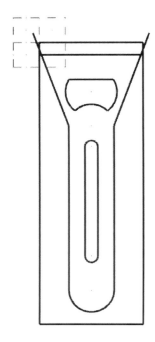

STEP 9: CREATE POLYGON

In this step, you will learn how to create a six sided polygon. To create a polygon, you need to specify the number of sides, the radius of the arc based on which polygon is created and how it is measured (Corner or Flat), and the center point.

Step Preview:

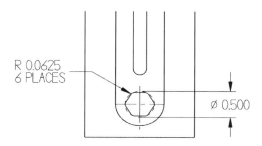

Wireframe

♦ From the **Shapes** group, select **Polygon** from the drop down menu beneath **Rectangle** as shown.

♦ Enter a radius of **0.25** and a **Corner Fillet** of **0.0625**. Ensure that the number of sides is set to **6** and **Corner radius** is selected. Click on the lock icon beside the radius field.

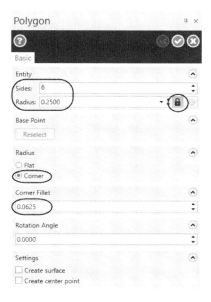

♦ [Select position of base point]: Using the mouse wheel, zoom into the lower portion of the geometry. Select the Center Point as shown.

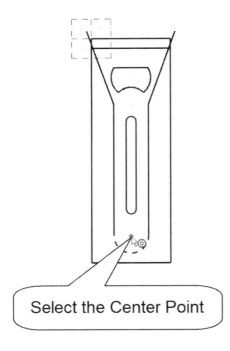

Select the Center Point

♦ Select the **OK** button to exit the command.
♦ Press **Alt + F1** to fit the geometry to the screen.
♦ The geometry should look as shown.

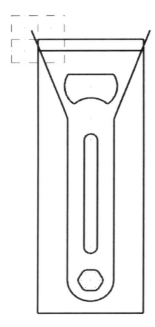

STEP 10: CREATE FILLETS

Fillets are used to round sharp corners.

Step Preview:

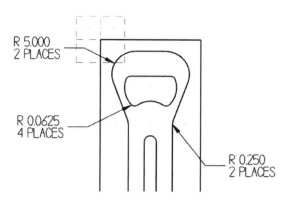

10.1 Fillet the large rounded section

Wireframe

♦ From the **Modify** group, select **Fillet Entities**.

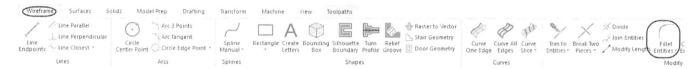

♦ Enter a **Radius** of **0.5** in the **Fillet Entities** panel as shown below. Make sure that **Normal** and **Trim entities** are enabled.

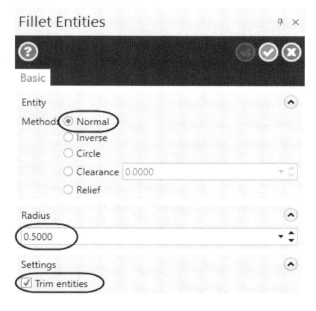

♦ [Fillet: Select an entity]: Select Entity A as shown in Figure: 10.1.1.
♦ [Fillet: Select another entity]: Select Entity B as shown in Figure: 10.1.1.

Figure: 10.1.1

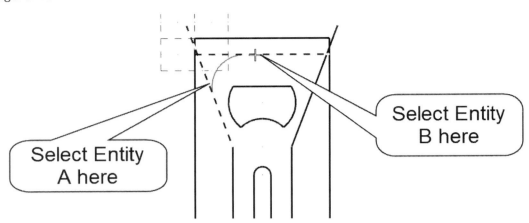

♦ Hit Enter or click the **OK and Create New Operation** button to continue in the command.

♦ [Fillet: Select an entity]: Select Entity B as shown Figure: 10.1.2.
♦ [Fillet: Select another entity]: Select Entity C as shown Figure: 10.1.2.

Figure: 10.1.2

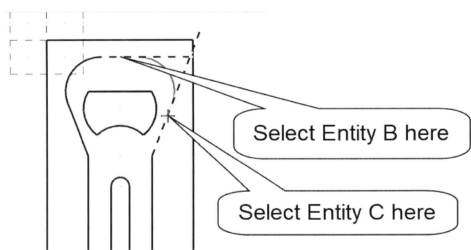

♦ Hit **Enter** or click the **OK and Create New Operation** button to continue in the command.

10.2 Fillet the sides

◆ In the **Fillet Entities** panel, change the radius to **0.25** as shown. Ensure all other parameters are kept the same as the previous operation.

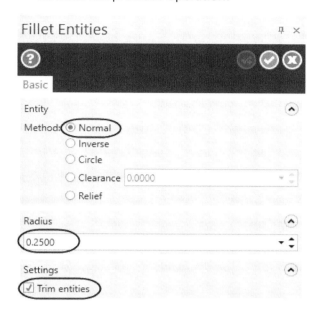

◆ [Fillet: Select an entity]: Select Entity D as shown Figure: 10.2.1.
◆ [Fillet: Select another entity]: Select EntityE as shown Figure: 10.2.1.

Figure: 10.2.1

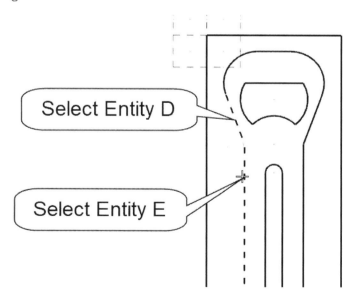

- ◆ [Fillet: Select an entity]: Select Entity F as shown Figure: 10.2.2.
- ◆ [Fillet: Select another entity]: Select Entity G as shown Figure: 10.2.2.

Figure: 10.2.2

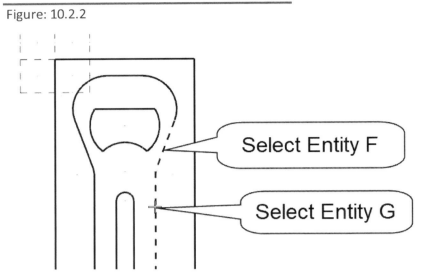

- ◆ Select the **OK** button to exit the **Fillet Entities** panel.

10.3 Use fillet chains for the remaining pocket

Wireframe

- ◆ From the **Modify** group, click on the drop down arrow beneath **Fillet Entities** and choose **Fillet Chains**.

♦ [Select chain 1]: Select the upper pocket as shown. You may wish to zoom in with the mouse wheel.

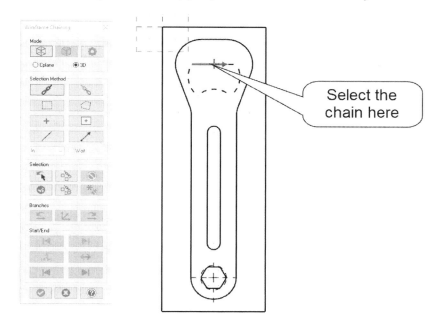

Select the chain here

♦ Click the **OK** button to continue.

♦ In the **Fillet Chains** panel, change the **Radius** value to **0.0625** as shown. Make sure other settings are enabled as follows. Press **Enter**.

♦ Click the **OK** button to exit the command.

- Press **Alt + F1** to fit the geometry to the screen.
- The geometry should look as shown.

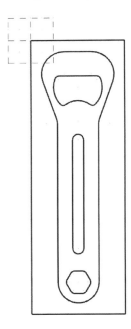

STEP 11: ROTATE THE PART

In this step you will rotate the part to have it orientated as it will be setup at the machine.

Step Preview:

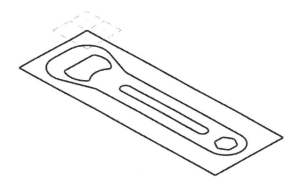

Transform

- From the **Position** group, select **Rotate**.

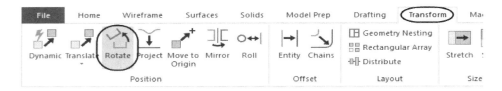

◆ Press Ctrl + A to select the entire part as shown.

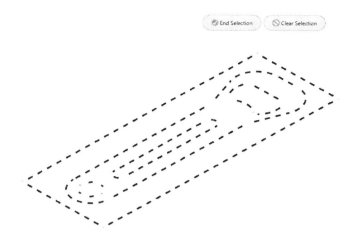

◆ Click on the **End Selection** button or press **Enter** to continue.

◆ In the **Rotate** panel, enable **Move** and set the **Angle** to **-90** degrees as shown.

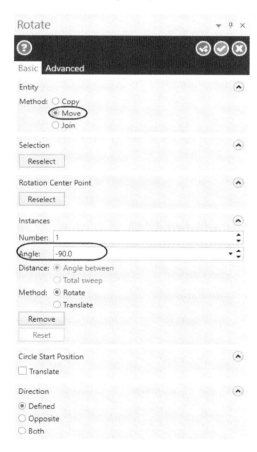

◆ Select the **OK** button to exit the **Rotate** command.

♦ The part should look as shown.

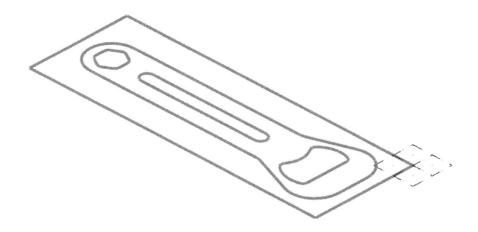

♦ To remove the result color, right mouse click in the graphics window and select **Clear color** icon as shown.

STEP 12: SAVE THE FILE

File

♦ **Save As.**

Note: You can also click on the *Save As* icon from the ***Quick Access Toolbar.***

♦ Click on the **Browse** icon as shown.
♦ Find a location on the computer to save your file. **File name:** "Your Name_2".

Note: It is highly recommended to save the file from time to time when going through the tutorial.
Click on the Save icon from the ***Quick Access Toolbar*** at the upper left corner to save the file.

TUTORIAL #2 REVIEW EXERCISE

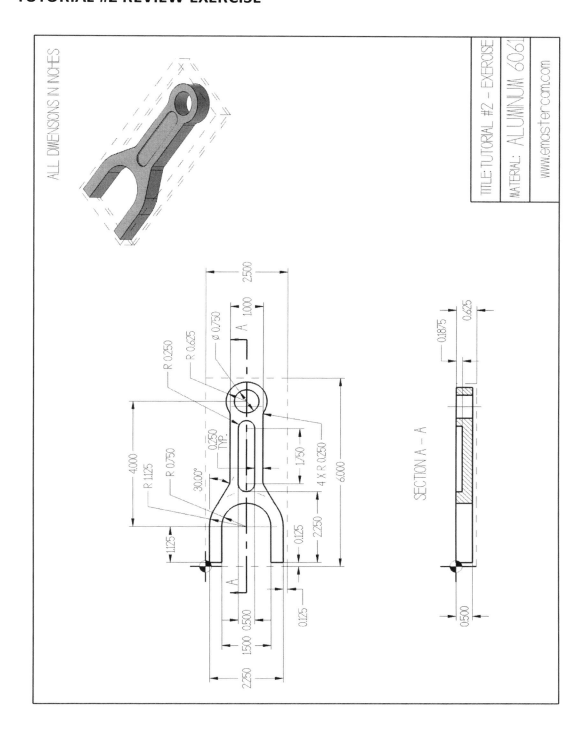

CREATE THE GEOMETRY FOR TUTORIAL #2 EXERCISE

Use these commands from the Wireframe tab to create the geometry.

- Rectangular Shapes.
- Circle Center Point.
- Line Endpoints (Tangent Angle).
- Trim Break Extend.
- Line Parallel.
- Fillet Entities.

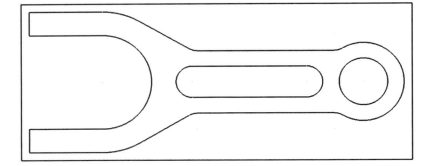

TUTORIAL #2 GEOMETRY CREATION QUIZ

- ◆ What do you need to know to create a rectangle?

- ◆ What command do you need to use to create an obround shape?

- ◆ What does Divide command allow you to do?

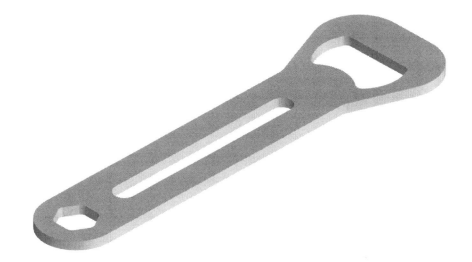

OVERVIEW OF STEPS TAKEN TO CREATE THE FINAL PART:

Create the necessary Toolpaths to machine the part:

◆ The student will set up the stock size to be used and the clamping method used.

Setup 1

◆ A Slot milling toolpath will be created to machine the slot.
◆ A Pocket toolpath will be created to machine the cut through pockets.
◆ A High Speed Dynamic Contour Mill toolpath will finish the cut through pockets.
◆ A High Speed Dynamic Mill toolpath will rough out the material outside of the part.
◆ A Contour toolpath will be created to finish the outside of the part.

Setup 2

◆ A Facing toolpath will be created to face the part.

Backplot and Verify the file:

◆ Backplot will be used to simulate a step-by-step process of the tool's movements.
◆ Verify will be used to watch a tool machine the part out of a solid model.

Post Process the file to generate the G-code:

◆ The student will then post process the file to obtain an NC file containing the necessary code for the machine.

TOOLPATH CREATION - SETUP #1

SUGGESTED FIXTURE

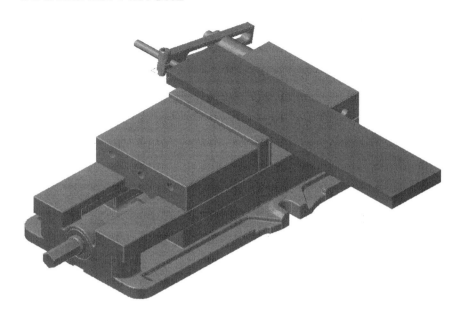

Note: In order to machine this part, we will have 2 setups and output 2 NC files. To view the second setup, see "toolpath Creation - Setup 2" on page 215.

SETUP SHEET

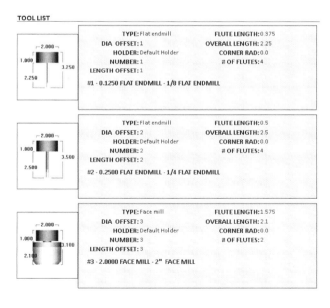

STEP 1: SELECT THE MACHINE AND SET UP THE STOCK

In Mastercam, you select a **Machine Definition** before creating any toolpath. The **Machine Definition** is a model of your machine's capabilities and features. It acts like a template for setting up your machine. The machine definition ties together three main components: the schematic model of your machine's components, the control definition that models your control capabilities, and the post processor that will generate the required machine code (G-code). For a Mill Essentials exercise (2D toolpaths), we need just a basic machine definition.

*Note: For the purpose of this tutorial, we will be using the **Default Mill** machine.*

1.1 Unhide the Toolpaths Manager panel

♦ From the left side of the graphics window, click on the **Toolpaths** tab as shown.

♦ To lock it, click on the Toolpaths tab and then click on the Auto Hide icon as shown.

1.2 Select the machine

Machine

---

*Note: Once you select the **Mill Default**, the **Ribbon bar** changes to reflect the toolpaths that could be used with **Mill Default**.*

◆ Select the plus sign (**+**) in front of Properties in the **Toolpaths Manager** to expand the **Toolpaths Group Properties**.

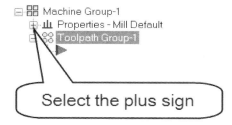

Select the plus sign

◆ Select **Tool settings** to set the tool parameters.

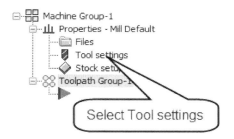

Select Tool settings

♦ Change the parameters to match the screen shot as shown.

Default program number is used to enter a number if your machine requires a number for a program name.

Assign tool numbers sequentially allows you to overwrite the tool number from the library with the next available tool number. (First operation tool number 1; second operation tool number 2, etc.).

Warn of duplicate tool numbers allows you to get a warning if you enter two tools with the same number.

Override defaults with modal values enables the system to keep the values that you enter.

Feed Calculation set to **From tool** uses feed rate, plunge rate, retract rate, and spindle speed from the tool definition.

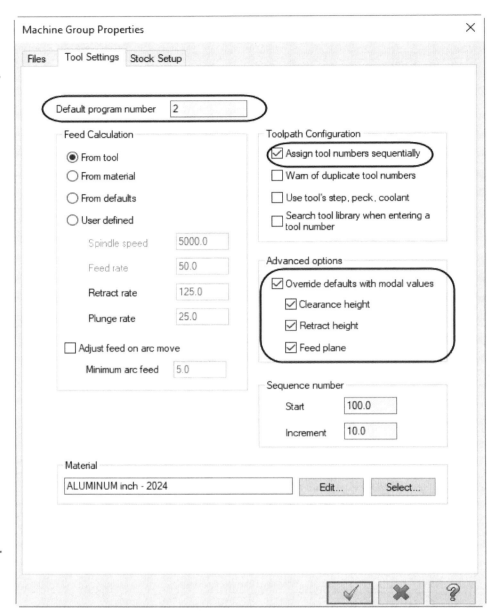

- Select the **Stock Setup** tab to define the stock.
- Select **All Entities** at the bottom of the dialog box.
- In the **Z** field, enter **0.25** as shown in Figure: 1.2.1. This will add **0.125"** of stock on the bottom of the model.
- Click in the **Stock Setup** window at the upper right corner of the stock to move the arrow where the origin is set and then change the **Stock Origin** values to zero as shown.

Figure: 1.2.1

The **X, Y, Z** values in the graphics area are the dimensions of the stock model. They are always positive values.

The **Stock Origin** values adjust the positioning of the stock, ensuring that you have an equal amount of extra stock around the finished part. In the graphics, the plus sign (**+**) shows you where the stock origin is. The default position is the middle of the stock.

Display options allow you to set the stock as Wireframe and to fit the stock to the screen. (Fit Screen)

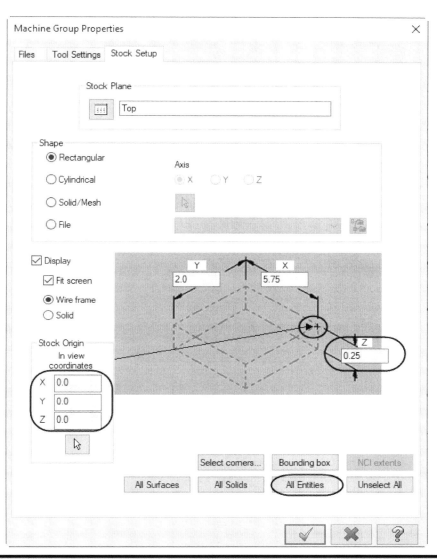

Note: The stock model that you create is displayed when viewing the file or the toolpaths, during backplot, or while verifying toolpaths.

- Select the **OK** button to exit **Machine Group Properties**.

♦ Right mouse click in the graphics window and select the **Isometric** view to see the stock.

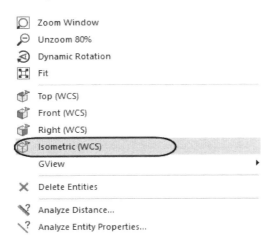

♦ Press **Alt + F1** to fit the drawing to the screen.
♦ The stock model will appear as shown.

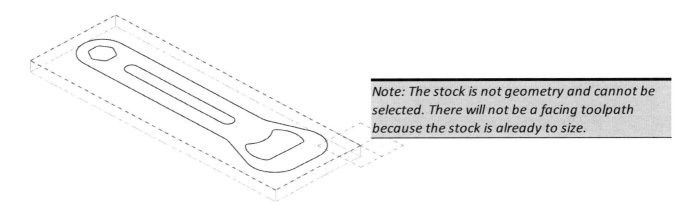

Note: The stock is not geometry and cannot be selected. There will not be a facing toolpath because the stock is already to size.

♦ Right mouse click again and select the **Top** view from the list to see the part from the top.

STEP 2: SLOT MILLING

Slot Mill toolpath allows Mastercam to efficiently machine obround slots. These are slots that consist of 2 straight lines and two 180-degree arcs at the ends.

Toolpath Preview:

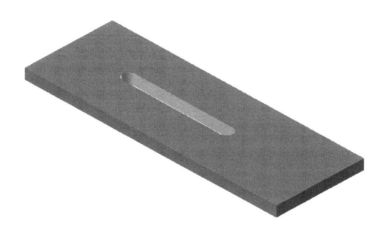

Toolpaths

♦ From the **2D** group, select the **Expand gallery** arrow as shown.

♦ Select the **Slot Mill** as shown.

♦ When the **Chaining** dialog box appears, leave **Wireframe Mode** and **Chain** as the only options selected.
♦ Select the chain as shown.

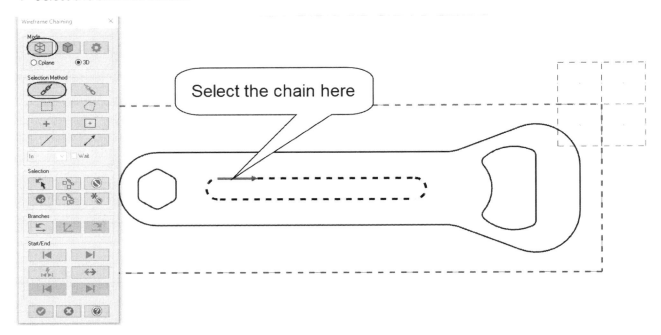

♦ Select the **OK** button to exit the **Chain Options** panel.
♦ In the **Toolpath Type** page, the **Slot Mill** icon will be automatically selected.

Contour   Pocket   Facing   Slot mill   Model Chamfer

Note: Mastercam updates the pages as you modify them and then marks them in the Tree View list with a green check mark. Pages that are not changed are marked with a red circle and slash.

2.1 Select a 1/8" Flat Endmill and set the Tool parameters

- ♦ Select **Tool** from the **Tree View list**.
- ♦ Click on the **Select library tool** button.

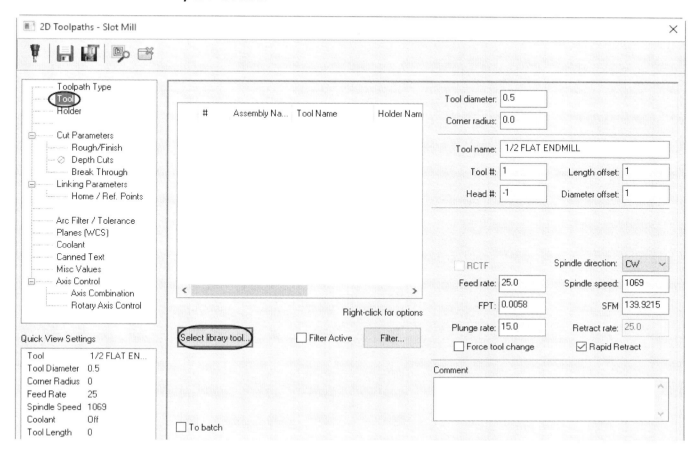

- ♦ Select the **Filter** button.

☑ Filter Active

427 of 427 tools

- ◆ Select the **None** button and then under **Tool Types**, choose the **Flat Endmill** icon.
- ◆ Under **Tool Diameter**, select **Equal** and input a value **0.125** as shown.

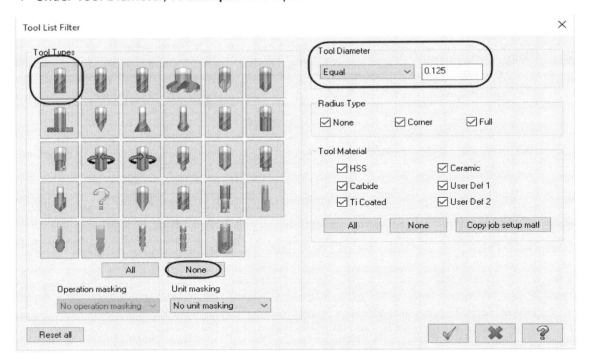

- ◆ Select the **OK** button to exit the **Tool List Filter**.
- ◆ In the **Tool Selection** dialog box you should only see a **1/8" Flat Endmill**.
- ◆ Select the **1/8" Flat Endmill** in the **Tool Selection** page and then select the **OK** button to exit.

#	Assembly Na...	Tool Name	Holder Name	Dia.
282	--	1/8 FLAT ENDMILL	--	0.125

♦ Input a comment and make all the necessary changes, as shown.

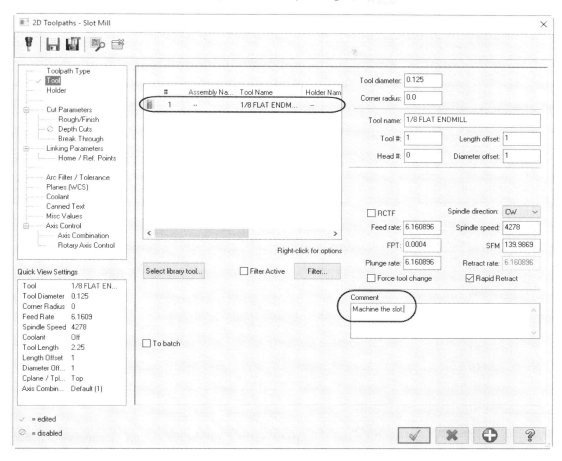

In the **Comment** field, enter a comment to help identify the toolpath in the **Toolpaths Manager** such as the one shown above.

The **Feed rate, Plunge rate, Retract rate,** and **Spindle speed** are based on the tool definition as set in the **Tool Settings**. You may change these values as per your part material and tools.

*Note: If by mistake you click the **OK** button, the toolpath will be generated without all the parameters set properly. To return and set the parameters, click on the **Parameters** in the **Toolpaths Manager** as shown below.*

2.2 Cut Parameters

♦ From the **Tree view list**, select **Cut Parameters** and make the necessary changes as shown.

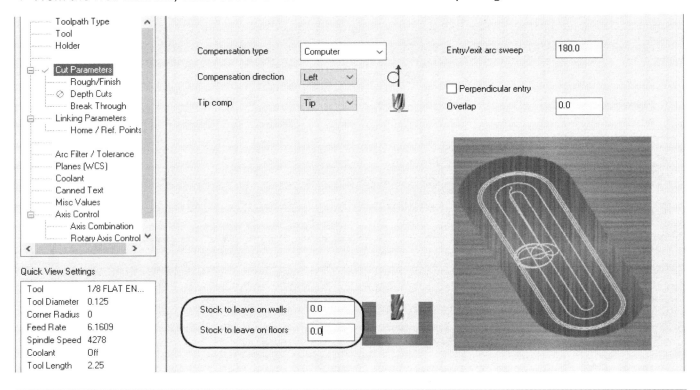

Compensation type allows you to choose how you want to handle cutter compensation. The computer sets Mastercam to compute the compensated toolpath and does not output control codes for compensation.

Entry/exit arc sweep sets the included angle of each entry and exit arc. If the entry/exit arc sweep is less than 180 degrees, the system applies an entry/exit line.

Perpendicular entry enters the toolpath perpendicular to the first tool move.

2.3 Rough/Finish

♦ Select **Rough/Finish** and make any necessary changes as shown.

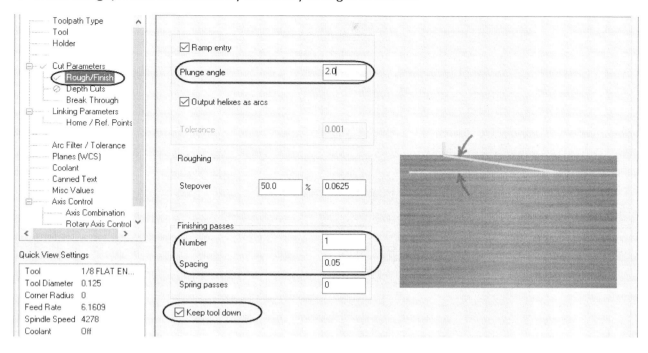

Ramp entry creates a smoother entry motion rather than plunging directly.

Plunge angle sets the angle of descent for the entry move and determines the pitch. A smaller plunge angle means that the entry move takes longer to descend in the Z axis. A recommended angle is 3 to 5 degrees.

Output helixes as arcs writes the entry helix to the NCI file as arcs. Using this option can create shorter NC files. If you turn off this option, the helix breaks into linear segments in the NCI file.

Roughing Stepover sets the distance between cutting passes in the X and Y axes. Enter a percentage of the tool diameter or a distance.

Finish passes allows you to set the finish cuts for the toolpath. This **Number** multiplied by the Finish Spacing value equals the total amount of stock cut by the finish passes. Setting the number of finish cuts to 0 creates no finish cuts.

Keep tool down enabled does not allow the tool to retract between multipasses.

Note: Toolpath display in the window may be different depending on the last field selected.

2.4 Depth Cuts

Choose **Depth Cuts** from the **Tree View list**. Enable **Depth cuts**. Input a **Max rough step** of **0.1**.

♦ Enable the option **Keep tool down** as shown.

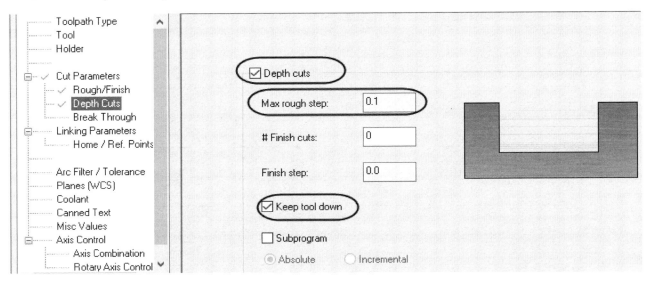

2.5 Break Through

♦ Select **Break Through** from the **Tree View list**. Enable this option and input a **Break through** amount of **0.125** as shown.

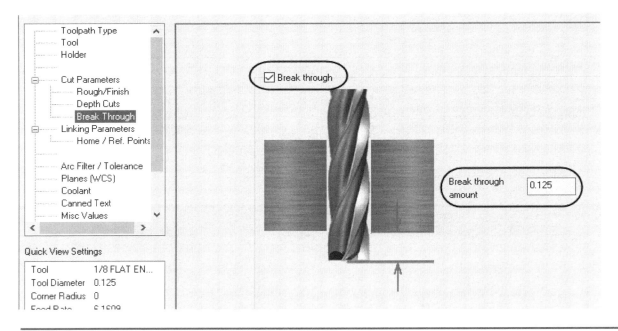

Break Through allows you to specify an amount by which the tool will completely cut through the material. This value is always a positive number.

2.6 Linking Parameters

♦ Select **Linking Parameters** and make the necessary changes as shown.

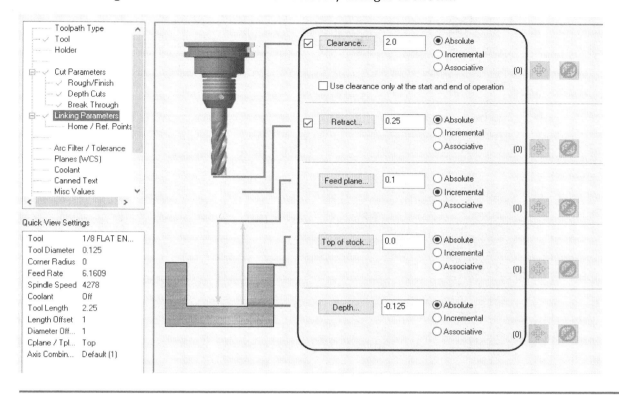

Clearance sets the height at which the tool moves to and from the part.

Retract sets the height to which the tool moves up to before the next tool pass.

Feed plane sets the height to which the tool rapids to before changing to the plunge rate to enter the part.

Top of stock sets the height of the material in the Z axis.

Depth determines the final machining depth that the tool descends into the stock.

2.7 Preview the Toolpath

♦ To quickly check how the toolpath will be generated, select the **Preview toolpath** icon as shown.

♦ To hide the dialog box, click on the **Hide** dialog icon as shown.

♦ To see the part from an **Isometric** view, right mouse click in the graphics window and select **Isometric**.

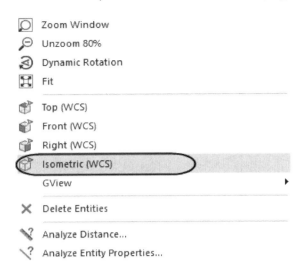

♦ The toolpath should look as shown.

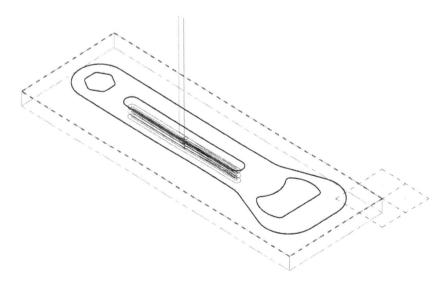

♦ Press **Esc** key to exit the preview.

Note: If the toolpath does not look as shown in the preview, check your parameters again.

♦ Select the **OK** button to exit the **Slot Mill** parameters.

STEP 3: BACKPLOT THE TOOLPATHS

Backplotting shows the path the tools take to cut the part. This display lets you spot errors in the program before you machine the part. As you backplot toolpaths, Mastercam displays additional information such as the X, Y, and Z coordinates, the path length, the minimum and maximum coordinates, and the cycle time.

♦ Make sure that the toolpath is selected (signified by the green check mark on the folder icon). If the operation is not selected, choose the **Select all operations** icon.

♦ Select the **Backplot selected operations** button.

♦ In the **Backplot** panel, enable **Display with color codes**, **Display tool** and **Display rapid moves** icons as shown.

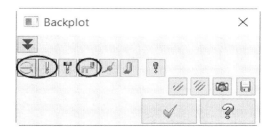

♦ To see the part from an **Isometric** view, right mouse click in the graphics window and select Isometric as shown.

- To fit the workpiece to the screen, if needed, right mouse click in the graphics window again and select the Fit.
- You can step through the **Backplot** by using the **Step forward** or **Step back** buttons.
- You can adjust the speed of the backplot.
- Select the **Play** button to run **Backplot**.

- The toolpath should look as shown.

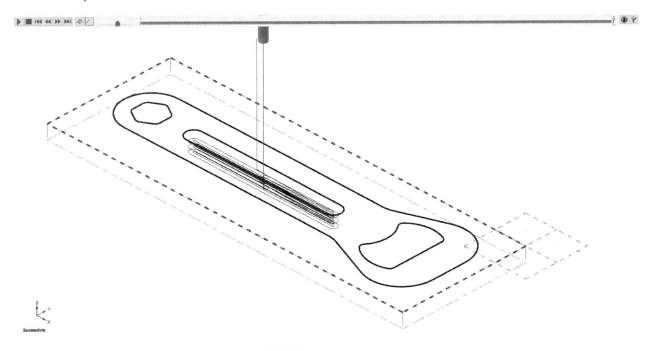

- Select the **OK** button to exit **Backplot**.

STEP 4: SIMULATE THE TOOLPATH IN VERIFY

Verify shows the path the tools take to cut the part with material removal. This display lets you spot errors in the program before you machine the part. As you verify toolpaths, Mastercam displays additional information such as the X, Y, and Z coordinates, the path length, the minimum and maximum coordinates, and the cycle time. It also shows any collision between the workpiece and the tool.

♦ From the **Toolpaths Manager**, select **Verify selected operations** icon as shown.

Note: Mastercam launches a new window that allows you to check the part using **Verify**.

♦ Select the **Play** button to run **Verify**.

♦ The part should appear as shown.

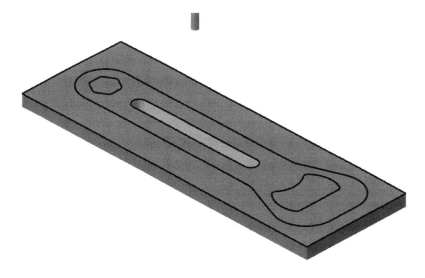

♦ To go back to Mastercam window, minimize **Mastercam Simulator** window as shown. ⊖ ☐ ✕

STEP 5: MACHINE THE CUTOUT POCKETS

In this step, you will use a **Pocket** toolpath to remove the material inside the enclosed trimmed shape near the top and the polygon near the bottom of the geometry.

Toolpath Preview:

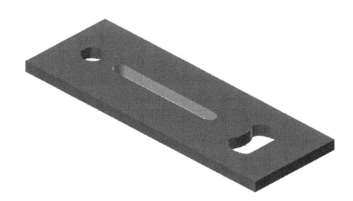

♦ Press **Alt + T** to remove the toolpath display.

Toolpaths

♦ From the **2D** group, select the **Expand** gallery arrow as shown.

♦ Select the **Pocket** icon as shown.

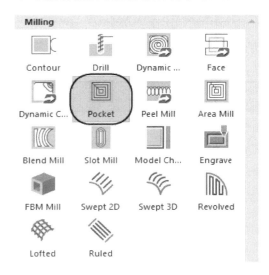

5.1 Select the Geometry

♦ In the **Chaining** dialog box, make sure the **Chains** option is chosen.

♦ [Select Pocket chain 1]: Select the two enclosed areas shown in Figure: 5.1.1. Make sure the chains are in the **CW** direction. Use the **Reverse** button to switch the direction if needed.

Figure: 5.1.1

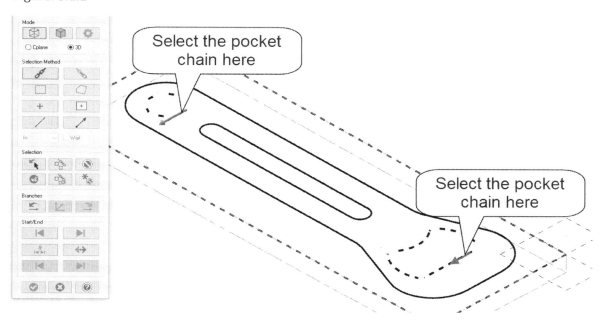

♦ Choose the **OK** button to exit the **Chaining** dialog box.

5.2 Toolpath Type

♦ On the **Toolpath Type** page, **Pocket** will be selected.

 Contour   Pocket   Facing   Slot mill   Model Chamfer

5.3 Select a 1/4" Flat Endmill from the library and set the Tool parameters

♦ Select **Tool** from the **Tree View list** and click on the **Select library tool** button. Select library tool...

♦ Select the **Filter** button.

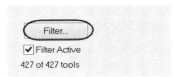

♦ Select the **None** button and then under **Tool Types** choose the **Flat Endmill** Icon.
♦ Under **Tool Diameter**, select **Equal** and input a value **0.25** as shown.

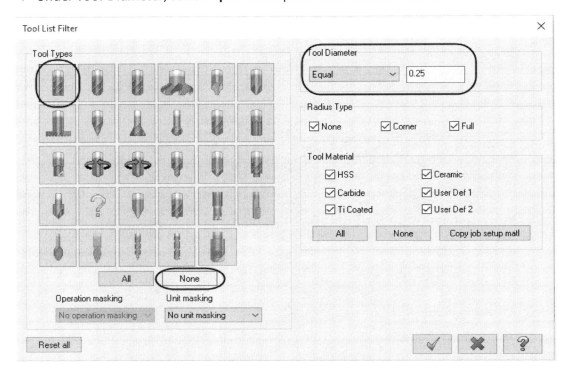

♦ Select the **OK** button to exit the **Tool List Filter**.
♦ In the **Tool Selection** panel you should only see a **1/4" Flat Endmill**.

#	Assembly Na...	Tool Name	Holder Name	Dia.
285	--	1/4 FLAT ENDMILL	--	0.25

♦ Select the **1/4" Flat Endmill** in the **Tool Selection** page and then select the **OK** button to exit.

♦ Set the **Tool** parameters as shown.

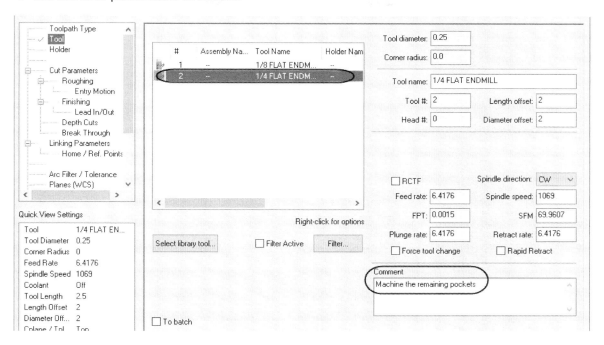

5.4 Set the Cut Parameters

♦ From the **Tree View list**, select **Cut Parameters** and ensure **Pocket** type is set to **Standard**, **Stock to leave on floors** and **Stock to leave on walls** are set to **0.0** as shown.

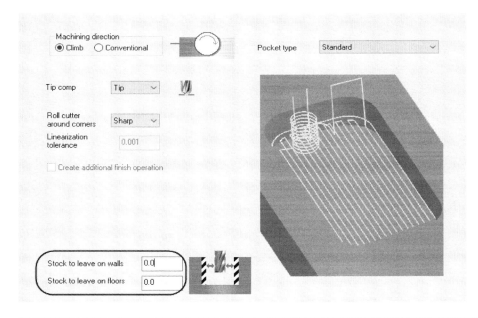

Pocket set to **Standard** will machine the inside of the of the pockets.

5.5 Set the Roughing Parameters

♦ From the **Tree View list**, select **Roughing**.

♦ Enable **Roughing** and set the parameters as shown.

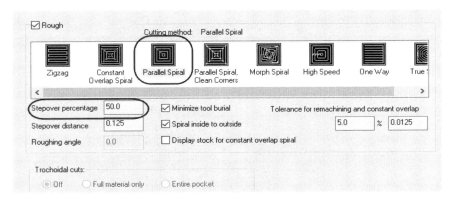

Parallel Spiral creates one roughing pass, determines the remaining stock and recalculates based on the new stock amount. This process repeats until the pocket is cleared.

5.6 Set the Depth Cuts Parameters

♦ Select **Depth Cuts** and enable this option. Set the **Max rough step** to **0.1**. Make sure the rest of the parameters appear as shown.

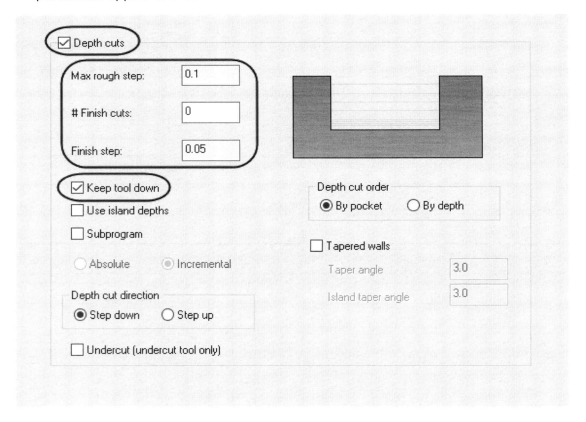

5.7 Break Through

♦ From the **Tree View list**, select **Break Through** and make the necessary changes as shown.

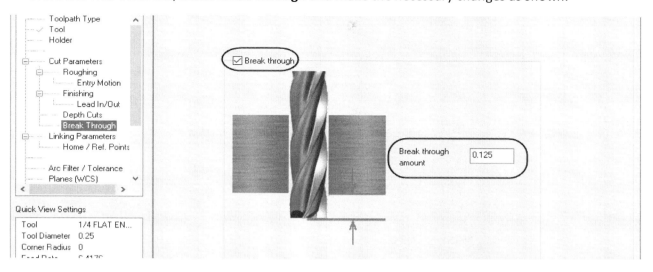

5.8 Set the Linking Parameters

♦ Choose **Linking Parameters** and input a final **Depth of -0.125** as shown.

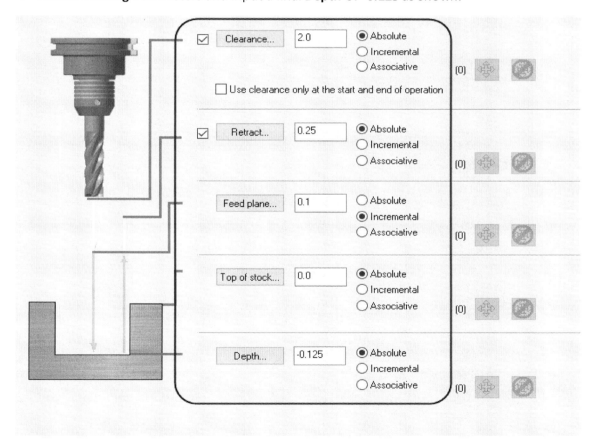

5.9 Preview the Toolpath

♦ Select the **Preview toolpath** icon as shown.

♦ Click on the **Hide dialog** icon as shown.

♦ The toolpath should look as shown.

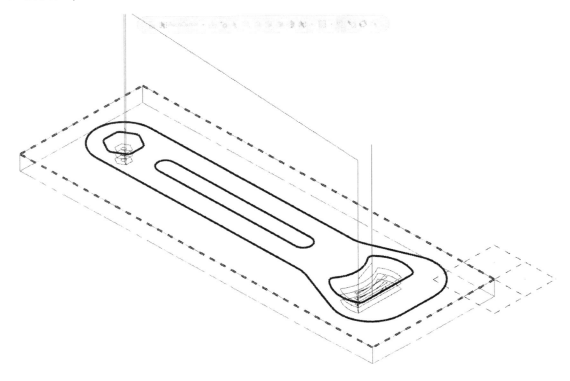

♦ Press **Esc** key to exit the preview.

> Note: If the toolpath does not look as shown in the preview, check your parameters again.

♦ Select the **OK** button to exit the **2D Toolpaths - Pocket** parameters.

5.10 Verify the Toolpaths

♦ From the **Toolpaths Manager**, click on the **Select all operations** icon.

♦ Click on the **Verify selected operation** icon.

♦ For information on how to set the **Verify** parameters and how to simulate the toolpath, please check **"Simulate the toolpath in Verify" on page 183**.

♦ Disable **Wireframe** as shown.

♦ Select the **Verify** tab, and enable **Color Loop** as shown.

Note: This option will change the material removal color. This can be set based on the operation or on the tool number used to machine the part. This makes it easier to spot if you forget to leave the stock in the finish operations.

♦ Select the **Play** button as shown.

♦ The part will appear as shown.

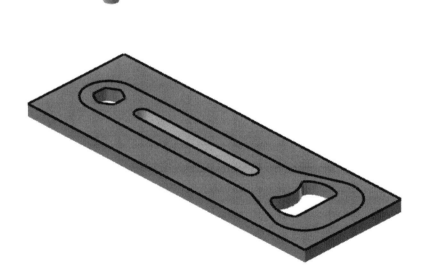

♦ To go back to Mastercam window, minimize **Mastercam Simulator** window as shown.

STEP 6: FINISH THE INSIDE SHAPES USING 2D HS DYNAMIC CONTOUR

2D HS Dynamic Contour toolpath utilizes the entire flute length of the cutting tools and is used to mill material off walls. It supports both closed or open chains.

Toolpath Preview:

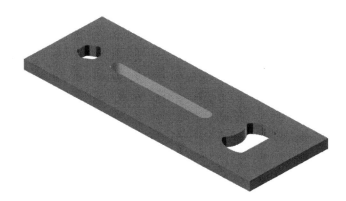

Toolpaths

♦ From the **2D** group, click on the drop-down arrow to see all the toolpaths and select the **Dynamic Contour** icon.

6.1 Select the Geometry

♦ In the Chain Options dialog box, in the Machining regions, click on the **Select machining chains** button as shown.

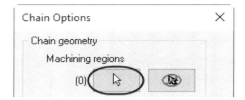

◆ Click the **Last** button in the **Chaining** dialog box as shown, to reselect the last chains selected.

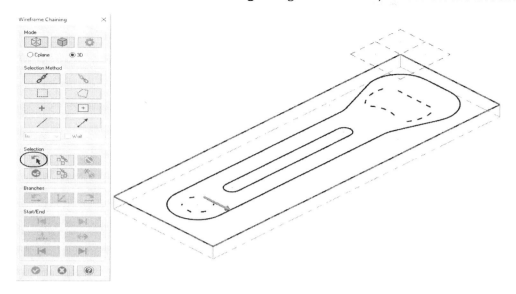

◆ Choose the **OK** button to exit the **Chaining** dialog box.

◆ Select the **OK** button to exit the **Chain Options** dialog box and to continue.

◆ On the **Toolpath Type** page, **Dynamic Contour** should already be selected.

6.2 Tool

◆ From the **Tree view list**, select **Tool**.

◆ Select the existing **1/8" Flat Endmill** and change the parameters as shown.

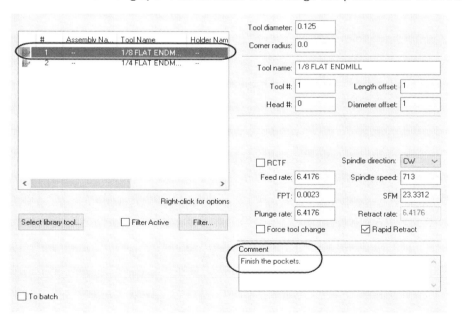

6.3 Cut Parameters

♦ From the **Tree View list**, select **Cut Parameters** and ensure the parameters are the same as shown.

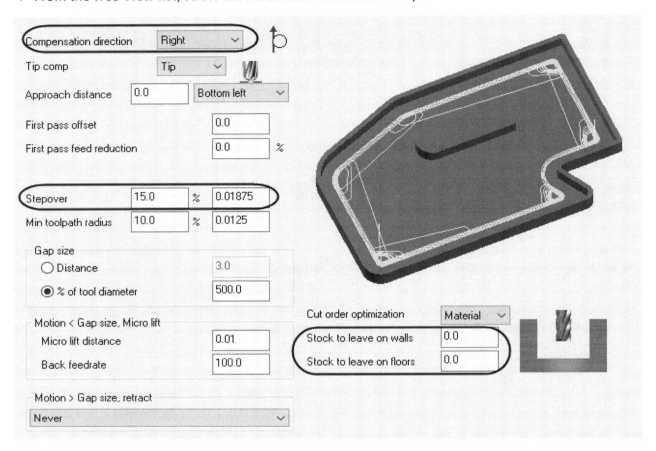

Compensation direction offsets the tool to the **Right** in our case.

Approach distance adds the specified absolute distance to the beginning of the toolpath's first cut.

First pass offset offsets out the machining region with a user defined distance for the tool to safely engage from the outside in the material.

First pass feed reduction allows you to slow the feed for the first pass on machining region material approached from the outside.

Stepover sets the distance between cutting passes in the X and Y axes. Enter a percentage of the tool diameter or an absolute distance.

Min toolpath radius sets the minimum toolpath radius used in combination with the **Micro lift distance** and **Back feedrate** parameters to calculate 3D arc moves between cut passes.

6.4 Contour Wall

◆ From the **Tree View list**, select **Contour Wall** and ensure your parameters appear as shown.

Note: The graphics in the toolpath pages change based on the parameter field you click on. Your graphic might look different.

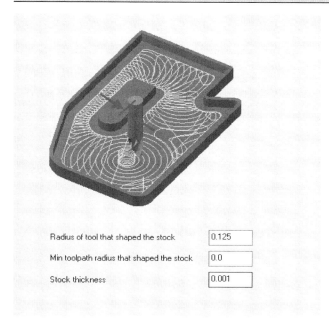

Radius of tool that shaped the stock	0.125
Min toolpath radius that shaped the stock	0.0
Stock thickness	0.001

Radius of tool that shaped the stock is the radius of the tool used in a toolpath that already cuts this area. Mastercam calculates the stock to remove along the contour wall using the **Stock Thickness** (required) and, if provided, the **Radius of the tool that shaped the stock** and the **Toolpath radius that shaped the stock**.

6.5 Break Through

◆ From the **Tree View list**, select **Break Through** and make the necessary changes as shown.

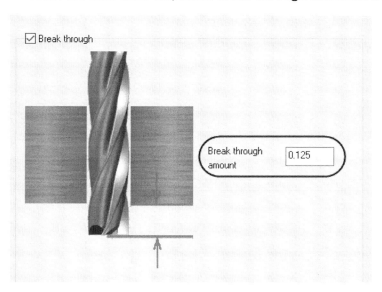

6.6 Linking Parameters

♦ Select **Linking Parameters** from the **Tree View list**.
♦ Set the **Depth to -0.125** as shown.

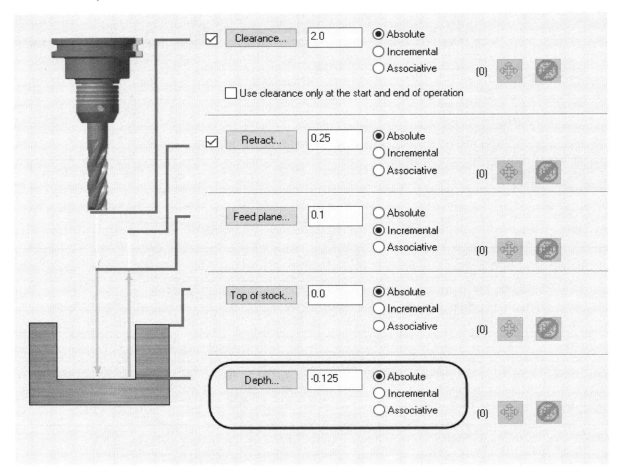

6.7 Preview the Toolpath

♦ To quickly check how the toolpath will be generated, select the **Preview toolpath** icon as shown.

♦ See **"Preview the Toolpath" on page 179** to review the procedure.
♦ The toolpath should look as shown.

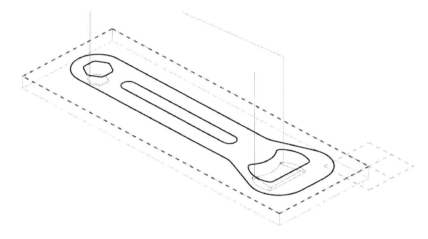

♦ Press **Esc** key to exit the preview.
♦ If the toolpath does not look as shown in the preview, check your parameters again.

♦ Select the **OK** button to exit the **Dynamic Contour** parameters.

6.8 Verify the toolpaths

♦ To **Backplot** and **Verify** your toolpath, see **"Simulate the toolpath in Verify" on page 183** to review the procedures.
♦ To select all the operations, from the **Toolpaths Manager**, click on the **Select all operations icon**.

♦ The part should look as shown.

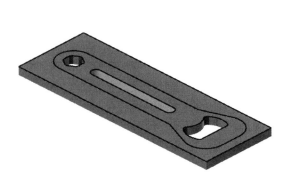

♦ See **"Simulate the toolpath in Verify" on page 183** to review the procedure.
♦ To go back to the Mastercam window, minimize the Mastercam Simulator window as shown.

STEP 7: ROUGH THE OUTSIDE USING HIGH SPEED DYNAMIC MILL

In this step, you will machine the outside profile using **2D HS Dynamic Mill toolpath**.

Dynamic Mill toolpath machines cores or pockets using the entire flute length. The toolpath supports many powerful entry methods, including a customized entry method. Entry methods and micro lifts support custom feeds and speeds to optimize and generate safe tool motion.

The toolpath depends on the **Machining strategy** that you choose in the **Chain Options**. If the strategy chosen is **From outside**, the toolpath starts at the outmost chain and works its way in, taking on the final shape of the part as it approaches the final pass. You can also machine pockets, in which case the strategy selected is **Start inside**, which keeps the tool inside the machining regions.

Toolpath Preview:

7.1 Chain selection

♦ Press **Alt + T** to remove the toolpath display.

Toolpaths

♦ In the **2D** group, click on the **Expand gallery** arrow as shown.

♦ Select the **Dynamic Mill** icon as shown.

♦ In the **Chain Options** dialog box, under **Machining regions**, click on the **Select machining chain**s button as shown to define the area to be machined.

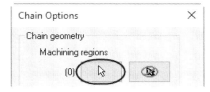

♦ In the **Chaining** dialog box, leave the **Chain** button enabled.

◆ Right mouse click in the graphics window and select the **Top** view as shown.

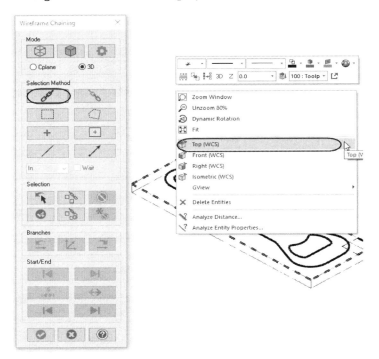

◆ [Select 2D HST machining chain 1]: Select the rectangle as shown.

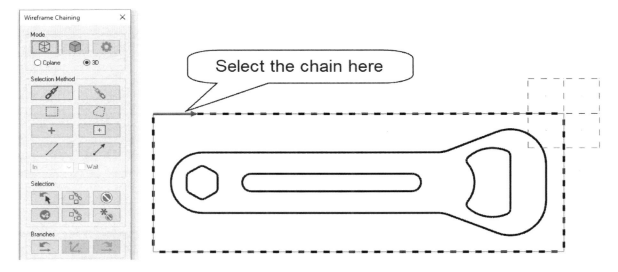

◆ Select the **OK** button to exit the **Chaining** dialog box.

◆ To start the toolpath from the outside, in the **Machining region strategy**, make sure that **From outside** is enabled.

♦ In the **Avoidance regions**, click on the **Select avoidance chains** button as shown.

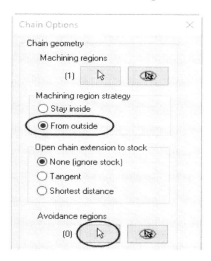

♦ [Select 2D HST avoidance chain 1]: Select the profile as shown.

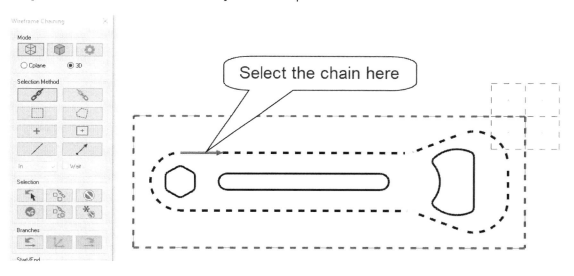

Select the chain here

♦ Select the **OK** button to exit the **Chaining** dialog box.

♦ Select the **OK** button to exit the **Chain Options** dialog box.

♦ In the **Toolpath Type** page, **Dynamic Mill** will be selected as shown.

 Dynamic Mill   Area Mill   Dynamic Contour   Peel Mill   Blend Mill

7.2 Preview Chains

The **Preview Chains** function is intended to give the user a quick visual representation of how Mastercam sees the various pieces of geometry that have been selected, how they interact with one another and a general overview of how the toolpath will be calculated with the selections presently made.

♦ Click on the **Color** icon to see the legend for **Preview chains** as shown.

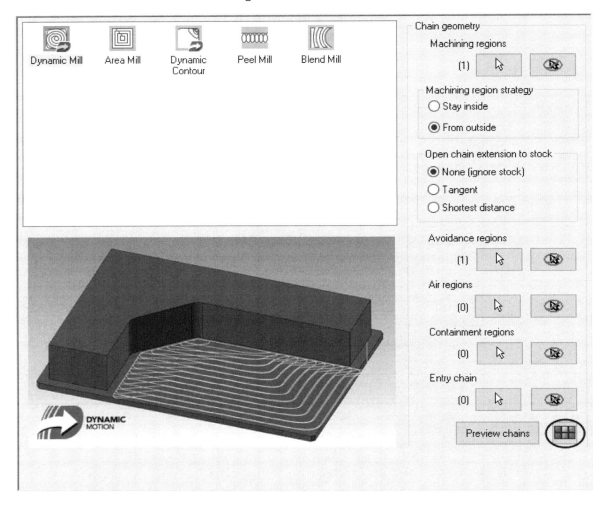

♦ The **Preview Chains Colors** dialog box should look as shown.

The **Material region** and **Material crosshatch** are the two colors that are used to define the material to be cut. The default colors are red for the background and black for the crosshatch.

The **Motion region** displays the area that Mastercam is making available to the toolpath for motion if it needs it. The color to represent it is dark blue. The primary reason for the display of the entire available (but not necessarily used) **Motion region** is to help the user visualize how the tool may move near or interact with any adjacent geometry.

The **Tool containment** is what you have selected as the **Containment region** in the chain geometry. If you have not selected a containment region, it will default to the outside of the **Motion region** since that is currently the default area the toolpath is being contained to. The color used to represent the **Tool containment** is yellow.

♦ Select the **OK** button to exit **Preview Chains Colors**.
♦ Select the **Preview chains** button as shown.

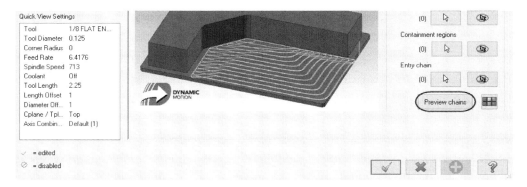

♦ Select the **Hide** dialog button to see the preview in the graphics window.

♦ The **Preview chain**s should look as shown.

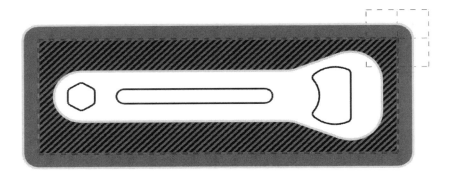

♦ Press **Esc** key to return to the toolpath parameters.

♦ Click on the **Preview chains** button again to clear the **Preview chains** display.

7.3 Select the 1/4" Flat Endmill and set the Tool parameters

♦ Select **Tool** from the **Tree View list** and select the **1/4" Flat Endmill.**

♦ Make all the necessary changes as shown.

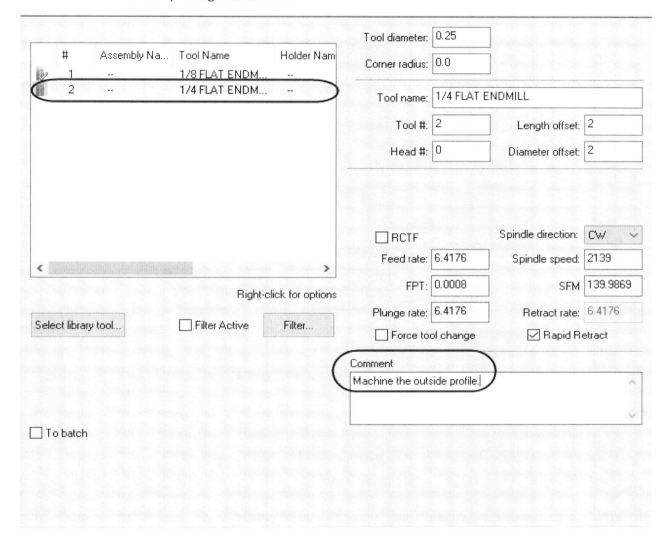

7.4 Set the Cut Parameters

♦ From the **Tree View list**, select **Cut Parameters**. Change the settings as shown.

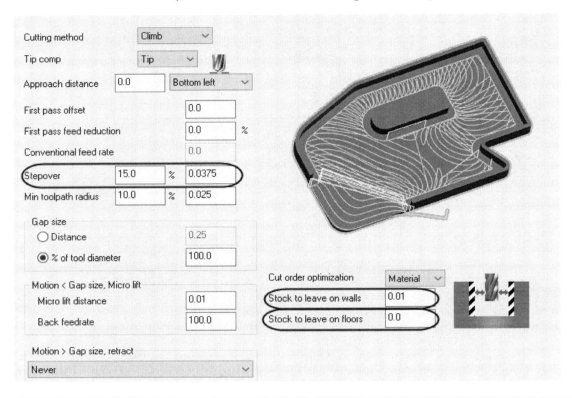

Stepover sets the distance between cutting passes in the X and Y axes.

Approach distance adds the specified absolute distance to the beginning of the toolpath's first cut.

First pass offset offsets out the machining region with a user defined distance for the tool to safely engage from the outside of the material.

First pass feed reduction allows you to slow the feed for the first pass on machining region material approached from the outside.

Min toolpath radius reduces sharp corner motion between cut passes.

Micro lift distance enters the distance the tool lifts off the part on the back moves.

Microlifts are slight lifts that help clear chips and minimize excessive tool heating.

Back feedrate controls the speed of the backfeed movement of the tool.

Motion > Gap Size, retract controls retracts in the toolpath when making a non-cutting move within an area where the tool can be kept down or microlifted.

7.5 Set the Linking Parameters

◆ Select **Linking Parameters**. Make sure the **Depth** is set to **-0.125, Absolute**, and the other parameters are set to the same values as shown.

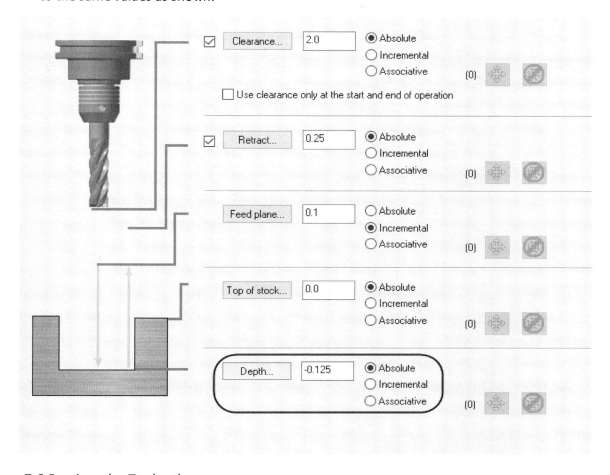

7.6 Preview the Toolpath

◆ To quickly check how the toolpath will be generated, select the **Preview toolpath** icon as shown.

◆ See **"Preview the Toolpath" on page 179** to review the procedure.

◆ The toolpath should look as shown.

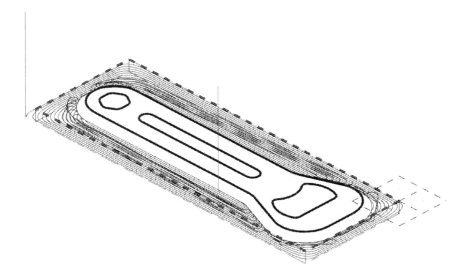

◆ Press **Esc** key to exit the preview.

Note: If the toolpath does not look as shown in the preview, check your parameters again.

◆ Select the **OK** button to generate the toolpath.
◆ To remove the toolpath display, press **Alt + T** or click on the **Toggle display on selected operations** icon.

7.7 Verify the toolpath

◆ From the **Toolpaths Manager**, click on the **Select all operations** icon before clicking on the **Verify** button.

◆ Follow **Mastercam Simulation** procedures as shown on **"Simulate the toolpath in Verify" on page 183** .

♦ The part will appear as shown.

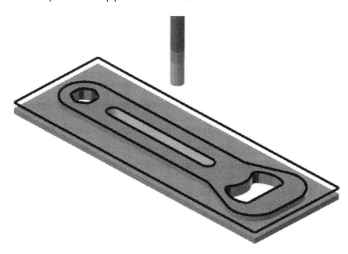

♦ To go back to the Mastercam window, minimize the **Mastercam Simulator** window as shown.

STEP 8: FINISH THE OUTSIDE PROFILE USING CONTOUR TOOLPATH

Contour toolpaths remove material along a path defined by a chain of curves. **Contour toolpaths** only follow a chain; they do not clean out an enclosed area.

Toolpath Preview:

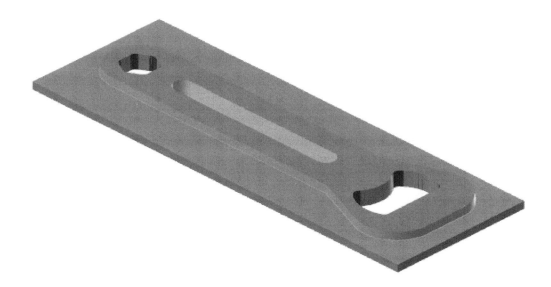

8.1 Chain selection

Toolpaths

♦ From the **2D** group, select **Contour** icon.

♦ [Select Contour chain 1]: Click on **Last** in the **Chaining** dialog box to select again the chain you last selected.

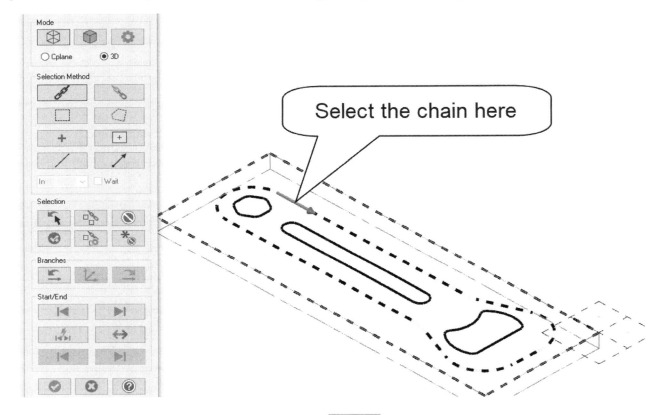

Select the chain here

♦ Select the **OK** button to exit the **Chaining** dialog box.
♦ In the **Toolpath Type** page, the **Contour** icon will be selected as shown.

Contour　　Pocket　　Facing　　Slot mill　　Model Chamfer

8.2 Tool

♦ From the **Tree View list**, select **Tool.**
♦ Select a **1/4" Flat Endmill** from the list and set the **Tool** page parameters.

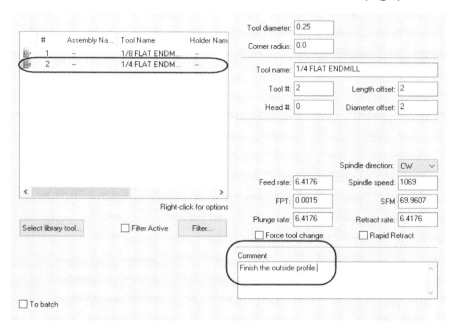

☐ To batch

8.3 Cut Parameters

♦ From the **Tree View list**, select **Cut Parameters** and ensure the settings appear as shown.

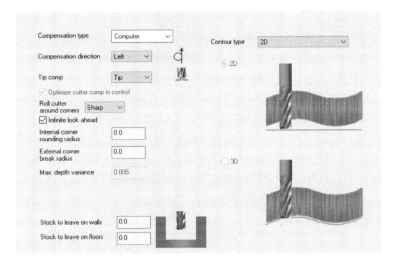

Note: For more information regarding these parameters, please check Step 10 in Tutorial #1.

8.4 Lead In/Out

♦ Select **Lead In/Out** from the **Tree View list.**
♦ Change the parameters as shown.

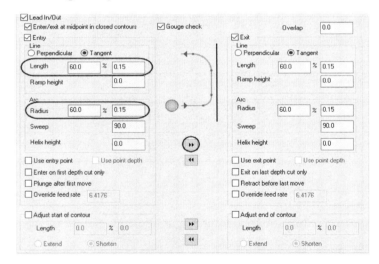

Note: Clicking on the circled arrows button near the center of the box will fill fields on the **Exit** category of the box with appropriate information copied from the **Entry** category.

8.5 Linking Parameters

♦ Select **Linking Parameters** and input the **Depth** as shown.

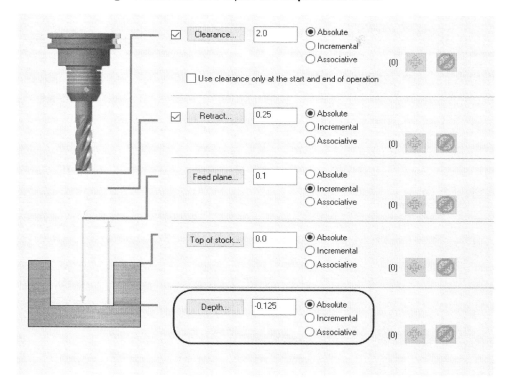

8.6 Preview the Toolpath

♦ To quickly check how the toolpath will be generated, select the **Preview toolpath** icon as shown.

♦ See **"Preview the Toolpath" on page 179** to review the procedure.

♦ The toolpath should look as shown.

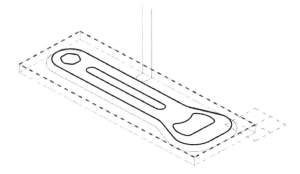

♦ Press **Esc** key to exit the preview.
♦ Once completed select the **OK** button to generate the toolpath.

8.7 Backplot and Verify the toolpaths

♦ To **Backplot** and **Verify** the toolpaths, see **"Backplot The Toolpaths" on page 181** and **"Simulate the toolpath in Verify" on page 183** to review the procedures.
♦ To select all the operations, from the **Toolpaths Manager**, click on the **Select all operations** icon.

♦ After running **Verify**, the part should look as shown.

♦ To go back to the Mastercam window, minimize the **Mastercam Simulator** window as shown.

*Note: There is still an extra **0.125** stock at the bottom of the part.*

TOOLPATH CREATION - SETUP 2

SUGGESTED FIXTURE:

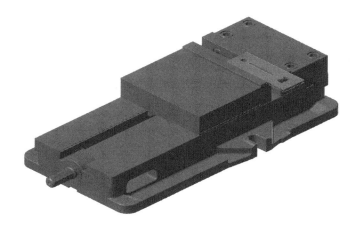

Note: In order to machine this part, we will have 2 setups and output 2 NC files.

SETUP SHEET:

TOOL LIST

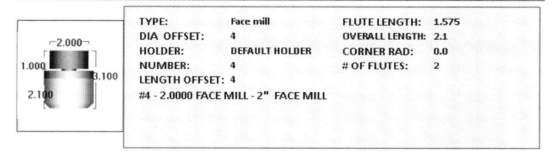

TYPE:	Face mill	FLUTE LENGTH:	1.575
DIA OFFSET:	4	OVERALL LENGTH:	2.1
HOLDER:	DEFAULT HOLDER	CORNER RAD:	0.0
NUMBER:	4	# OF FLUTES:	2
LENGTH OFFSET:	4		

#4 - 2.0000 FACE MILL - 2" FACE MILL

STEP 9: CREATING AND RENAMING TOOLPATH GROUPS

To machine the part in two different setups, we will need to have two separate programs. To be able to post process the operations of each setup separately, we will create them under different toolpath groups with different NC names.

9.1 Rename the current Toolpath Group - 1 and NC file

♦ Click once on the **Toolpath Group - 1** to highlight it and then click on it again to rename it "Setup #1" as shown.

♦ Right mouse click on the **Setup #1 Toolpath group** and select **Edit selected operations** and then select **Change NC file name**.

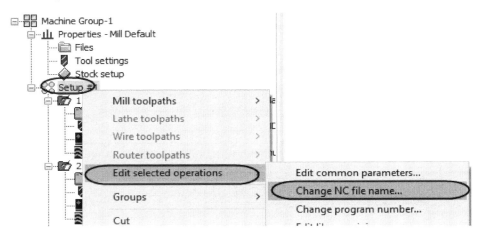

♦ Enter the new **NC name: Setup #1**.

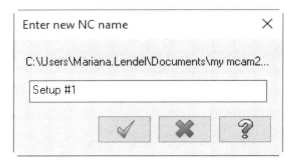

♦ Select the **OK** button to accept the new **NC name**.

9.2 Create a new Toolpath Group

♦ Right mouse click on the **Machine Group-1** and select **Groups** and then **New Toolpath group** as shown.

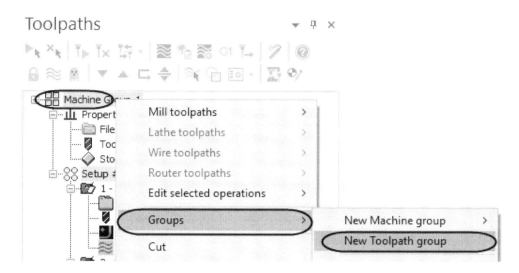

♦ Rename the toolpath group "**Setup #2**" as shown in the previous step.

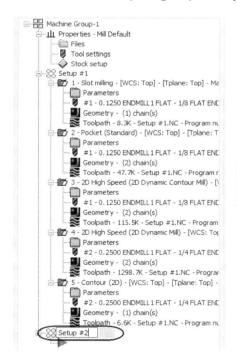

Note: The red insert arrow controls where the new operation will be inserted. In our case it should be located below the Setup #2 group.

◆ If the insert arrow needs to be relocated, from the **Toolpaths Manager**, click on the **Move insert arrow down** icon.

STEP 10: CREATE AND SET WCS TO BOTTOM

Work coordinate system (WCS) is the active coordinate system in use by Mastercam at any given time. The **WCS** contains the orientation of the X-Y-Z axes plus the location of the zero point (the origin). This tells Mastercam how your part is positioned or oriented in the machine.

Construction plane (Cplane) is the plane in which the geometry is created.

Tool plane (Tplane) is the plane normal to Z or to the vertical tool axis in which the tool moves. When creating a toolpath, both **Cplane** and **Tplane** should be set to the same plane. If the **Tplane** is different than the **WCS**, the post will produce a rotary motion code. By setting the **Cplane**, **Tplane** and **WCS** to one plane, no rotary move will be generated in the code which is what you want when machining parts with multiple setups.

In this step you will set the **WCS**, the **Construction plane (Cplane)** and the **Tool plane (Tplane)** to a new plane that can be defined using existing geometry. In our case, we will define the plane using two lines.

◆ Select **Planes** tab located at the bottom of the **Toolpaths Manager** or, if it is floating, to the left of it.

♦ To create a new plane based on existing geometry, click on the **+** sign as shown.

♦ Select **From Geometry** as shown.

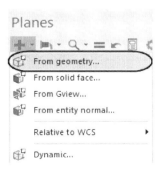

♦ Right mouse click in the graphics window and select the **Isometric** view.

♦ [Set construction plane by geometry/Select an entity]: Select the first line along the X axis of the new view and then select the line along the Y axis of the new view as shown.

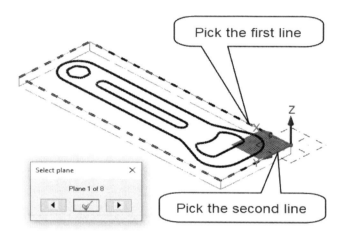

♦ In **Select plane**, click on the **Next** plane button until the axes are oriented as shown.

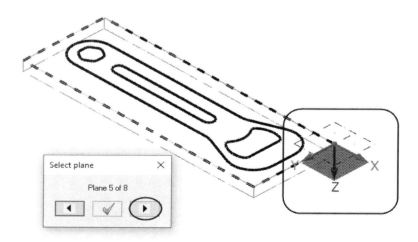

♦ From the **Select plane**, click on the **OK** button to continue.

♦ In the **New Plane** panel in the **Name** field, input **Setup 2 Plane** as shown. To maintain the origin at the upper right corner of the part, change the **Y** coordinate for the **Origin** to **2.0**.

♦ Select the **OK** button to continue.

◆ Set the **Work Coordinate System (WCS)**, **Tool plane**, and **Construction plane** to the newly created **Setup 2 Plane** by clicking on the = icon, with **Setup 2 Plane** highlighted in blue, as shown in Figure: 10.0.1.

◆ Set the **Z Origin** to **0.125** as shown in Figure: 10.0.1.

Figure: 10.0.1

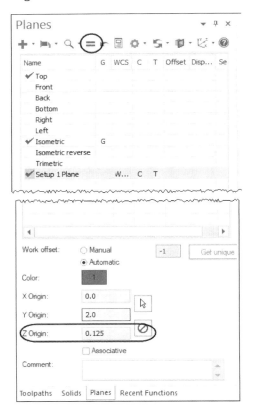

◆ Right mouse click and select the **Isometric** view to see the part in its new orientation.

The menu shows:
- Zoom Window
- Unzoom 80%
- Dynamic Rotation
- Fit
- Top (WCS)
- Front (WCS)
- Right (WCS)
- Isometric (WCS)
- GView ▶
- Delete Entities
- Analyze Distance...
- Analyze Entity Properties...

◆ The part should look as shown.

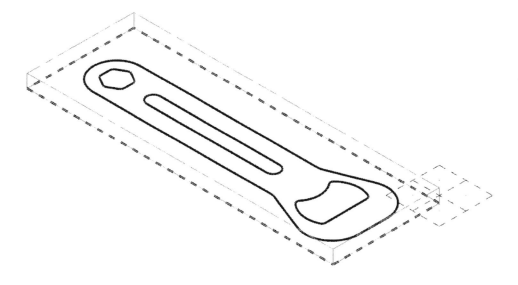

◆ Select the **Toolpath** tab to open the **Toolpaths Manager**.

*Note: Z zero is at **0.125** below the stock.*

STEP 11: FACE THE PART

A **Facing** toolpath quickly removes material from the top of the part to create an even surface.

Toolpath Preview:

Toolpaths

♦ From the **2D** group, click on the upper arrow until you see the Face icon and select it as shown.

♦ When the **Chaining** dialog box appears, choose the **OK** button to use defined stock and exit the **Chaining** dialog box.

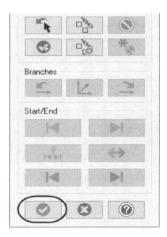

Note: *If no chain is selected, Mastercam will create the Facing toolpath defined from the stock setup.*

- In the **Toolpath Type** page, the **Facing** icon will be automatically selected.

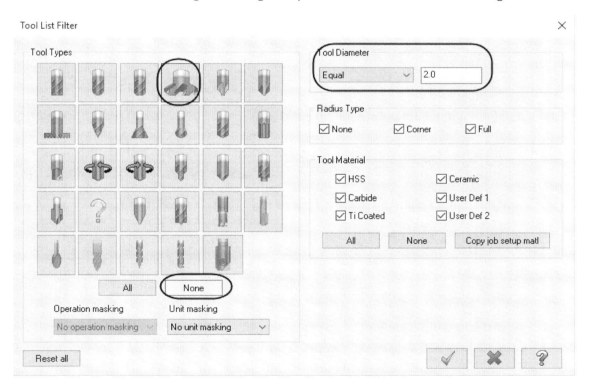

Contour   Pocket   Facing   Slot mill   Model Chamfer

11.1 Select a 2.0" Face Mill from the library and set the Tool parameters

- Select **Tool** from the **Tree View list**.

- Click on the **Select library tool** button.
- Select the **Filter** button.

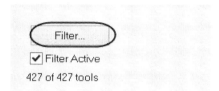

- In the **Tool List Filter** dialog box change the parameters to match the following screensheet.

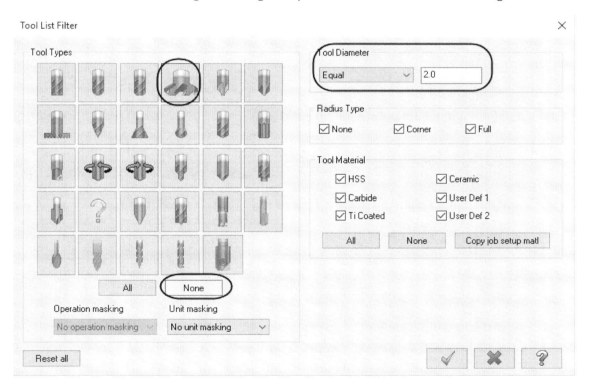

♦ Select the **2" Face Mill** in the **Tool Selection** page and then select the **OK** button to exit as shown.

♦ Make all the necessary changes as shown.

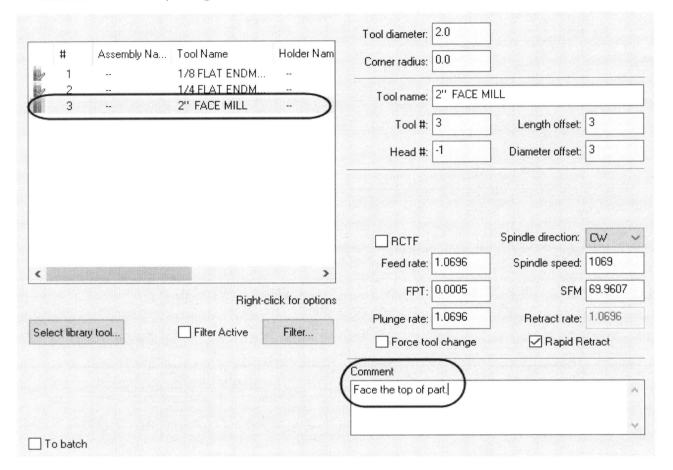

11.2 Cut Parameters

♦ Select **Cut Parameters** and make the necessary changes as shown.

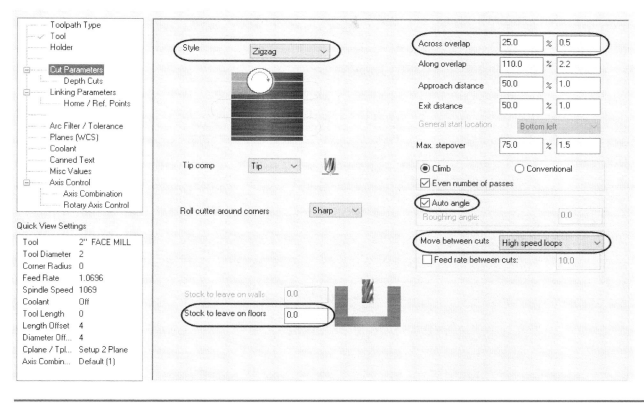

The **Style** (facing cutting method) **Zigzag** creates a back and forth cutting motion.

Auto angle determines the angle to machine along the larger side of the stock.

Move between cuts determines how the tool moves between each cut. This is only available if you select the zigzag cutting method.

High speed loops creates 180 degree arcs between each cut.

11.3 Linking Parameters

♦ Select the **Linking Parameters** page and make the necessary changes as shown.

*Note: The top of stock is set to **0.125"** because in our **Setup 2 Plane** we have the **Z Origin** value set to **0.125"** above the first setup origin. The depth is set to **0.0"** because this is the depth of the finish part we want the tool to go to.*

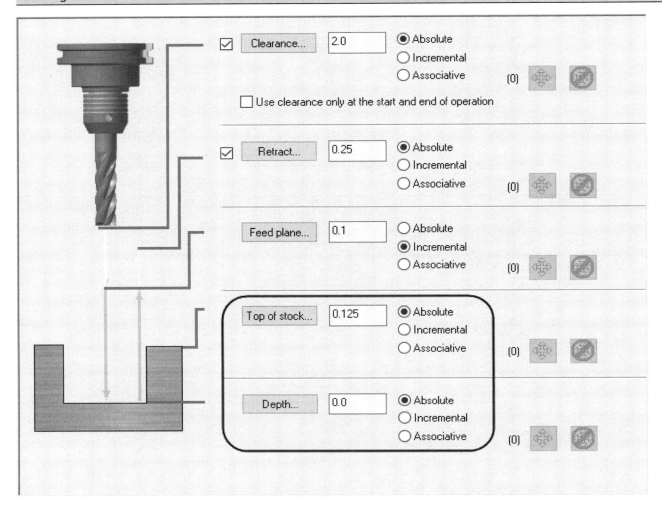

Clearance sets the height at which the tool moves to and from the part.

Retract sets the height to which the tool moves up before the next tool pass.

Feed plane sets the height to which the tool rapids before changing to the plunge rate to enter the part.

Top of stock sets the height of the material in the Z axis.

Depth determines the final machining depth that the tool descends into the stock.

11.4 Preview the Toolpath

♦ To quickly check how the toolpath will be generated, select the **Preview toolpath** icon as shown.

♦ See **"Preview the Toolpath" on page 179** to review the procedure.

♦ The toolpath should look as shown.

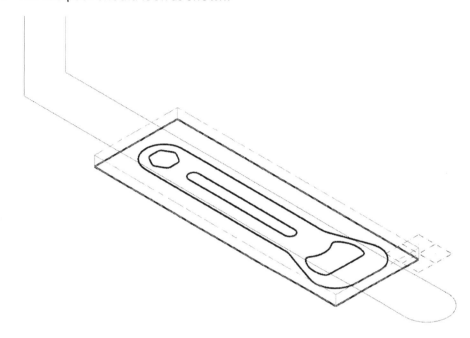

♦ Press **Esc** key to exit the preview.

♦ Once completed select the **OK** button to generate the toolpath.

11.5 Backplot and Verify the toolpaths

♦ To **Backplot** and **Verify** the toolpaths, see **"Backplot The Toolpaths" on page 181** and **"Simulate the toolpath in Verify" on page 183** to review the procedures.

♦ To select all the operations, from the **Toolpaths Manager**, click on the **Select all operations** icon.

♦ The finish part should look as shown.

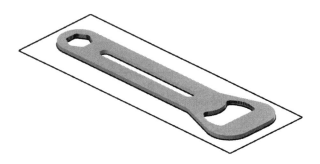

♦ To go back to the Mastercam window, close **Mastercam Simulator** window as shown.

STEP 12: RENAME THE NC FILE

The **Facing** operation in Setup #2 kept the NC name from Setup #1. We need to rename this operation.

♦ Right click on **Setup #2** group, choose the option **Edit selected operations** and then select **Change NC file name**.

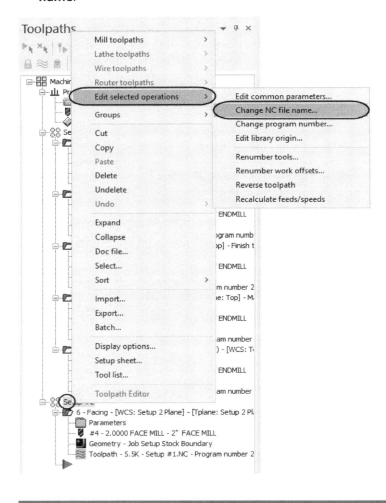

♦ When the **Enter new NC name** panel appears, enter "**Setup #2**" in the input field.

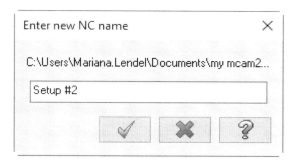

♦ Select the **OK** button to apply the change and exit the panel.
♦ As a result, you should see **Setup #2.NC** in the last item of text for **Operation #6**.

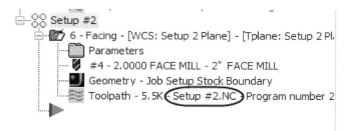

STEP 13: POST THE FILE

♦ Ensure all operations are selected. If not, use the button **Select all operations** in the **Toolpaths Manager**.
♦ Select the **Post selected operations** icon from the **Toolpaths Manager** as shown.

Note: The HLE/Demo version of Mastercam does not support post processing. The G1 button does not work and no G-code can be created in the HLE/Demo version.

♦ In the **Post processing** window, make necessary changes as shown.

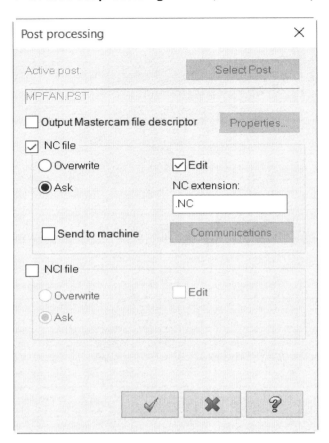

NC file enabled allows you to keep the NC file and to assign the same name as the MCAM file.

Edit enabled allows you to automatically launch the default.

♦ Select the **OK** button to continue.
♦ Save Setup #1 NC file.
♦ Save Setup #2 NC file.

♦ A window with **Mastercam Code Expert** will be launched and the NC program will appear as shown.

♦ Select the "X" box at the upper right corner to exit the editor.

STEP 14: SAVE THE UPDATED MCAM FILE

CREATE THE TOOLPATHS FOR TUTORIAL #2 EXERCISE

Create the Toolpaths for Tutorial #2 Exercise as per the instructions below.

Setup #1
Set the machine properties including the stock setup.
Remove the material in the slot using Slot Mill.

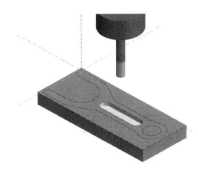

- ♦ Use a **1/4" Flat Endmill**.
- ♦ **Stock to leave on walls/floors = 0.0**.
- ♦ Set the **Depth** according to the drawing.

Circle Mill the 3/4" Hole.

- ♦ Choose a **3/8" Flat Endmill**.
- ♦ **Stock to leave on walls/floors = 0.0**.
- ♦ Enable **Roughing**.
- ♦ Set appropriate **Depth cuts** and **Break through amount**.
- ♦ Input a **Depth** according to the drawing.

Rough the outside profile using 2D HS Dynamic Mill.

- ♦ Select the outside rectangle in the **Machining regions**.
- ♦ Enable **From outside**.
- ♦ Select the profile in the **Avoidance regions.**
- ♦ Use a **1/2" Flat Endmill**.
- ♦ **Leave stock on the wall** only.
- ♦ Set the **Depth** according to the drawing.

Finish the outside profile using Contour.

- ♦ Use a **1/2" Flat Endmill**.
- ♦ Set the final **Depth** according to the drawing.

Setup #2.

- ◆ Rename the previous **Toolpath Group Setup #1**.
- ◆ Rename all the existing operation **NC file Setup #1**.
- ◆ Create a new **Toolpath Group** and rename it **Setup #2**.

Use the Plane Manager and set the Setup #2 plane.

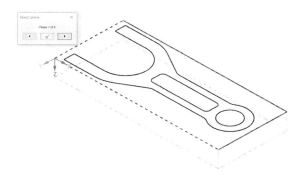

- ◆ Use **Geometry** to define the plane.
- ◆ Set **WCS**, **Cplane** and **Tplane** to the new view.
- ◆ Set the **Z origin** to **-0.5**.

Face the part.

- ◆ Select the **2.0" Face Mill** from the **Tool** page.
- ◆ **Stock to leave on floors = 0.0.**
- ◆ Set the **Depth** according to the drawing.

TUTORIAL #2 TOOLPATH CREATION QUIZ

♦ What does a Slot Mill toolpath do?

♦ What does the 2D HS Dynamic Mill do?

♦ What does the 2D HS Dynamic Contour Mill do?

♦ What is the process used to be able to post different operations as different programs?

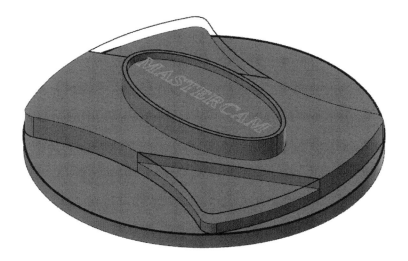

OVERVIEW OF STEPS TAKEN TO CREATE THE PART GEOMETRY:

From Drawing to CAD Model:

♦ The student should examine the drawing on the following page to understand what part is being created in the tutorial.

♦ From the drawing we can decide how to create the geometry in Mastercam.

Create the 2D CAD Model:

♦ The student will create the Top 2D geometry needed to create the toolpaths.

♦ Geometry creation commands such as Rectangle, Arc Endpoints, Mirror, Ellipse, Letters and Translate will be used.

Create the Solid Model:

♦ The student will create the solid geometry using Extrude - Create Body, Extrude - Add Boss and Extrude Cut Body.

TUTORIAL #3 DRAWING

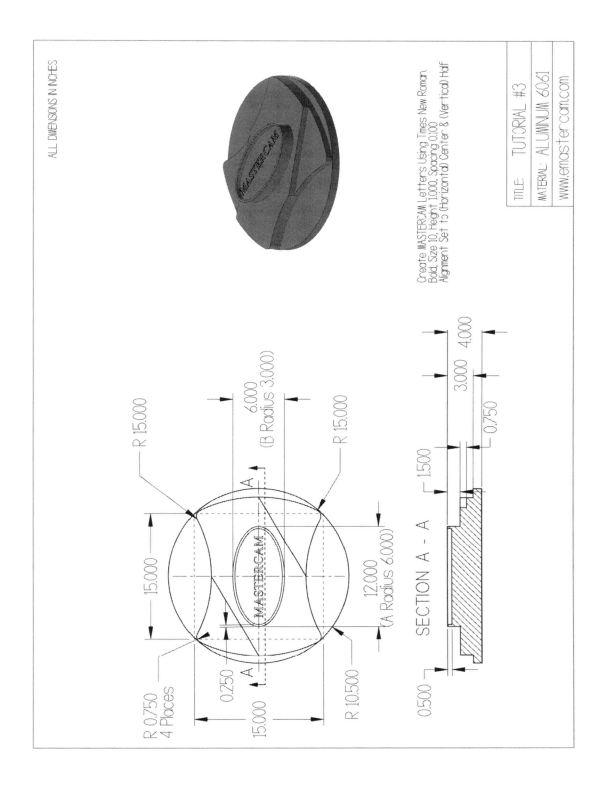

ALL DIMENSIONS IN INCHES

Create MASTERCAM Letters Using Times New Roman,
Bold, Size 10, Height 1.000, Spacing 0.100
Alignment Set to (Horizontal) Center & (Vertical) Half

TITLE: TUTORIAL #3
MATERIAL: ALUMINUM 6061
www.emastercam.com

R 15.000

6.000
(B Radius 3.000)

R 15.000

15.000

12.000
(A Radius 6.000)

R 0.750
4 Places

0.250

15.000

R 10.500

MASTERCAM

A

A

1.500

3.000

4.000

0.750

0.500

SECTION A - A

STEP 1: SETTING UP THE GRAPHICAL USER INTERFACE

Please refer to the **Getting Started** section to set up the graphical user interface.

*Note: In the next few steps you will create a quarter of the entire geometry. You will then use the **Mirror** command to generate the rest.*

STEP 2: CREATE A RECTANGLE

In this step, you will learn how to create a rectangle given the width, the height, and the anchor position.

Step Preview:

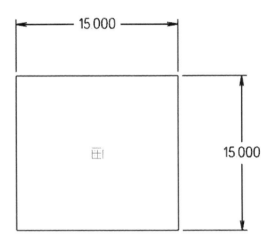

Wireframe

♦ From the **Shapes** group, select **Rectangle**.

♦ In the **Rectangle** panel, enter the **Width** and **Height** and enable **Anchor to center** as shown.

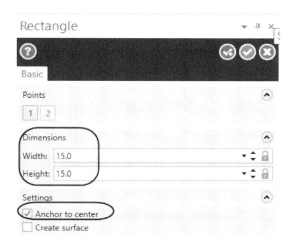

♦ Press **Enter** after typing the values.
♦ Select the **Origin** as shown.

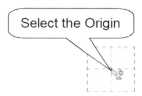

Select the Origin

♦ Select the **OK** button to exit the command.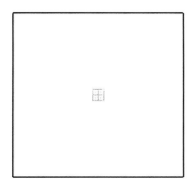
♦ Press **Alt + F1** to fit the geometry to the screen.
♦ The geometry should look as shown.

STEP 3: CREATE ARCS KNOWING ENDPOINTS

In this step you will create two arcs knowing the Radius and two Endpoints.

Step Preview:

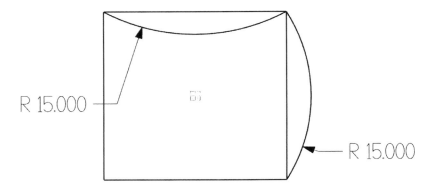

3.1 Create the 15.0" Radius arc

Wireframe

♦ From the **Arcs** group, click on the drop down arrow next to **Circle Edge Point** and select **Arc Endpoints** as shown.

♦ [Enter the first point}: Select Endpoint1 as shown.

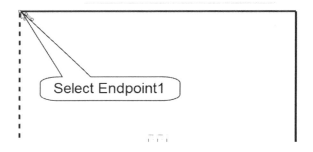

◆ [Enter the second point]: Select Endpoint2 as shown.

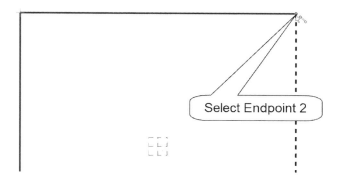

Select Endpoint 2

◆ [Enter the third point]: Select a third point somewhere below the top line as shown.

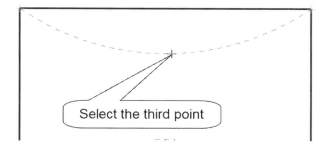

Select the third point

◆ Change the values in the **Arc Polar** panel as shown.

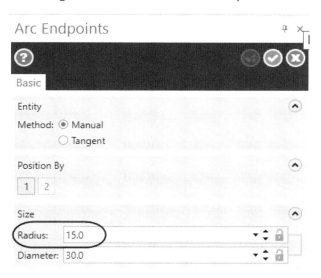

◆ Press **Enter**.

♦ The arc will appear as shown.

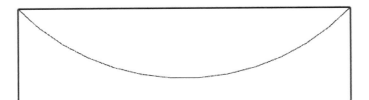

♦ Select the **OK and Create New Operation** button to continue with the same command.

Note: While creating geometry for this tutorial, if you make a mistake, you can undo the last step using the **Undo** icon. ⤺ You can undo as many steps as needed. If you delete or undo a step by mistake, just use the **Redo** icon. ⤻ To delete unwanted geometry, select the geometry first and then press **Delete** from the keyboard.

3.2 Create another 15.0" diameter arc on the right side of the rectangle.

♦ Select the first and second endpoints as shown.

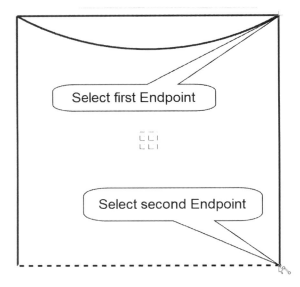

♦ Select the third point as shown.

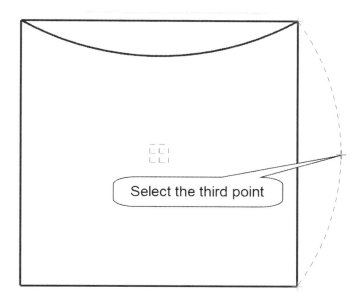

♦ Change the **Radius** to **15.0**in the panel and press Enter.
♦ The drawing will appear as shown.

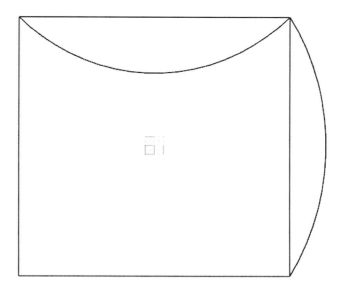

♦ Choose the **OK** button to exit the command.

STEP 4: DELETE THE RECTANGLE

In this step, you will learn how to select and delete the rectangle.

Step Preview:

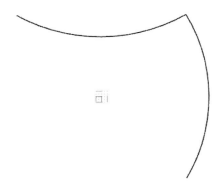

♦ To select all four lines as shown.

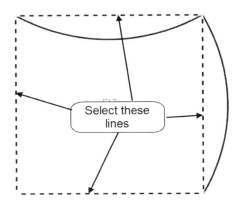

♦ Click on the **Delete** key from the keyboard.

♦ The geometry should look as shown.

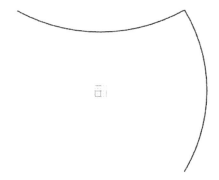

STEP 5: MIRROR THE GEOMETRY

In this step you will **Mirror** the geometry about the X axis.

Step Preview:

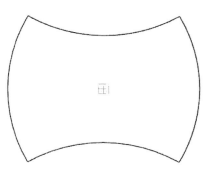

Transform

♦ From the **Position** group, select **Mirror** as shown.

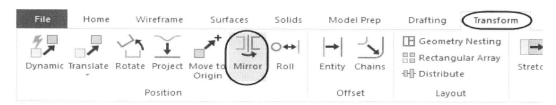

♦ [Mirror: select entities to mirror]: Select the first entity as shown.

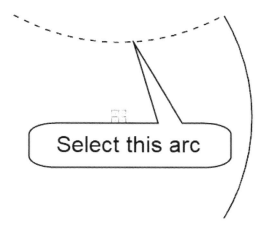

Select this arc

♦ Click on the **End Selection** button to finish the selection to continue.

♦ Select the option to mirror the entities about the **X axis** as shown.

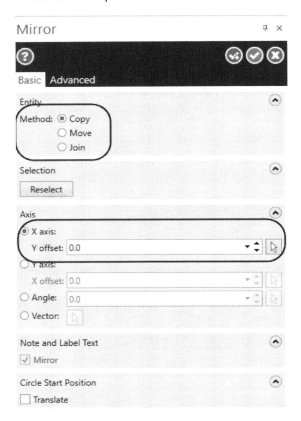

♦ Select the **OK and Create New Operation** button to continue with the same command.

♦ Select the second entity as shown.

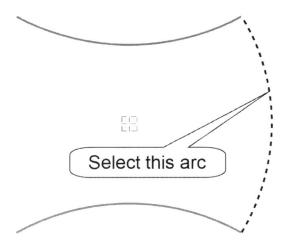

♦ Click on the **End Selection** button to finish the selection to continue.

♦ Select the option to mirror the entities about the **Y axis** as shown.

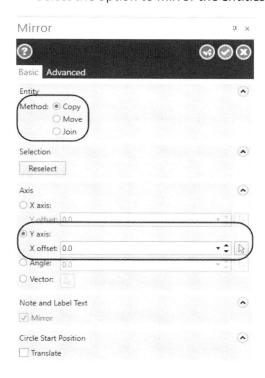

♦ Select the **OK** button to exit the **Mirror** panel.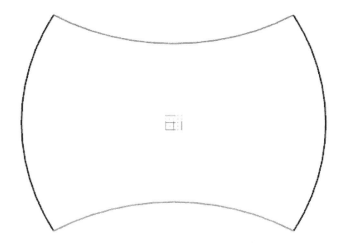
♦ Press **Alt + F1** to fit the drawing in the graphics window.

♦ The geometry should look as shown.

♦ Right mouse click in the graphics window and from the **Mini Toolbar** select **Clear Colors** to return the colors

   to the original system colors.

STEP 6: CREATE A FILLET

In this step you will use the **Create Fillet Entities** command to create a fillet with the radius 0.75. Fillets are used to round sharp corners.

Step Preview:

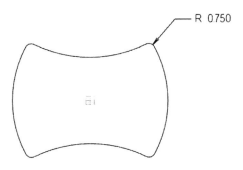

— R 0750

Wireframe

♦ From the **Modify** group, select **Fillet Entities** drop down menu and select **Fillet Chains**..

♦ Make sure **Chain** is enabled and select one arc. The entire geometry will be automatically selected as shown.

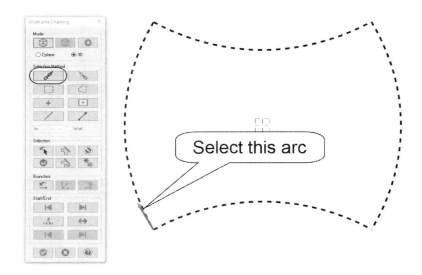

Select this arc

♦ Click the **OK** button to continue.

Mill Essentials

♦ In the **Fillet Chains** panel, change the **Radius** value to **0.75** as shown. Make sure other settings are enabled as follows. Press **Enter**.

♦ Select the **OK** button to exit the command.

♦ The geometry should look as shown.

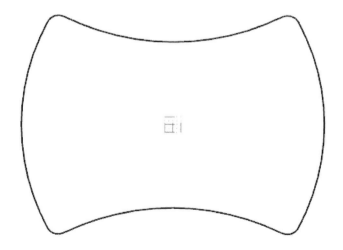

STEP 7: CREATE THE ELLIPSES

In this step you will learn how to create an ellipse given the point of origin, A radius, and B radius.

Step Preview:

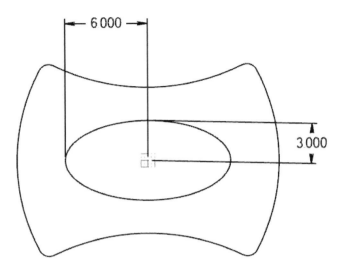

Wireframe

♦ From the **Shapes** group, click on the drop down arrow under **Rectangle** and select **Ellipse**.

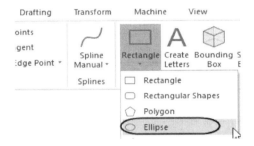

♦ Select the **Origin** as the position of base point.

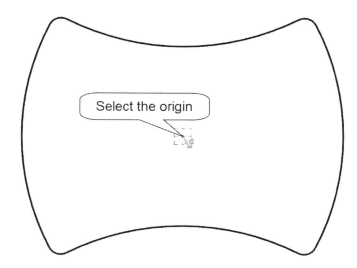

♦ [Enter X axis radius or select point]: Select a point in the graphics window as shown.

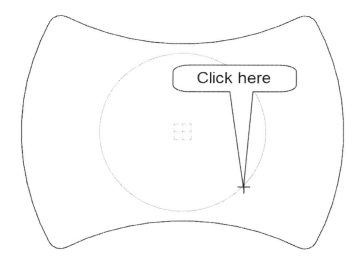

♦ [Enter Y axis radius or select point]: Select a point in the graphics window as shown.

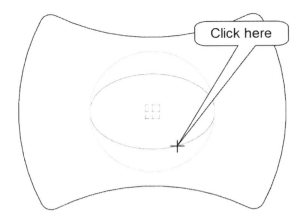
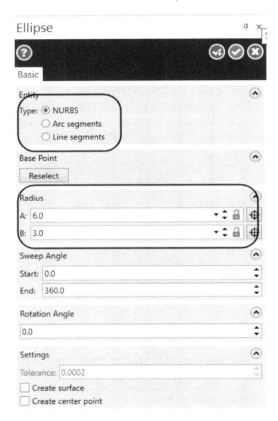

♦ Enter an **A radius** of **6.0**, a **B radius** of **3.0** and press **Enter** as shown.

♦ Select the **OK** button to exit the **Ellipse** command.

STEP 8: OFFSET THE ELLIPSE

In this step you will offset the ellipse with a given distance.

Step Preview:

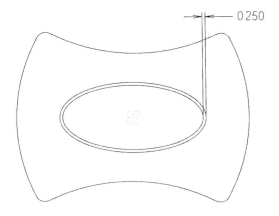

Transform

♦ From the **Offset** group, select **Entity**.

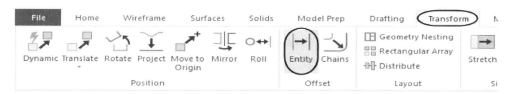

♦ [Select the line, arc, spline or curve to offset]: Select the ellipse as shown.
♦ [Indicate the offset direction]: Click inside of the ellipse as shown.

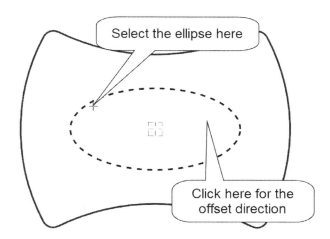

♦ Change the distance in the **Offset** dialog box to **0.25** and leave **Copy** enabled as shown.

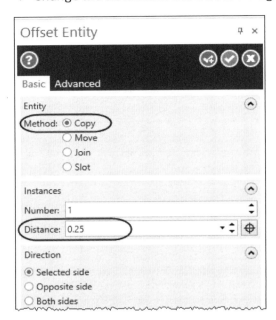

♦ Select the **OK** button to exit the **Offset** panel.

♦ Right mouse click in the graphics window and from the **Mini Toolbar** select **Clear Colors** to return the colors

to the original system colors.

♦ The geometry should look as shown.

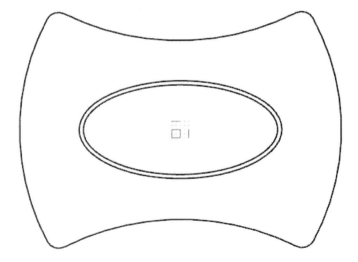

STEP 9: CREATE LINES KNOWING THE ENDPOINTS

In this step you will use the **Line Endpoint** command to create two lines that start at the midpoints of the arcs.

Step Preview:

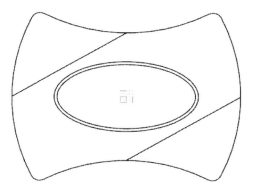

Wireframe

♦ From the **Lines** group, select **Line Endpoints** as shown.

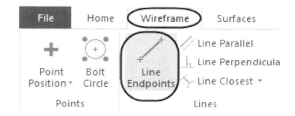

♦ In the **Line Endpoints** panel, leave the **Entity type** set to **Freeform** and the **Method** set **Two endpoints**.
♦ [Specify the first point]: Select the arc as shown. Make sure that only the arc as a whole is selected and the Midpoint point sign appears while selecting the arc.

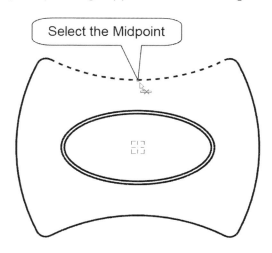

Select the Midpoint

♦ Sketch the line by moving the cursor to the left of the arc and click to select the second point at the Midpoint of the arc as shown.

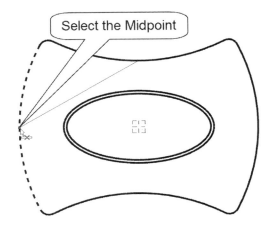

♦ Select the **OK and Create New Operation** button to continue with the same command.

♦ Select the Midpoint of the arc as shown.

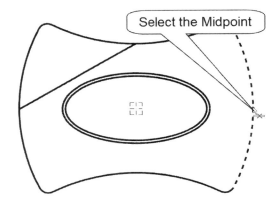

♦ Sketch the line by moving the cursor to the left of the arc and click to select the second Midpoint as shown.

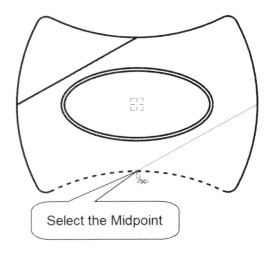

- Select the **OK** button to exit the command.

- The geometry should look as shown.

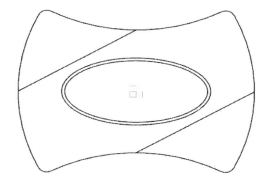

STEP 10: ADD THE TEXT

In this step you will create the **Letters**, then by using **Bounding box**, you will create a point at the center of these letters. You will then use the **Translate** command to move the letters to the center of the part. Creating letters uses lines, arcs and **NURBS** splines. There are various fonts found in this command as well. When using **TrueType** fonts, the height of the letters may not match the value you entered for the letter height because Mastercam scales the letters based on all the information encoded into the **TrueType** font.

Step Preview:

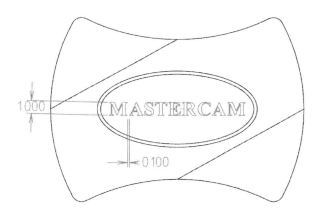

10.1 Change the wireframe color to red

Home

♦ From the **Attributes** group, click on the drop down arrow next to the **Wireframe color** and select color red as shown.

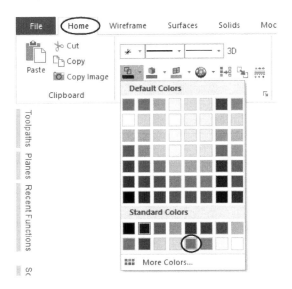

10.2 Create the letters

Wireframe

♦ From the **Shapes** group, select **Create Letters** as shown.

♦ When the **Create Letters** panel appears, select **True Type Font** icon as shown.

- ◆ Scroll down the **Font** list and find the font **Times New Roman**.
- ◆ Select **Bold** for the **Font style** as shown.

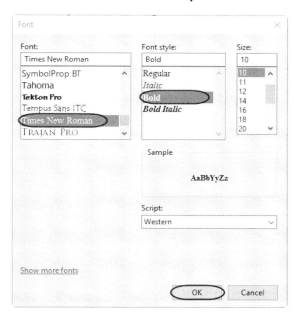

- ◆ Select the **OK** button to exit **Font** dialog box.
- ◆ Input the word **MASTERCAM** in the field under **Letters** as shown.

- ◆ Change the **Height** to **1.0** and the **Spacing** to **0.1**.
- ◆ Make sure the **Alignment** is set to **Horizontal**.

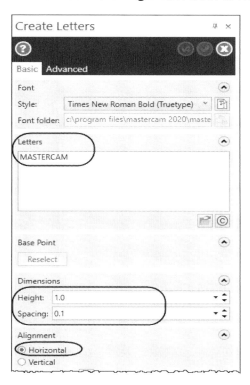

♦ [Enter the starting location]: Select a point to the right of the part as the text starting location as shown.

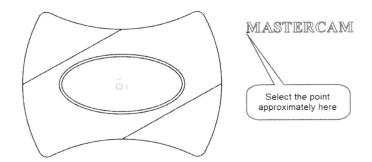

Select the point
approximately here

♦ Select the **OK** button to end the command.

Note: Next we will move the text within the part.

♦ Press **Alt + F1** to fit the geometry in the graphics window if needed.

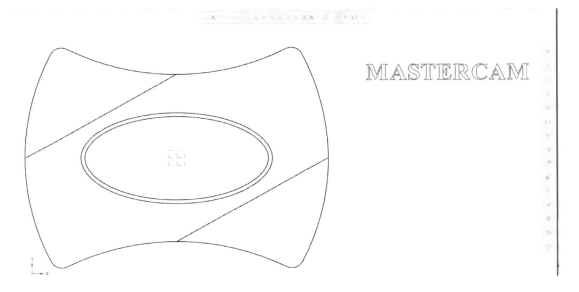

10.3 Move the letters using Translate

♦ Make a window outside the letters, as shown.

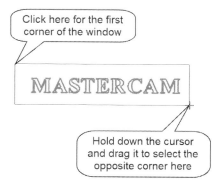

Transform

♦ From the **Position** group, select **Translate** icon as shown.

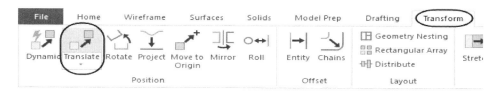

♦ When the **Translate** panel appears, select the **Move** button and then click on **Reselect** button under **Vector From/To** shown.

◆ Move the cursor to the center of the letters and scroll the mouse up to zoom in as shown. The center point

icon should look as shown.

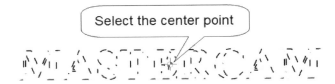

◆ [Select the point to translate from]: Select the Origin as shown.

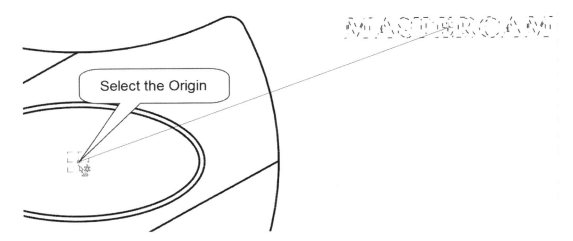

◆ Select the **OK** button in the **Translate** panel.

◆ Press **Alt + F1** to see the geometry.

◆ Right mouse click in the graphics window and from the **Mini Toolbar** select **Clear Colors** to return the colors

to the original system colors.

◆ Once complete, the geometry should look as shown.

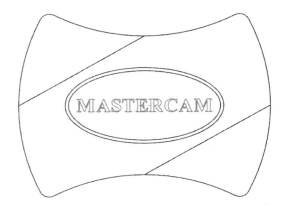

STEP 11: BREAK AT INTERSECTION

In this step you will use **Break at Intersection** command to break the 15" Radius arcs. The arcs have to be broken to create the solid.

Break at Intersection allows you to select entities and automatically break them at each intersection.

Step Preview:

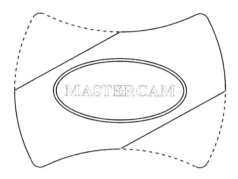

Wireframe

♦ From the **Modify** group, select the arrow next to **Break Two Pieces** and select **Break at Intersection** as shown.

♦ [Select the entities to break]: Select the arcs and the lines as shown. (No fillets should be selected.)

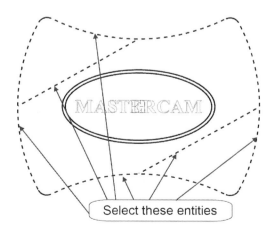

Select these entities

♦ Press **Enter** to finish the selection.

- ◆ The selected arcs will be automatically broken at the intersection with the lines.

Note: Hover the cursor about the arcs as shown to check if they are broken.

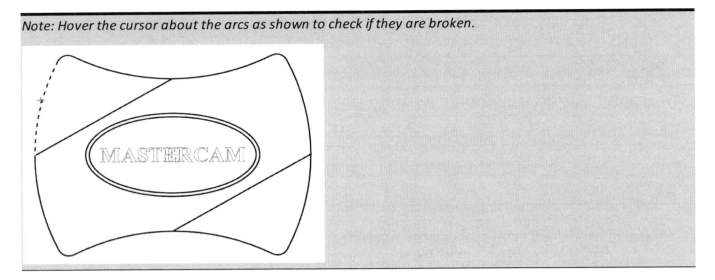

STEP 12: TRANSLATE

In this step you will learn how to translate entities to a different Z depth. This geometry will be used to create the solid and the toolpaths.

Step Preview:

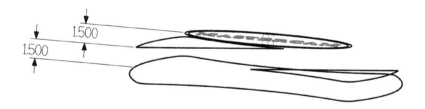

12.1 Translate the outside geometry and the lines at Z -1.5

Transform

- ◆ From the **Position** group, select **Translate** as shown.

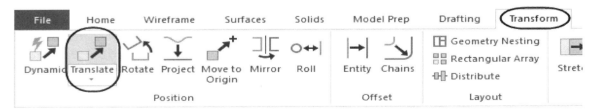

♦ [Translate: select entities to translate]: Hold down the **Shift** key and select the arc as shown.

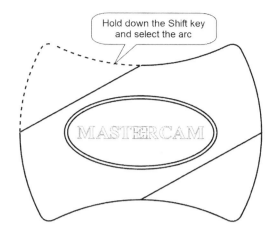

*Note: If you hold the **Shift** key the system select all the entities that form a chain with the entity selected. It stops at a branch point where three or more entities have their endpoints.*

♦ Repeat the step and select the rest of the outside profile as shown.

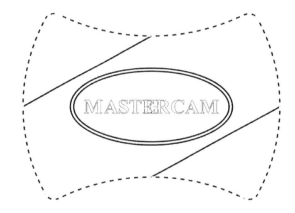

♦ Select the two lines as shown.

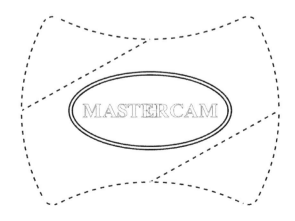

♦ Click on the **End Selection** button or press **Enter**.
♦ In the **Translate** panel, enable **Move** and set the **Z** to **-1.5** as shown.

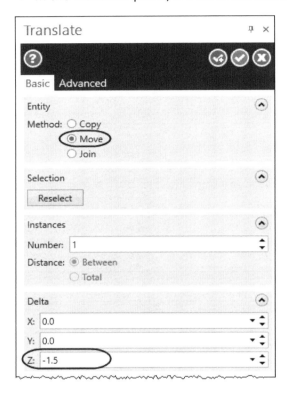

♦ Right click in the graphics area, and select the graphic view **Isometric** as shown.

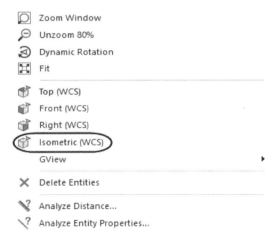

- The geometry should look as shown.

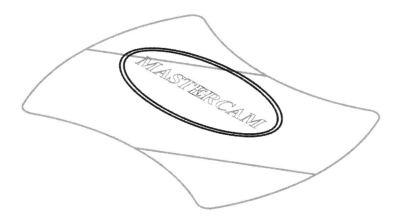

- Select the **OK and Create New Operation** button.

12.2 Translate - Copy the open chains of the pockets at Z -1.5

- Select the two chains as shown.

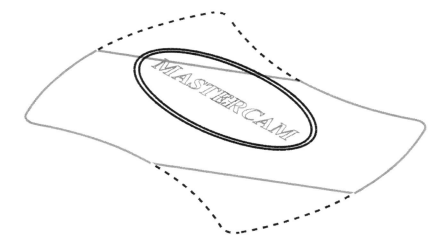

- Click on the **End Selection** button or press **Enter**.

♦ When the **Translate** panel appears, ensure **Copy** is enabled and input a **Z depth** of **-1.5**

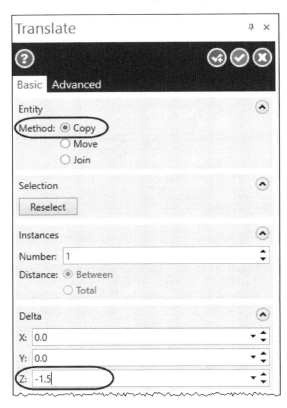

♦ Select **OK and Create New Operation** or press **Enter** to remain in the command.

12.3 Translate-Move the rest of the ouside geometry at Z -1.5.

♦ [Translate: select entities to translate]: Hold down the **Shift** key and select the rest of the outside profile as shown.

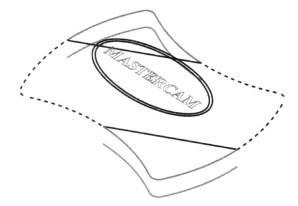

♦ Click on the **End Selection** button or press **Enter**.

♦ Enable **Move**.
♦ Change the **Z depth** to **-1.5**.

♦ Select **OK** to exit the command.
♦ Right mouse click in the graphics window and from the **Mini Toolbar**, select the **Clear Colors** icon to reset the colors back to the original colors.
♦ Press **Alt + F1** to fit the entire geometry in the graphics window.
♦ The geometry should look as shown.

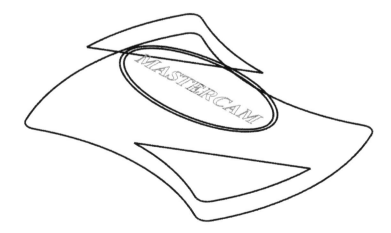

STEP 13: CHANGE THE MAIN LEVEL TO 2

Levels are a primary organizational tool in Mastercam. A Mastercam file can contain separate levels for wireframe, surfaces, drafting entities, solids, and toolpaths. By organizing your files into levels, you can easily control which areas of the drawing are visible at any time and which parts are selectable. By doing so, you will not inadvertently make changes to areas of the drawing you do not want to change.
In this step we will change the **Main Level** to **2**, to create the solid on **Level 2**.

♦ Right mouse click in the graphics area and in the **Mini Toolbar**, change the **Level** number to **2** as shown.

♦ Press the **Enter** key on your keyboard.

CREATE THE SOLID BODY

STEP 14: EXTRUDE THE BASE GEOMETRY

Solid Extrude: Uses planar chains to create one or more solid bodies, create cuts in an existing solid or create bosses to an existing solid. Mastercam extrudes entities by driving the shapes of the entity along a linear path using a specified direction, distance, and other parameters that further define the results.

Step Preview:

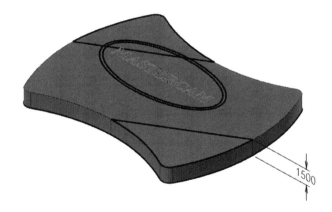

Solids

♦ From the **Create** group, select **Extrude** as shown.

♦ Leave the default settings in the **Chaining** dialog box as shown.

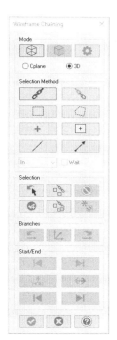

Chaining is the process of selecting and linking geometry entities such that they form the foundation of a toolpath, a surface, or a solid. When you chain the geometry, you can select one or more sets of curves (lines, arcs, and splines) that have adjoining endpoints.

Chaining differs from other selection methods because it assigns order and direction to the selected curves. Chaining order and direction determine how surfaces, solids, and toolpaths are generated.

♦ [Select chain(s) to extrude 1]: Select the outside profile as shown.

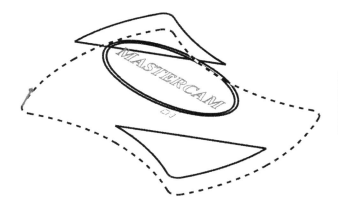

Note: If you did not select the chain correctly, you can use the **Unselect** button ⊘ from the Chaining dialog box to undo the previous selection.

♦ Select the **OK** button to exit the **Chaining** dialog box. ✓
♦ The **Solid Extrude** panel will display. An arrow will appear on the geometry. This arrow indicates the direction of the extrusion.

Note: Make sure that the arrow points upwards. Otherwise, in the Solid Extrude panel, click on the **Reverse all** button.

♦ In the **Solid Extrude** panel, set the **Distance** to **1.5** as shown.

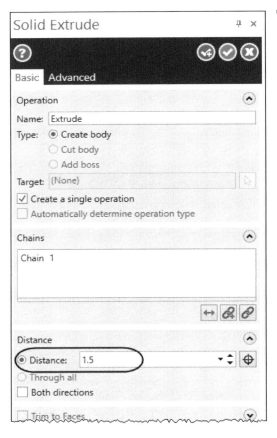

Extrusion Operation is used to create a solid body, cut a solid body, or add a boss to another solid.

Reverse Direction extrudes the solid in the opposite direction from the arrow on the chain indicating the extrusion direction.

Distance allows you to control the length of extrusion, by specifying a **Distance**, extending **Through all**, extending in **Both directions**, or trimming to selected faces.

Both Directions allows you to extrude in both directions from the chain.

♦ Select the **OK** button to exit the **Extrude** panel.
♦ The part, in the unshade mode, should appear as shown below.

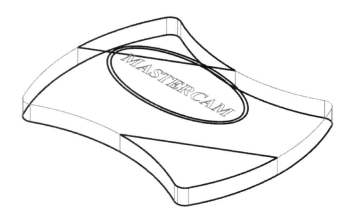

♦ To display the part in the shaded/unshade mode, press **Alt + S**.

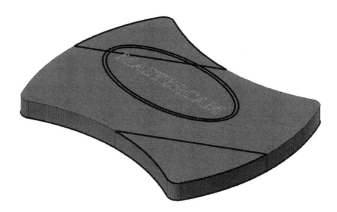

♦ Click on the **Solids** tab at the bottom of the **Toolpaths Manager** or at the right side of the graphics window.

♦ If the **Solids Manager** is not yet in the display, select the **View** tab, then from the **Managers** group, click on **Solids** as shown.

♦ In the **Solids Manager**, you should see one **Solid** as shown.

♦ To see the solid history with all the operations listed, click on the plus sign (+) in front of the **Solid**.

*Note: To modify any of the solids operation, first make sure the **Solids** panel is locked, then double click on the operation. The corresponding panel will appear on the screen, and hence the parameters can be modified. To update the solid after modifying the parameters, click on the **Regen** button from the **Solids Manager**.*

STEP 15: EXTRUDE CUT THE BODY

In this step another extrusion operation will be performed to cut the pockets and through holes from the solid body to a specific depth.

Step Preview:

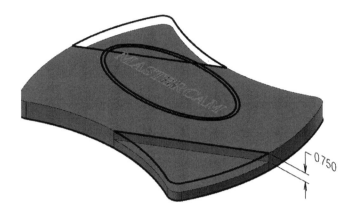

Solids

♦ From the **Create** group, select **Extrude**.

♦ Leave the default settings in the **Chaining** dialog box and select the chain as shown.

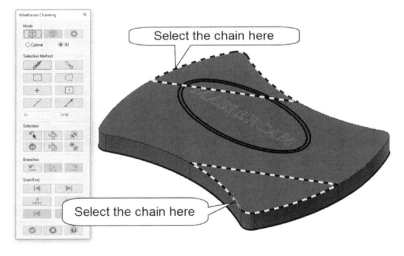

Select the chain here

Select the chain here

♦ Select the **OK** button to exit the **Chaining** dialog box.

♦ The **Solid Extrude** panel will appear. Change the **Type** to **Cut body** and enter the **Distance 0.75** as shown.

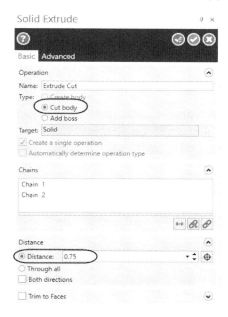

Note: Make sure that the arrow points downwards. Otherwise, in the Solid Extrude panel, click on the **Reverse all** button.

♦ Select the **OK and Create New Operation** button to remain in the command.
♦ The part should appear as shown in the **Isometric** view.

♦ To display the part in the unshaded mode, press **Alt + S**.

STEP 16: ADD THE ELLIPSE AS A BOSS SHAPE

Step Preview:

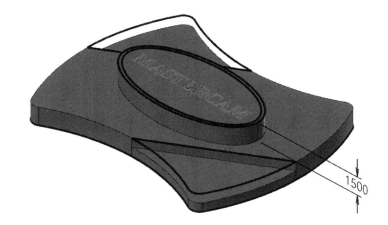

♦ Leave the default settings in the **Chaining** dialog box and select the arc as shown.

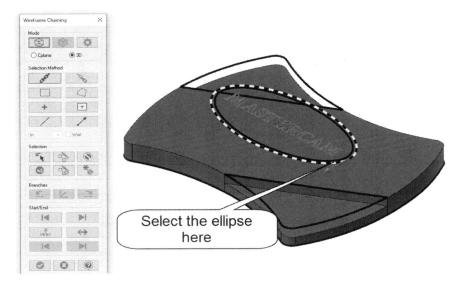

Select the ellipse here

♦ Select the **OK** button to exit the **Chaining** dialog box.

♦ The **Solid Extrude** panel will appear. Change the **Type** to **Add boss** and enter the **Distance 1.5** as shown.

*Note: Make sure that the arrow points downwards. Otherwise, in the Solid Extrude panel, click on the **Reverse all** button.*

♦ Select the **OK and Create New Operation** button to remain in the command.

♦ The part should appear as shown below.

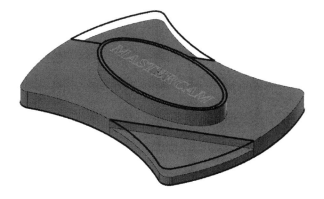

STEP 17: EXTRUDE CUT THE ELLIPSE

Step Preview:

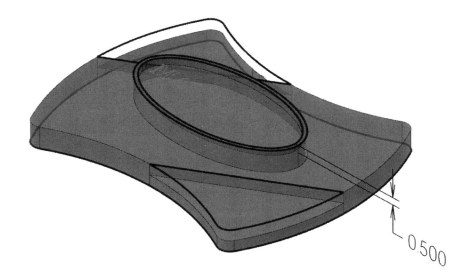

♦ Leave the default settings in the **Chaining** dialog box and select the inside ellipse as shown.

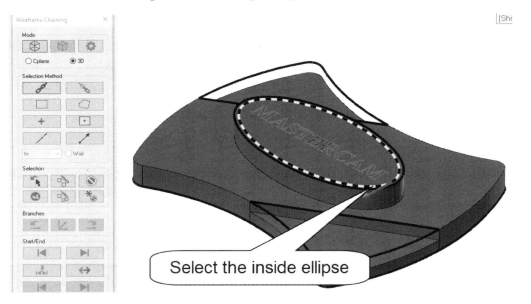

Select the inside ellipse

♦ Select **OK** to exit the **Chaining** dialog box.

♦ Ensure the arrow points downwards. Click on the **Reverse All** button, if needed, to change the arrow direction as shown.

♦ In the **Solid Extrude** panel, ensure **Cut body** is enabled and set **Distance** to **0.5.**

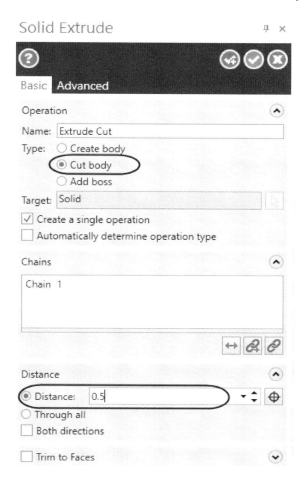

♦ Select **OK** to exit the command.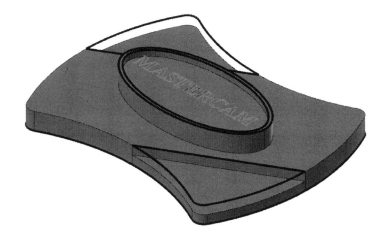
♦ The part should appear as shown below.

STEP 18: CREATE THE BOTTOM CYLINDER

In this step you will create a circle at the bottom of the solid. You will use the circle and add a boss to the existing solid.

Step Preview:

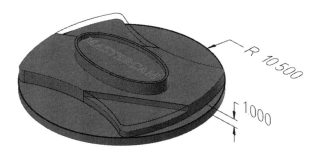

18.1 Move Z depth at the bottom of the solid

♦ In the **Status bar** select **Z** as shown.

| X: 12.35262 | Y: 3.51944 | Z: 0.00000 | 3D | CPLANE: TOP |

♦ Select an Endpoint at the bottom of the solid.

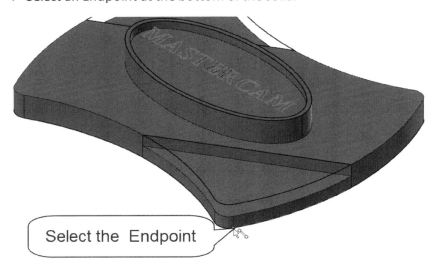

Select the Endpoint

♦ The Z value should change as shown.

| X: 8.51212 | Y: -7.01718 | Z: -3.00000 | 3D | CPLANE: TOP |

18.2 Set the Construction mode to 2D

Note: To create the circle at the proper depth, you have to change the construction mode to 2D.

♦ In the **Status bar** select **3D** as shown.

| X: 19.01107 | Y: -10.08174 | Z: -3.00000 | 3D | CPLANE: TOP |

♦ The construction mode will be automatically change to **2D**.

| X: 15.24451 | Y: 4.52252 | Z: -3.00000 | 2D | CPLANE: TOP |

18.3 Create the circle

Wireframe

♦ From the **Arcs** group, select the **Circle Center Point** icon.

♦ In the **Circle Center Point** panel, enter the **Radius** as shown.

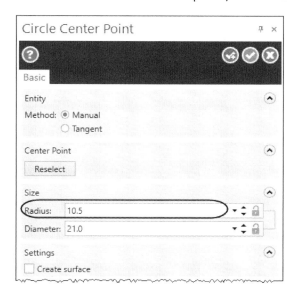

♦ [Enter the center point]: In the **General Selection** bar, select the drop down next to the **AutoCursor** and select **Origin**.

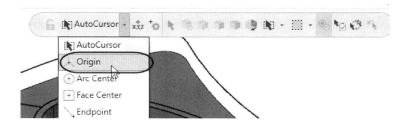

♦ In the **Circle Center Point** panel, click on the **OK** button to exit the command.

◆ The geometry should look as shown.

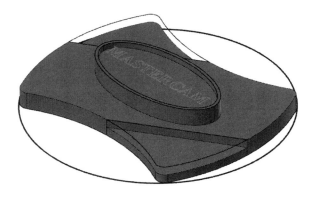

18.4 Add the boss to the solid

Solids

◆ From the **Create** group, select **Extrude** icon.

◆ Select the circle as shown.

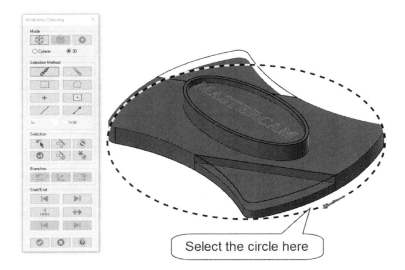

Select the circle here

◆ In the **Chaining** dialog box, select the **OK** button.

♦ If the arrow points upwards, as shown, click on the reverse icon in the **Solid Extrude** panel.

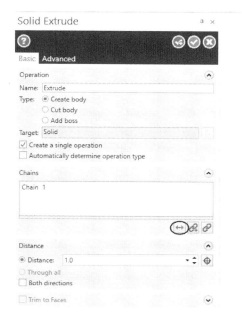

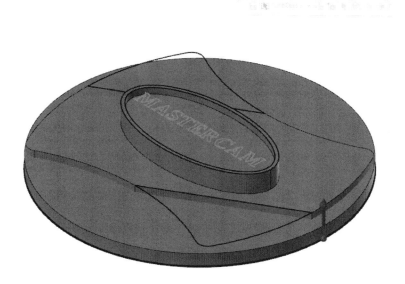

♦ In the **Solid Extrude** panel enable **Add boss** and set the **Distance** to **1.0** as shown. The arrow should point downwards as shown.

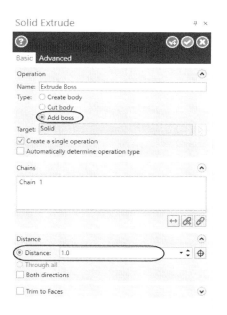

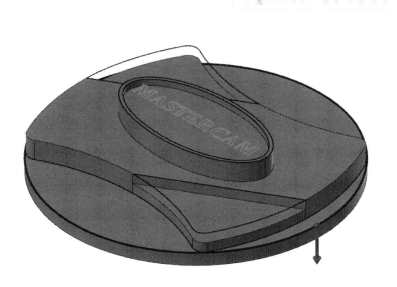

♦ Select the **OK** button to exit the command.

♦ The final geometry should look as shown.

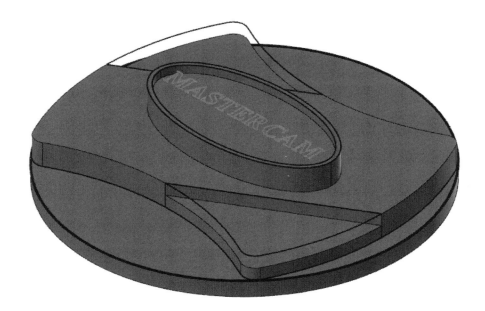

♦ In the Status bar change the construction mode back to **3D**.

STEP 19: SAVE THE FILE

File

♦ **Save As.**

♦ Click on the **Browse** icon as shown.

♦ Find a location on the computer to save your file. **File name:** "Your Name_3".

TUTORIAL #3 REVIEW EXERCISE

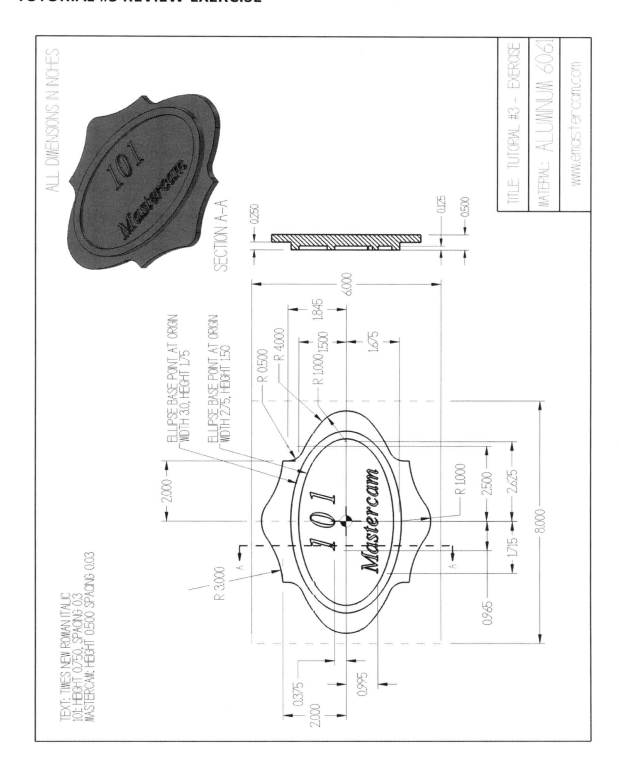

ALL DIMENSIONS IN INCHES

SECTION A-A

TITLE: TUTORIAL #3 - EXERCISE
MATERIAL: ALUMINUM 6061
www.emastercam.com

ELLIPSE BASE POINT AT ORIGIN
WIDTH 3.0, HEIGHT 1.75

ELLIPSE BASE POINT AT ORIGIN
WIDTH 2.75, HEIGHT 1.50

TEXT:- TIMES NEW ROMAN ITALIC
101: HEIGHT 0.750, SPACING 0.3
MASTERCAM: HEIGHT 0.500 SPACING 0.03

CREATE THE GEOMETRY FOR TUTORIAL #3 EXERCISE

Use these commands from the Wireframe tab to create the geometry.

- Circle Center Point.
- Rectangle.
- Arc Tangent 2 Entities or Fillet Entities.
- Arc one point.
- Trim.
- Mirror.
- Ellipse.
- Create Letters
- Translate.
- Solid Extrude.

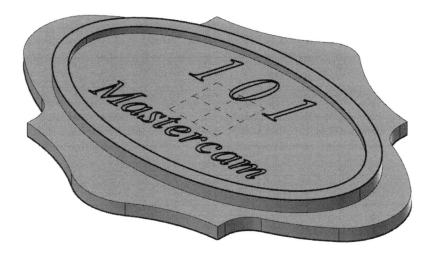

TUTORIAL #3 GEOMETRY CREATION QUIZ

◆ What does Break at intersection command do?

◆ What does Mirror command do?

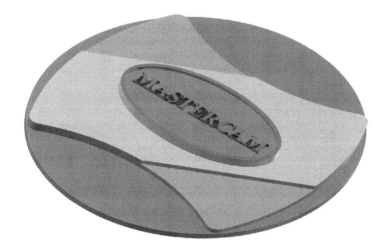

OVERVIEW OF STEPS TAKEN TO CREATE THE FINAL PART:

Create the necessary Toolpaths to machine the part:

♦ The student will set up the stock size to be used and the clamping method used.
♦ A 2D High Speed Area Mill toolpath will be created to remove the material from the outside step.
♦ A Pocket Island Facing toolpath will be created to machine the pocket and face the letters.
♦ A Pocket Remachining toolpath will be used to machine the remaining material.
♦ A 2D High Speed Dynamic Mill toolpath will be created to remove the outside material.

Backplot and Verify the file:

♦ Backplot will be used to simulate a step-by-step process of the tool's movements.
♦ Verify will be used to watch a tool machine the part out of a solid model.

Post Process the file to generate the G-code:

♦ The student will then post process the file to obtain an NC file containing the necessary code for the machine.

SUGGESTED FIXTURE

SETUP SHEET

TOOL LIST

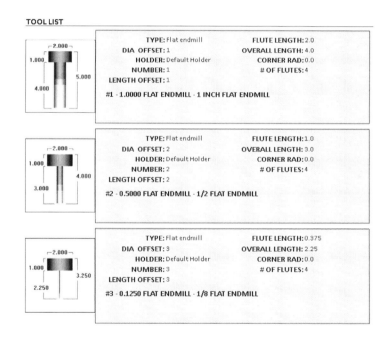

TYPE: Flat endmill	**FLUTE LENGTH:** 2.0	
DIA OFFSET: 1	**OVERALL LENGTH:** 4.0	
HOLDER: Default Holder	**CORNER RAD:** 0.0	
NUMBER: 1	**# OF FLUTES:** 4	
LENGTH OFFSET: 1		

#1 - 1.0000 FLAT ENDMILL - 1 INCH FLAT ENDMILL

TYPE: Flat endmill	**FLUTE LENGTH:** 1.0	
DIA OFFSET: 2	**OVERALL LENGTH:** 3.0	
HOLDER: Default Holder	**CORNER RAD:** 0.0	
NUMBER: 2	**# OF FLUTES:** 4	
LENGTH OFFSET: 2		

#2 - 0.5000 FLAT ENDMILL - 1/2 FLAT ENDMILL

TYPE: Flat endmill	**FLUTE LENGTH:** 0.375	
DIA OFFSET: 3	**OVERALL LENGTH:** 2.25	
HOLDER: Default Holder	**CORNER RAD:** 0.0	
NUMBER: 3	**# OF FLUTES:** 4	
LENGTH OFFSET: 3		

#3 - 0.1250 FLAT ENDMILL - 1/8 FLAT ENDMILL

STEP 1: SELECT THE MACHINE AND SET UP THE STOCK

In Mastercam, you select a **Machine Definition** before creating any toolpath. The **Machine Definition** is a model of your machine's capabilities and features. It acts like a template for setting up your machine. The machine definition ties together three main components: the schematic model of your machine's components, the control definition that models your control capabilities, and the post processor that will generate the required machine code (G-code). For a Mill Essentials exercise (2D toolpaths), we need just a basic machine definition.

*Note: For the purpose of this tutorial, we will be using the **Default Mill** machine.*

1.1 Un-hide the Toolpaths Manager panel

♦ From the left side of the graphics window, click on the **Toolpaths** tab as shown.

♦ Pin the **Toolpaths Manager** by clicking on the **Auto Hide** icon as shown.

1.2 Select the machine

*Note: Select the **Mill Default** only if there is no **Machine Group** in the **Toolpaths Manager**.*

Machine

*Note: Once you select the **Mill Default**, the **Ribbon bar** changes to reflect the toolpaths that could be used with **Mill Default**.*

♦ Select the plus sign (**+**) in front of Properties in the **Toolpaths Manager** to expand the **Toolpaths Group Properties**.

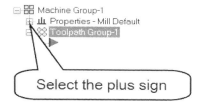

Select the plus sign

♦ Select **Tool settings** to set the tool parameters.

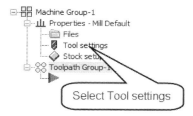

Select Tool settings

♦ Change the parameters to match the screen shot as shown.

Default program number is used to enter a number if your machine requires a number for a program name.

Assign tool numbers sequentially allows you to overwrite the tool number from the library with the next available tool number. (First operation tool number 1; second operation tool number 2, etc.).

Warn of duplicate tool numbers allows you to get a warning if you enter two tools with the same number.

Override defaults with modal values enables the system to keep the values that you enter.

Feed Calculation set to **From tool** uses feed rate, plunge rate, retract rate, and spindle speed from the tool definition.

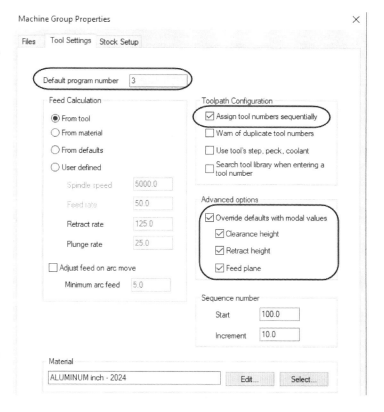

♦ Select the **Stock Setup** tab to define the stock.
♦ Select the **Cylindrical Shape** and enter the values as shown.

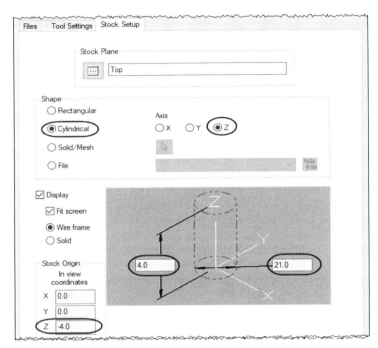

The **Stock Origin** values adjust the positioning of the stock, ensuring that you have an equal amount of extra stock around the finished part.

Display options allow you to set the stock as Wireframe and to fit the stock to the screen. (Fit Screen)

♦ Select the **OK** button to exit **Machine Group Properties**.

♦ Right mouse click in the graphics window and select the **Isometric** view to see the stock.

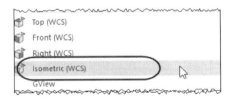

♦ The stock model will appear as shown.

> *Note: The stock model will appear as shown. The stock is not geometry and cannot be selected.*

STEP 2: 2D HIGH SPEED AREA MILL

2D High Speed Area Mill generates the free-flowing motion needed to machine features, such as standing bosses and cores or pockets in a single operation. With **Area Mill High Speed**, smaller depth of cuts are recommended, versus **Dynamic Mill** in which the depth cuts can be the size of the flute.

The toolpath depends on the **Machining strategy** that you choose in the **Chain Options**. If the strategy chosen is **From outside**, the toolpath starts at the outmost chain and works its way in, taking on the final shape of the part as it approaches the final pass. You can also machine pockets, in which case the strategy selected is **Start inside** which keeps the tool inside the machining regions.

Toolpath Preview:

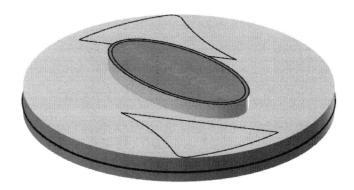

Toolpaths

♦ From the **2D** group, select the **Expand gallery** arrow.

♦ Select the **Area Mill** icon as shown.

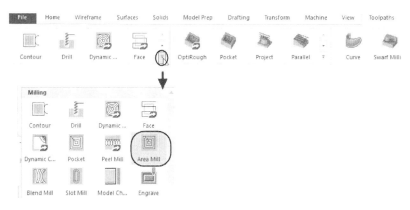

2.1 Select the geometry

♦ In the **Chain Options**, enable **From outside** as shown.

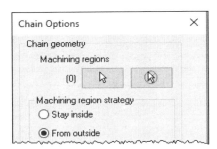

Note: No selection is required in the **Machining regions**. To determine the **Machining region,** the system will use the defined stock. You have to set the stock in the **Stock setup** to be able to use this option.

♦ From the **Chain Options**, click on the **Select avoidance chains** button in the **Avoidance regions** as shown.

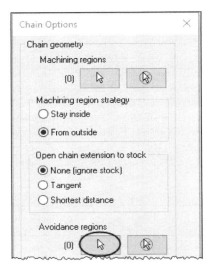

- In the **Chaining** dialog box, enable **Solids**.
- Enable only the **Loop** button as shown.

- [Select 2D HST machining faces]: Select the solid edge as shown.

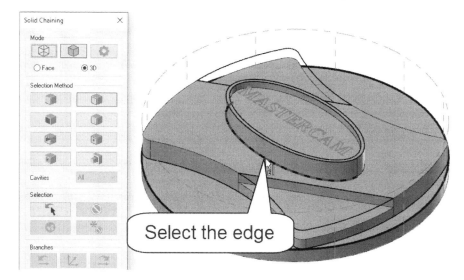

- If the selected geometry looks as shown, select the **OK** button to accept the face.

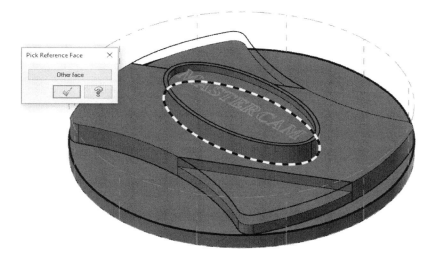

- Select the **OK** button to exit the **Solid Chaining** dialog box.

2.2 Preview Chains

The **Preview Chains** function is intended to give the user a quick visual representation of how Mastercam sees the various pieces of geometry that have been selected, how they interact with one another and a general overview of how the toolpath will be calculated with the selections presently made.

♦ Click on the **Color** icon to see the legend for **Preview chains** as shown. The **Preview Chains Colors** dialog box should look as shown.

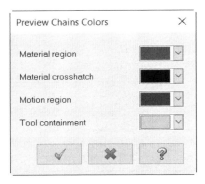

The **Material region** and **Material crosshatch** are the two colors that are used to define the material to be cut. The default colors are red for the background and black for the crosshatch.

The **Motion region** displays the area that Mastercam is making available to the toolpath for motion if it needs it. The color to represent it is dark blue. The primary reason for the display of the entire available (but not necessarily used) **Motion region** is to help the user visualize how the tool may move near or interact with any adjacent geometry.

The **Tool containment** is what you have selected as the containment region in the chain geometry. If you have not selected a containment region, it will default to the outside of the **Motion region** since that is currently the default area the toolpath is being contained to. The color used to represent the **Tool containment** is yellow.

♦ Select the **OK** button to exit **Preview Chains Colors**.
♦ Select the **Preview chains** button as shown.
♦ The **Preview chains** should look as shown.

- Press **Esc** key to return to the toolpath parameters.

- Select the **OK** button to exit the **Chain Options** panel.
- In the **Toolpath Type** page, **Area Mill** will be selected as shown.

2.3 Select a 1.0" Flat Endmill from the Tool Library and set the Tool Parameters

- From the **Tree View list**, select **Tool**.

- Click on the **Select library tool** button.
- Select the **Filter** button.

- Select the **None** button and then under **Tool Types**, choose the **Flat Endmill** icon.
- Under **Tool Diameter**, select **Equal** and input a value of **1.0** as shown.

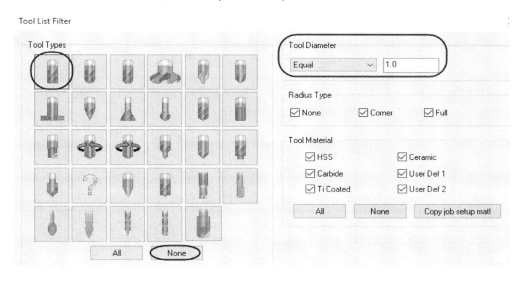

- Select the **OK** button to exit the **Tool List Filter**.
- In the **Tool Selection** panel you should only see a **1.0" Flat Endmill**.

#	Assembly Na...	Tool Name	Holder Name	Dia.	Cor. rad.	Length	# Flutes	Type	Rad. Type
297	--	1 INCH FLA...	--	1.0	0.0	2.0	4	Flat endmill	None

- Select the **1.0" Flat Endmill** in the **Tool Selection** page and then select the **OK** button to exit.

♦ Make all the necessary changes as shown.

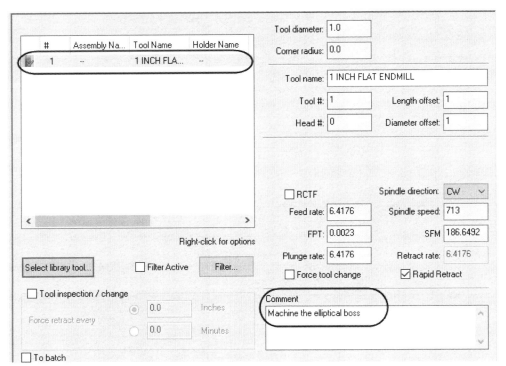

2.4 Set the Cut Parameters

♦ Select **Cut Parameters** and enable **Corner rounding**. Make all the necessary changes as shown.

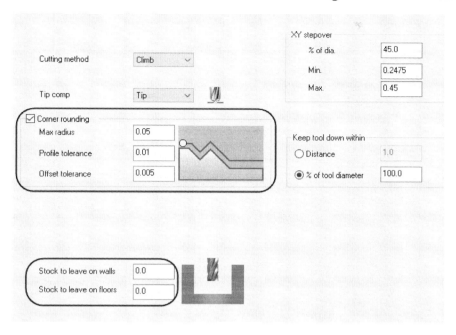

Corner Rounding replaces sharp corners with arcs for faster and smoother transitions in tool direction.

Max Radius is the largest arc that you allow Mastercam to insert to replace a corner. Larger arcs will create a smoother toolpath but with greater deviation from the originally programmed toolpath.

Profile Tolerance represents the maximum distance that the outermost profile of a toolpath created corner with a corner rounding can deviate from the original toolpath.

Offset Tolerance represents the maximum distance that a profile of a toolpath created with corner rounding can deviate from the original toolpath. This is the same measurement as the profile tolerance but is applied to all the profiles except the outermost one.

XY Stepover expresses the maximum XY stepover as a percentage of the tool diameter. Mastercam will use the largest value possible that does not leave unwanted upstands of material between the passes.

Keep Tool Down Within keeps the tool down if the distance from the end pass to the start of the next pass is less than the value here. Mastercam will not create a retract move as defined on the linking parameters page. Instead the tool will stay down and move directly between the passes at the feed rate.

2.5 Set the Depth Cuts Parameters

♦ Enable **Depth cuts** and make the necessary changes as shown.

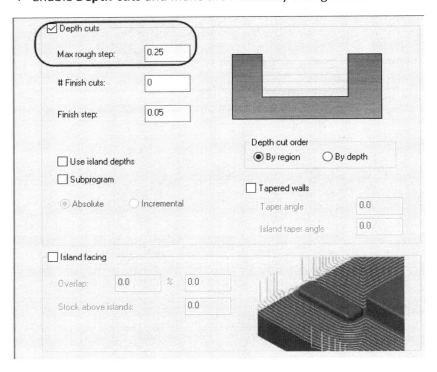

2.6 Set the Transitions Parameters

Note: You can leave the default parameters for transitions. In this operation you are machining from outside and the tool will automatically plunge outside the stock.

2.7 Set the Linking Parameters

♦ Select **Linking Parameters** and make any necessary changes as shown.

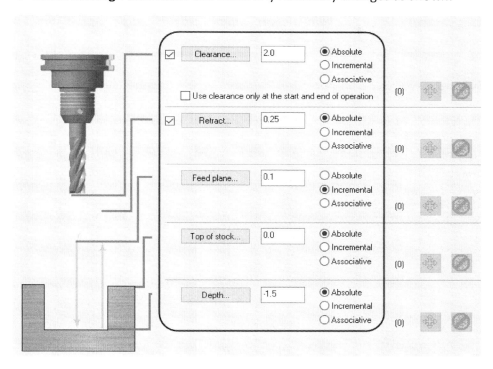

2.8 Set the HST Leads

♦ From the **Tree View list**, select **HST Leads** and make any necessary changes as shown.

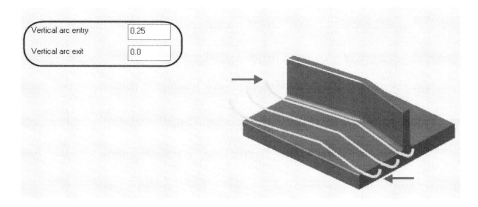

HST Leads page allows you to specify an entry and exit arc radius value for the **2D High Speed Toolpaths**. The arc is created vertically to lead on and off the material.

2.9 Set the Arc Filter / Tolerance

♦ Choose **Arc Filter / Tolerance** from the **Tree View list**.

♦ Select **Line/Arc Filter Settings** as shown.

♦ Select the **OK** button to accept the warning and make the necessary changes as shown.

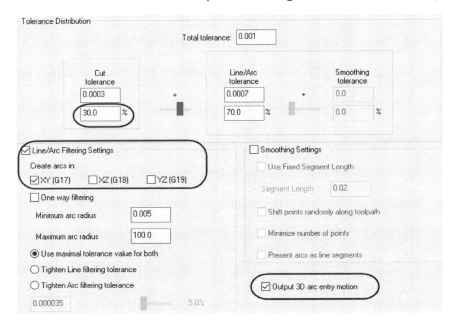

Tolerance Distribution allows you to dynamically adjust the toolpath's total tolerance. Total tolerance is the sum of the cut tolerance and the line/arc and smoothing tolerances. Move the sliders between the **Cut tolerance, Line/Arc tolerance** and/or **Smoothing tolerance** fields. The ratios update in 5% increments and the toolpath's total tolerance remains at its current value.

Line/Arc Filtering Settings allows you to activate Line/Arc filtering for the toolpath and apply the settings you define in this section to the toolpath refinement. Toolpath filtering lets you replace multiple very small linear moves — within the filter tolerance — with single arc moves to simplify the toolpath. Smoothing distributes a toolpath's node points, avoiding the clustering and grouping of points that can cause marks and other imperfections.

Create arcs in creates arcs in the selected plane. Your post processor must be able to handle arcs and output the code G17, G18, G19 to select this option.

2.10 Preview the Toolpath

♦ To quickly check how the toolpath will be generated, select the **Preview toolpath** icon as shown.

♦ To hide the dialog box, click on the **Hide dialog** icon as shown.

♦ The toolpath should look as shown.

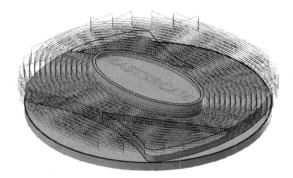

♦ Press **Esc** key to exit the preview.

Note: If the toolpath does not look as shown in the preview, check your parameters again.

♦ Select the **OK** button to exit the **2D High Speed Toolpath - Area Mill**.

STEP 3: BACKPLOT THE TOOLPATHS

3.1 Backplot the toolpath

Backplotting shows the path the tools take to cut the part. This display lets you spot errors in the program before you machine the part. As you backplot toolpaths, Mastercam displays additional information such as the X, Y, and Z coordinates, the path length, the minimum and maximum coordinates and the cycle time.

♦ Make sure that the toolpath is selected (signified by the green check mark on the folder icon). If the operation is not selected, choose the **Select all operations** icon.

♦ Select the **Backplot selected operations** button.

♦ In the **Backplot** dialog box, enable **Display with color codes, Display tool, Display Holder** and **Display rapid moves** icons as shown.

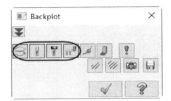

♦ To see the part from an **Isometric view**, right mouse click in the graphics window and select **Isometric** as shown.

♦ To fit the workpiece to the screen, if needed, right mouse click in the graphics window again and select **Fit**.
♦ You can step through the **Backplot** by using the **Step forward** ▶▶ or **Step back** ◀◀ buttons.
♦ You can adjust the speed of the backplot. ▬▬▬▬ ♦ ▬▬▬
♦ Select the **Play** button to run **Backplot**. ▶ ■ ◀◀◀ ◀◀ ▶▶ ▶▶▶ 〰 ✎
♦ After **Backplot** is completed, the toolpath should look as shown.

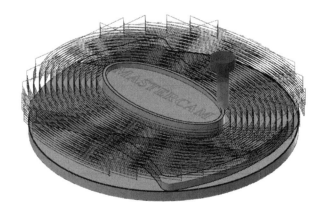

♦ Select the **OK** button to exit **Backplot** dialog box. ✓

STEP 4: SIMULATE THE TOOLPATH IN VERIFY

Verify shows the path the tools take to cut the part with material removal. This display lets you spot errors in the program before you machine the part. As you verify toolpaths, Mastercam displays additional information such as the X, Y, and Z coordinates, the path length, the minimum and maximum coordinates and the cycle time. It also shows any collision between the workpiece and the tool.

♦ From the **Toolpaths Manager**, select **Verify selected operations** icon as shown.

> Note: Mastercam launches a new window that allows you to check the part using **Backplot** or **Verify**. For more information on how to set and use **Backplot** and **Verify**, please check **"Simulate the toolpath in Verify" on page 78.**

♦ Change the settings for **Visibility** as shown.

♦ Select the **Play** button to run **Verify**.

♦ The part should appear as shown.

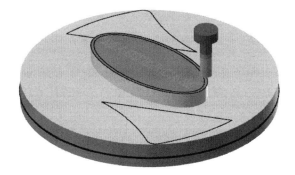

♦ To go back to the Mastercam window, minimize the **Mastercam Simulator** window as shown.

STEP 5: POCKET WITH ISLANDS

In this step, you will use a **Pocket** toolpath to remove the material inside of the inner ellipse leaving the letters as islands.

Toolpath Preview:

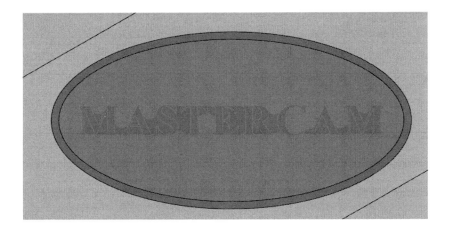

♦ Press **Alt + T** to remove the toolpath display.

Toolpaths

♦ From the **2D** group, select the **Expand gallery** arrow as shown.

♦ Select the **Pocket** icon as shown.

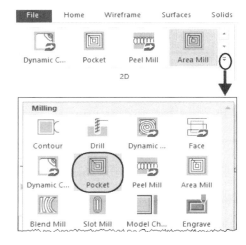

5.1 Select the Geometry

◆ Right mouse click in the graphics window and select the **Top** graphics view.

◆ In the **Chaining** dialog box Solid mode, enable **Face**.
◆ Select the bottom of the pocket.

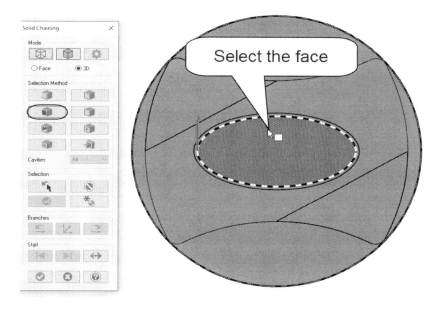

Select the face

♦ Change the **Mode** to **Wireframe** and select the **Window** button as shown.

♦ Create a window around the letters and the inner ellipse as shown.

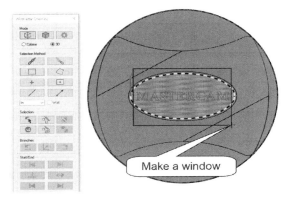

Make a window

Note: Make sure that the window is big enough to include the inside letters but avoid parts of the ellipses.

♦ [Sketch approximate start point]: Select an approximate starting point near the bottom of the letter "M" as shown.

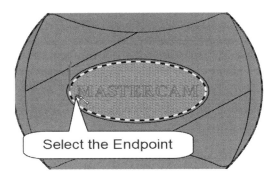

Select the Endpoint

♦ The geometry should be selected as shown.

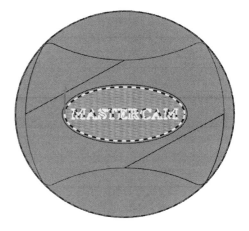

♦ Choose the **OK** button to exit the **Chaining** dialog box.

♦ On the **Toolpath Type** page, **Pocket** will be selected.

Contour   Pocket   Facing   Slot mill   Model Chamfer

5.2 Select a 1/2" Flat Endmill from the library and set the Tool Parameters

♦ Select **Tool** from the **Tree View list**.

♦ Click on the **Select library tool** button.

♦ Select the **Filter** button.

♦ Select the **None** button and then under **Tool Types** choose the **Flat Endmill** icon.

♦ Under **Tool Diameter**, select **Equal** and input a value of **0.5** as shown.

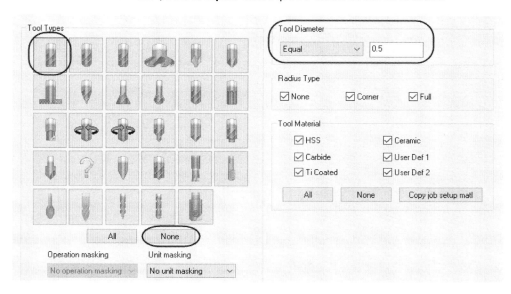

♦ Select the **OK** button to exit the **Tool List Filter**.

♦ In the **Tool Selection** panel you should only see a **1/2" Flat Endmill**.

#	Assembly Na...	Tool Name	Holder Name	Dia.	Cor. rad.	Length	# Flutes	Type	Rad. Type
290	--	1/2 FLAT E...	--	0.5	0.0	1.0	4	Flat endmill	None

♦ Select the **1/2" Flat Endmill** in the **Tool Selection** page and then select the **OK** button to exit.

♦ Make all the necessary changes as shown.

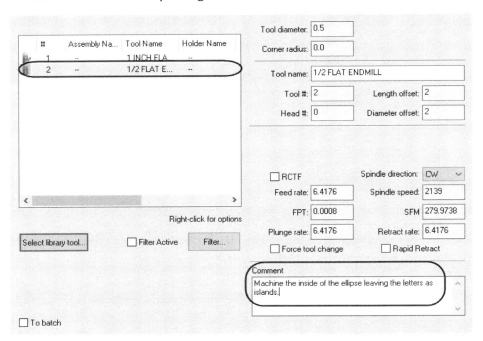

5.3 Set the Cut Parameters

♦ From the **Tree View list**, select **Cut Parameters** and ensure **Pocket type** is set to **Standard**, and **Stock to leave on walls/floors** is set to **0.0** as shown.

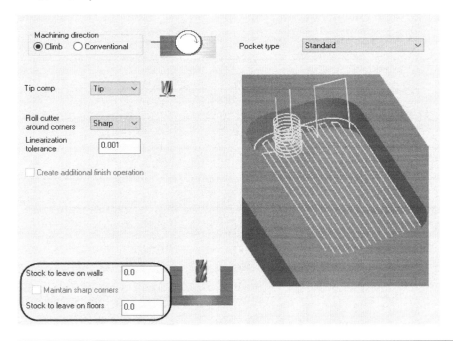

*Note: **Pocket** set to **Standard** will machine the inside of the ellipse and leave the letters as islands with heights at the same level as the top of the pocket.*

5.4 Set the Roughing Parameters

♦ From the **Tree View list**, select **Roughing**.
♦ Enable **Rough.**
♦ Select the **Constant Overlap Spiral** and set the **Stepover percentage** to **65%** as shown.

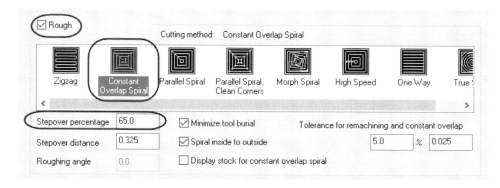

Constant Overlap Spiral creates one roughing pass, determines the remaining stock and recalculates based on the new stock amount. This process repeats until the pocket is cleared.

5.5 Set the Entry Motion

♦ Choose **Entry Motion** from the **Tree View list**. Ensure your settings appear as shown.

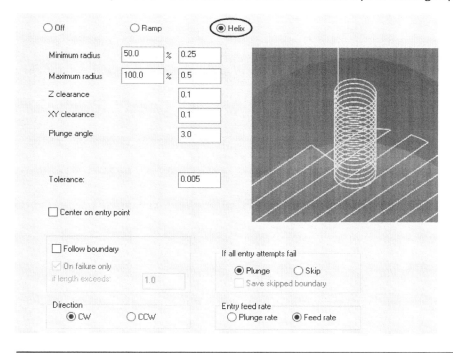

Minimum radius sets the smallest possible radius for the entry helix.

Maximum radius sets the largest possible radius for the entry helix.

5.6 Set the Finishing Parameters

♦ Select **Finishing** and ensure your options appear as shown.

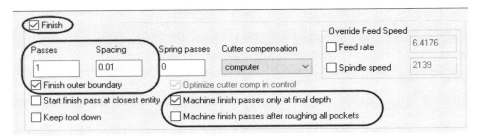

5.7 Set the Lead In/Out Parameters

♦ Select **Lead In/Out** from the **Tree View list**. Set the length and arc percentage to **60%** and input an **Arc Sweep** of **90** degrees as shown.

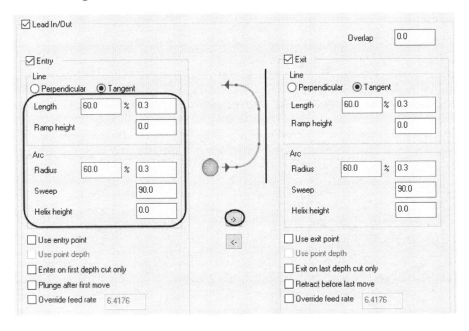

5.8 Setup Depth Cuts Parameters

♦ Select **Depth Cuts** and enable this option. Set the **Max rough step** to **0.05** as shown.

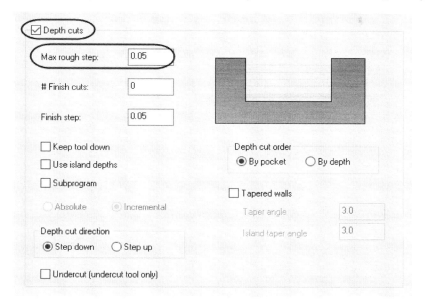

5.9 Set the Linking Parameters

♦ Choose **Linking Parameters** and input a final **Depth** of **-0.5** as shown. Make sure that all the values are set to Absolute.

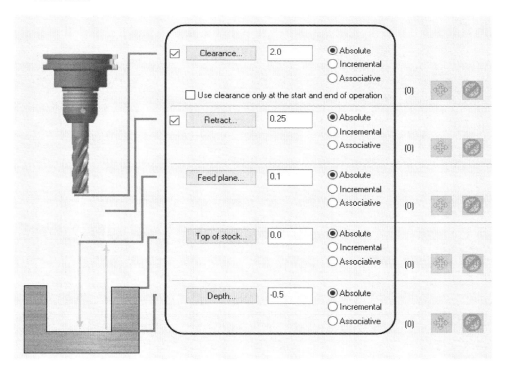

5.10 Preview the Toolpath

◆ To quickly check how the toolpath will be generated, select the **Preview toolpath** icon as shown.

◆ See **"Preview the Toolpath" on page 307** to review the procedure.
◆ The toolpath should look as shown.

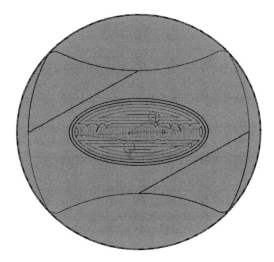

◆ Press **Esc** key to exit the preview.

Note: If the toolpath does not look as shown in the preview, check your parameters again.

◆ Select the **OK** button to exit the **2D Toolpath - Pocket** parameters.

5.11 Backplot and Verify the toolpath

◆ To **Backplot** and **Verify** your toolpath, see **"Backplot The Toolpaths" on page 307** and **"Simulate the toolpath in Verify" on page 309** to review these procedures.

*Note: To better see the machined part, make the tool invisible by clicking twice on the square in front of the Tool in the **Visibility** area.*

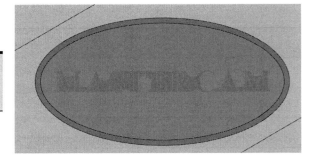

STEP 6: POCKET REMACHINING

Pocket Remachining is only used with closed chains. It calculates areas where the pocket roughing tool could not machine the stock and creates a remachining pocket toolpath to clear the remaining material.

Toolpath Preview:

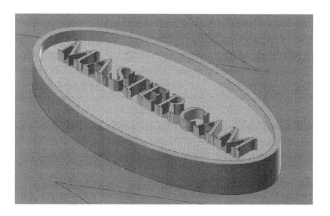

6.1 Copy the Pocket

◆ Press **Alt + T** to remove the toolpath display.

◆ In the **Toolpaths Manager**, select only the **Pocket**.

◆ Right mouse click in the **Toolpaths Manager** and select **Copy**.

◆ Right mouse click in the **Toolpaths Manager** and select **Paste**.

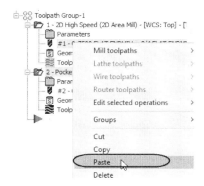

♦ Select the **Parameters** of the third operation.

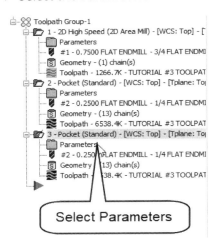

6.2 *Select a 1/8" Flat Endmill from the library and set the Tool Parameters*

♦ Select **Tool** from the **Tree View list**.

♦ Click on the **Select library tool** button.

♦ Select the **Filter** button.

♦ Select the **None** button and then under **Tool Types** choose the **Endmill Flat** icon.

♦ Under **Tool Diameter**, select **Equal** and input a value of . Make all the necessary changes as shown.

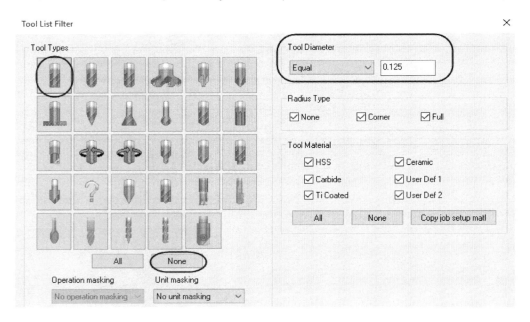

6.3 Set the Cut Parameters

♦ Select **Cut Parameters** and change the **Pocket type** to **Remachining**. Disable **Display stock**.

Note: The standard pocket removes the material inside of a closed boundary while the remachining pocket removes only the remaining material that a previous toolpath could not clean due to the tool size.

♦ Ensure your settings appear as shown.

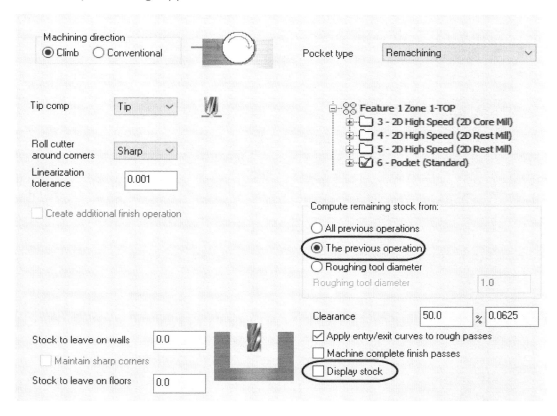

Compute remaining stock from set to **The previous operation** determines remaining stock for remachining by calculating stock removed during the previous toolpath.

Clearance extends the remachining toolpath at the beginning and end to prevent cusps of material from being left behind.

6.4 Set the Roughing Parameters

♦ Choose **Roughing** and change the **Stepover percentage** to **55.0** as shown.

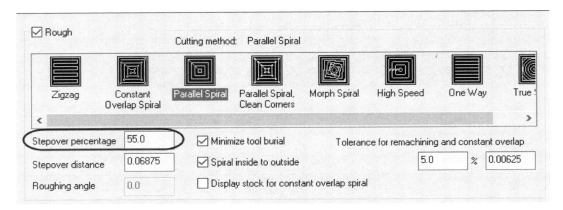

> Note: The **Cutting method** is defined by the **Pocket type** and cannot be modified for **Remachining**. The **Finishing, Lead In/Out** and **Depth Cuts** parameters are the same as the previous toolpath. Therefore, we do not need to view them.

6.5 Preview the Toolpath

♦ To quickly check how the toolpath will be generated, select the **Preview toolpath** icon as shown.

♦ See **"Preview the Toolpath" on page 307** to review the procedure.
♦ The toolpath should look as shown.

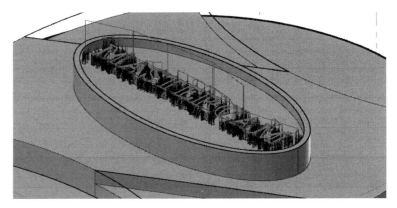

♦ Press **Esc** key to exit the preview.

> Note: If the toolpath does not look as shown in the preview, check your parameters again.

♦ Select the **OK** button to exit the **2D Toolpaths - Pocket**.

6.6 Regenerate, Backplot and Verify the toolpaths

♦ To **Backplot** and **Verify** your toolpath, see"Backplot The Toolpaths" on page 307 and **"Simulate the toolpath in Verify" on page 309** to review these procedures.

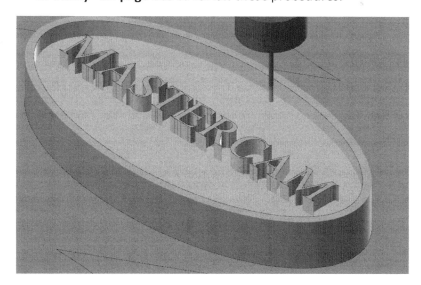

♦ To go back to the Mastercam window, minimize the **Mastercam Simulator** window as shown.

STEP 7: 2D HS DYNAMIC MILL - OUTSIDE PROFILE

In this step you will machine the outside profile using **2D High Speed Dynamic Mill** toolpath which machines pockets, material that other toolpaths left behind, and standing bosses or cores using the entire flute length. The toolpath supports many powerful entry methods, including a customized entry method. Entry methods and micro lifts support custom feeds and speeds to optimize and generate safe tool motion.

The toolpath depends on the **Machining strategy** that you choose in the **Chain Options**. If the strategy is **From outside**, the toolpath starts at the outmost chain and works its way in taking on the final shape of the part as it approaches the final pass. You can also machine pockets with the strategy set to be **Start inside**, which keeps the tool inside the machining regions.

Toolpath Preview:

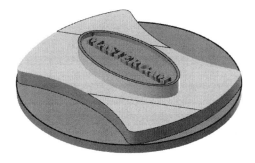

♦ Press **Alt + T** to remove the toolpath display.

Toolpaths

♦ In the **2D** group, click on the **Expand gallery** arrow as shown.

♦ Select the **Dynamic Mill** icon as shown.

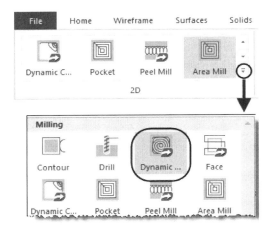

♦ In the **Chain Options** panel, enable **From outside**.

*Note: You do not need to select any **Machining regions**. The system will look at the defined stock from the **Stock setup**.*

♦ In the **Chain Options** panel, **Avoidance regions**, click on the **Select avoidance chains** button as shown.

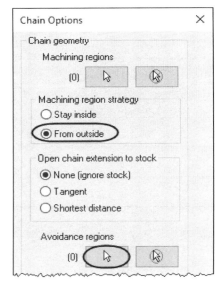

♦ [Select 2D HST avoidance faces]: Select the arc as shown.

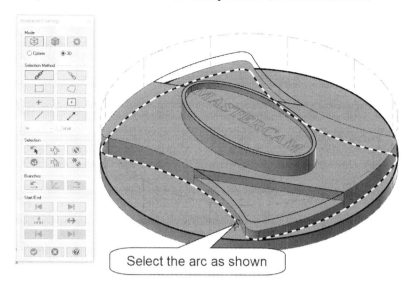

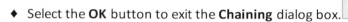

Select the arc as shown

♦ Select the **OK** button to exit the **Chaining** dialog box.

♦ Select the **Preview chains** button as shown.

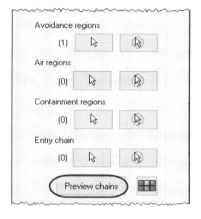

♦ The **Preview chains** should look as shown.

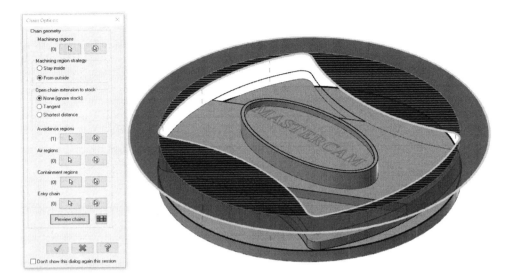

♦ Select the **OK** button to exit **Chain Options**.

7.1 Select the 1.0" Flat Endmill and set the Tool Parameters

♦ Select the **1.0" Flat Endmill**.
♦ Make all the necessary changes as shown.

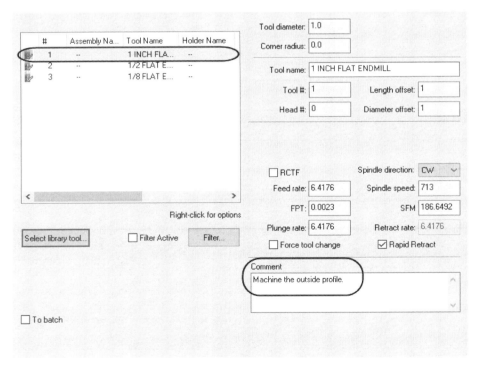

7.2 Set the Cut Parameters

♦ From the **Tree View list**, select **Cut Parameters**. Set the **Stock to leave on** both **walls** and **floors** to **0** as shown.

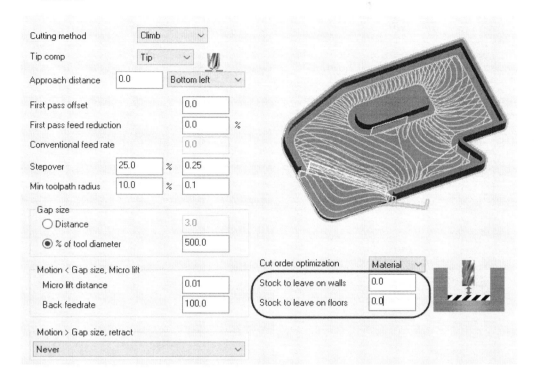

Approach distance is available only when open pocket machining is selected. It adds the specified absolute distance to the beginning of the toolpath's first cut.

First pass offset offsets out the machining region with a user defined distance for the tool to safely engage in the material from the outside.

First pass feed reduction allows you to slow the feed for the first pass on machining region material approached from the outside.

Stepover sets the distance between cutting passes in the X and Y axes.

Min toolpath radius reduces sharp corner motion between cut passes.

Micro lift distance enters the distance the tool lifts off the part on the back moves. Microlifts are slight lifts that help clear chips and minimize excessive tool heating.

Back feedrate controls the speed of the backfeed movement of the tool.

Motion > Gap size, retract controls retracts in the toolpath when making a non-cutting move within an area where the tool can be kept down or microlifted.

Cut order optimization defines the cut order Mastercam applies to different cutting passes in the Dynamic Mill Toolpath.

7.3 Depth cuts parameters disabled

♦ From the **Tree View list**, select the **Depth Cuts** and make sure **Depth cuts** is disabled as shown.

7.4 Set the Entry Motion

Note: Because we choose to machine from the outside the tool will automatically plunge in.

7.5 Set the Linking Parameters

♦ Select **Linking Parameters** and input the **Depth** and **Top of stock** values as shown.

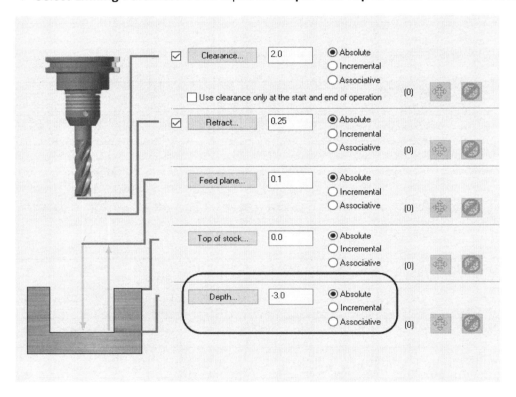

7.6 Preview the Toolpath

♦ To quickly check how the toolpath will be generated, select the **Preview toolpath** icon as shown.

♦ See**"Preview the Toolpath" on page 307** to review the procedure.
♦ The toolpath should look as shown.

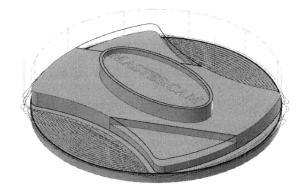

♦ Press **Esc** key to exit the preview.

Note: If the toolpath does not look as shown in the preview, check your parameters again.

♦ Once complete, select the **OK** button to generate the toolpath. ✓

7.7 Backplot the toolpath

♦ Make sure that the toolpath is selected (signified by the green check mark on the folder icon).

♦ Select the **Play** button to run **Backplot**. ▶ ■ ◄◄ ◄◄ ►► ►►| ⟲ ✓
♦ After **Backplot** is completed, the toolpath should look as shown.

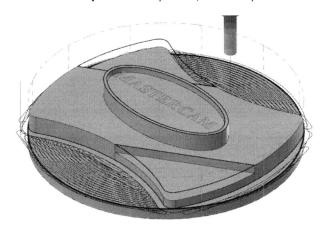

♦ Select the **OK** button to exit **Backplot.**

7.8 Simulate the toolpaths using Verify

♦ Select all operations.

♦ Select the **Play** button to run **Verify**.

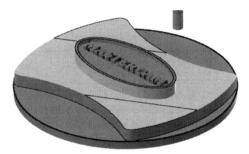

♦ The part should appear as shown.

♦ To go back to the Mastercam window, minimize the **Mastercam Simulator** window as shown.

STEP 8: 2D HS DYNAMIC MILL - OPEN POCKETS

In this step you will machine the two open pockets using the 2D HS Dynamic Mill. You will learn how to machine the machine the open pockets setting the air regions accordingly. Air regions are area where there is no material. This allows the tool to travel through it when machining. You can have multiple open and closed air region chains for each closed machining region chain.

Toolpath Preview:

♦ Press **Alt + T** to remove the toolpath display.

Toolpaths

♦ From the **2D** group, select the **Dynamic Mill**.

♦ In the **Chain Options** dialog box, Machining regions, enable **Stay inside** and click on the **Select machining chains** button as shown.

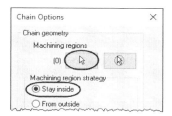

♦ Make sure **Chain** is enabled in the **Wireframe Chaining** dialog box.

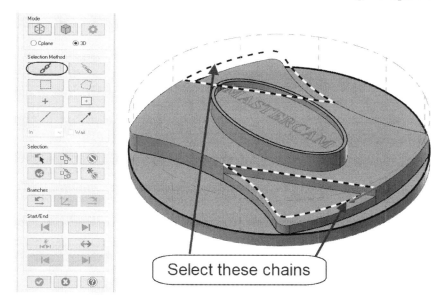

Select these chains

♦ Select the **OK** button to exit the **Chaining** dialog box.

8.1 Select the Air regions

♦ In the **Chain Options** click on the **Air regions Select** button.

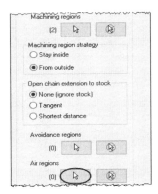

♦ In the **Wireframe Chaining** dialog box, enable **Partial** button as shown.
♦ Select the first entity of the chain as shown.

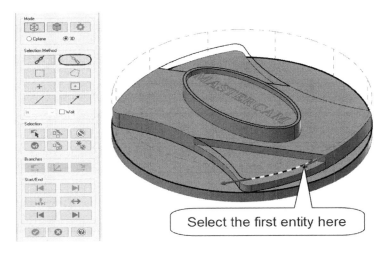

Select the first entity here

♦ Select the last entity of the chain as shown.

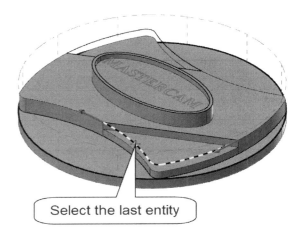

Select the last entity

♦ Select the first entity of the second chain as shown.

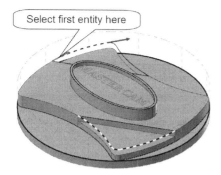

Select first entity here

♦ Select the last entity of the chain as shown.

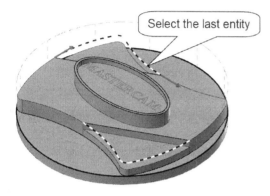

Select the last entity

♦ Select the **OK** button to exit the **Chaining** dialog box. ✓
♦ Select the **OK** button to exit the **Chain Options** dialog box. ✓

8.2 Preview Chains

♦ Select the **Preview chains** button as shown.

♦ The **Preview chains** should look as shown.

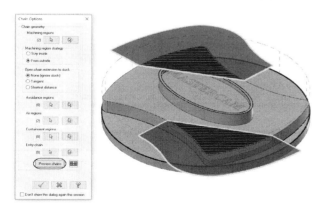

♦ Press **Esc** key to return to the toolpath parameters.

8.3 Select the existing 1" Flat Endmill from the list and set the Tool Parameters

♦ From the **Tree View list**, select **Tool**.

♦ Make all the necessary changes as shown.

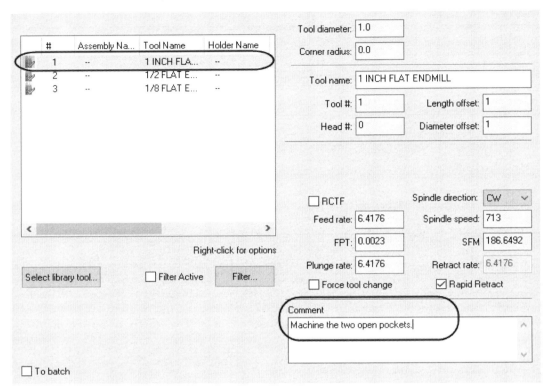

8.4 Set the Cut Parameters

♦ From the **Tree View list**, select **Cut Parameters**. Input a **Stepover** value of **25%** and make sure the rest of the parameters are set as shown.

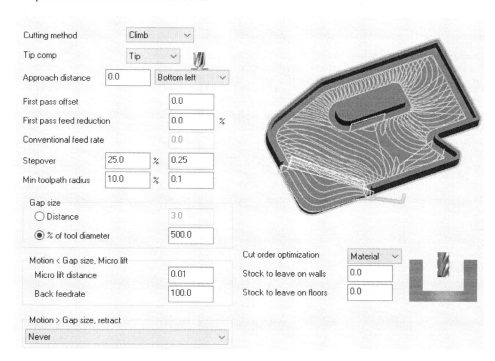

8.5 Disable the Depth cuts parameters

♦ From the **Tree View list**, select the **Depth Cuts** and make sure **Depth cuts** is disabled as shown.

8.6 Set the Linking Parameters

♦ Select **Linking Parameters** and input the **Depth** value as shown.

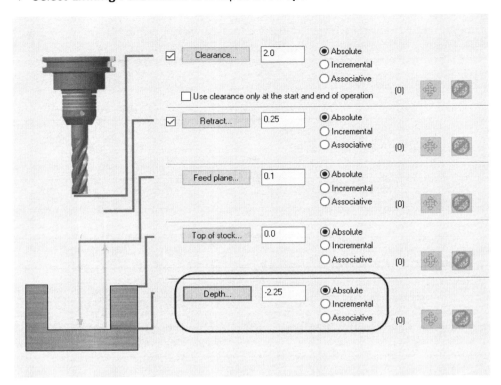

8.7 Preview the Toolpath

♦ To quickly check how the toolpath will be generated, select the **Preview toolpath** icon as shown.

♦ The toolpath should look as shown.

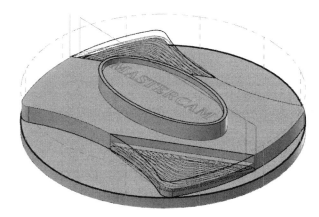

♦ Press **Esc** key to exit the preview.

Note: If the toolpath does not look as shown in the preview, check your parameters again.

♦ Once complete, select the **OK** button to generate the toolpath.

8.8 Backplot the toolpath

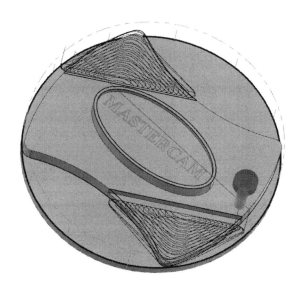

Note: The tool overlaps the air regions.

♦ Select the **OK** button to exit **Backplot**.

8.9 Simulate the toolpaths using Verify

♦ To select all operations, in the **Toolpaths Manager**, click on the **Select all operations** icon.

♦ To **Verify** the toolpath, see **"Simulate the toolpath in Verify" on page 309**.
♦ In the **Visibility** group disable **Wireframe**.
♦ The part should look as shown.

♦ To go back to the Mastercam window, close **Mastercam Simulator** window as shown.

STEP 9: POST THE FILE

♦ Ensure all operations are selected. If not, use the button **Select all operations** in the **Toolpaths Manager**.
♦ Select the **Post selected operations** icon from the **Toolpaths Manager** as shown.

◆ In the **Post processing** window, make necessary changes as shown.

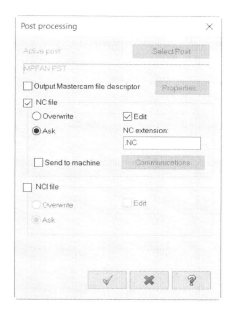

NC file enabled allows you to keep the NC file and to assign the same name as the MCAM file.

Edit enabled allows you to automatically launch the default.

◆ Select the **OK** button to continue.

◆ Save the **NC** file.

◆ A window with **Mastercam Code Expert** will be launched and the NC program will appear as shown.

◆ Select the "**X**" box at the upper right corner to exit the editor.

STEP 10: SAVE THE UPDATED MCAM FILE

CREATE THE TOOLPATHS FOR TUTORIAL #3 EXERCISE

Create the Toolpaths for Tutorial #3 Exercise as per the instructions below.

Set the machine properties including the stock setup.

- Remove the material around the part using **2D HS Area Mill**.
- Use a **1" Flat Endmill**.
- Enable **Corner rounding**.
- Set the **Entry method**.
- Use **Depth Cuts**.
- Enable **Break through**.
- Set the depth according to the drawing.

Remove the material at the step using Dynamic Mill.

- Chain the outer profile in **Machining regions**.
- Enable **From outside**.
- Chain the outer ellipse in the **Avoidance regions**.
- Use the **1" Flat Endmill**.
- Disable **Depth cuts**.
- Set your **Entry method**.
- Disable **Break through**.
- Set the depth according to the drawing.

Pocket out the center.

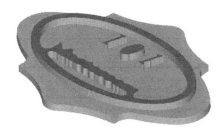

- Select the inner ellipse and the letters.
- Use a **1/4" Flat Endmill**.
- Choose the **Cutting method** in the **Rough** settings to **Parallel Spiral Clean Corners**.
- Change the **Stepover percentage** to **25%**.
- Set the **Entry Motion**. Disable **Finishing**.
- Enable Depth cuts and set a **Max rough step** of **0.125**.
- Set the depth according to the drawing.

Remachine the pocket.

- Use a **1/16"** Flat Endmill.
- Change the **Pocket Type** to **Remachining**.
- Enable **Machine complete finish passes**.
- Disable **Display stock**.
- Change the **Stepover percentage** to **55%**.
- Enable **Depth cuts** and set a **Max rough** step of **0.0625**.
- Set the depth according to the drawing.

TUTORIAL #3 TOOLPATH CREATION QUIZ

♦ What does Area Mill do?

♦ What does smoothing do?

♦ What does Pocket Remachining do?

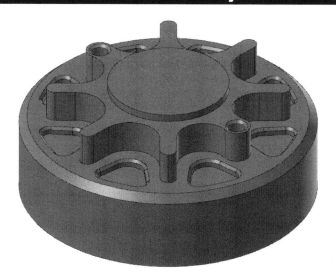

OVERVIEW OF STEPS TAKEN TO CREATE THE PART GEOMETRY:

From Drawing to CAD Model:

♦ The student should examine the drawing on the following page to understand what part is being created in the tutorial.
♦ From the drawing we can decide how to create the geometry in Mastercam.

Create the 2D CAD Model:

♦ The student will create the Top 2D geometry needed to create the toolpaths.
♦ Geometry creation commands such as Rectangle, Circle Center Point, Arc Endpoints, Line Tangent, Mirror, Arc Polar Endpoints, Arc Tangent, Arc Polar, Trim, Fillet, Rotate, and Translate will be used.
♦ Create a solid using Solid Extrude command.

TUTORIAL #4 DRAWING

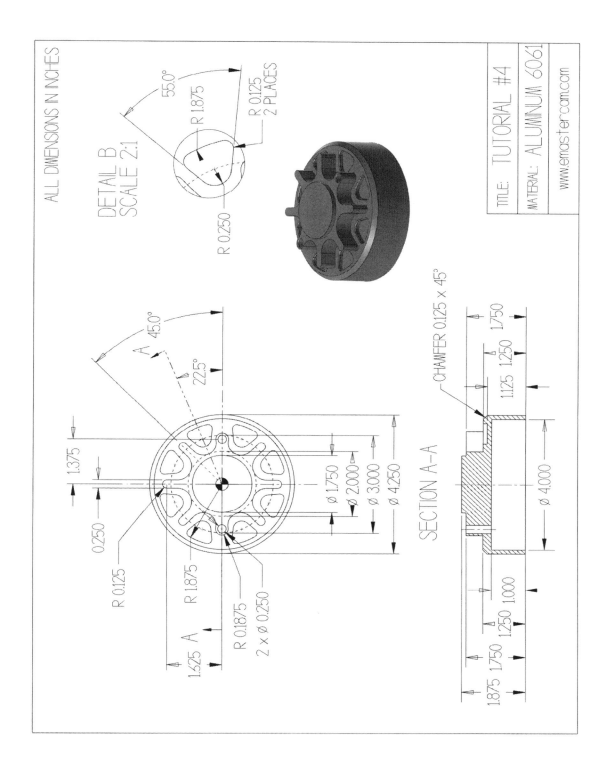

STEP 1: SETTING UP THE GRAPHICAL USER INTERFACE

Please refer to the **Getting Started** section to set up the graphical user interface.

*Note: In the next few steps you will create a quarter of the entire geometry. You will then use the **Mirror** command to generate the rest.*

STEP 2: CREATE TWO ARCS

In this step you will create the arcs used for the main body of the part.

Step Preview:

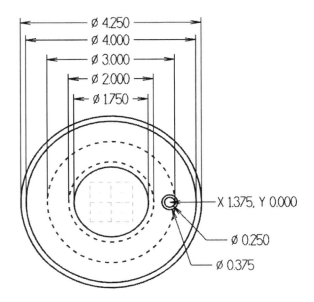

2.1 Create Circles centered on the Origin

Wireframe

♦ From the **Arcs** group, select **Circle Center Point** as shown.

♦ In the **Circle Center Point** panel, input a **Diameter** of **4.25**. Press **Enter**.

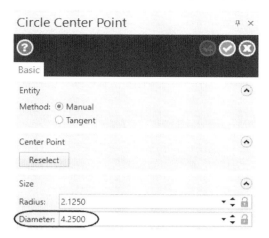

♦ [Enter the center point]: Select the **Origin** as shown.

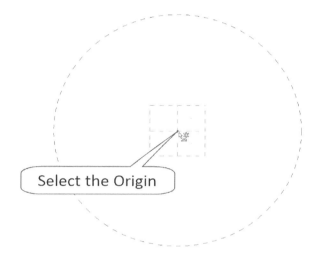

Select the Origin

♦ Press **Alt + F1** to fit the geometry to the graphics window.

♦ Press **Enter** or select the **OK and Create New Operations** icon to continue in the same command.

♦ Move the cursor to the center of the circle and scroll down the mouse wheel to unzoom the geometry as shown.

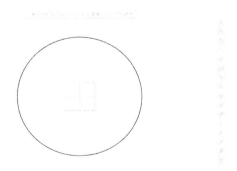

♦ Change the **Diameter** value to **1.75** and press **Enter**.

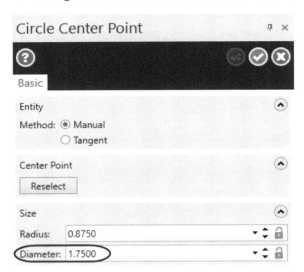

♦ [Enter the center point]: Select the **Origin**. The cursor may snap to the center of the first circle, which is also acceptable.

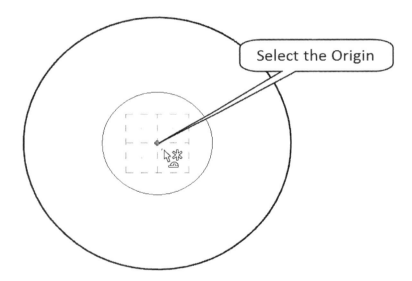

Select the Origin

♦ Press **Enter** or select the **OK and Create New Operations** icon to continue in the same command.

♦ Change the **Diameter** value to **4.00** and press **Enter**.

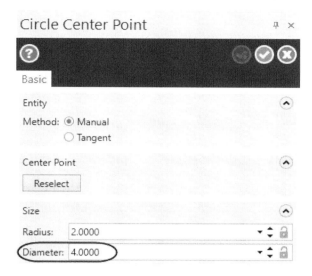

♦ Select the **Origin** again as shown before.

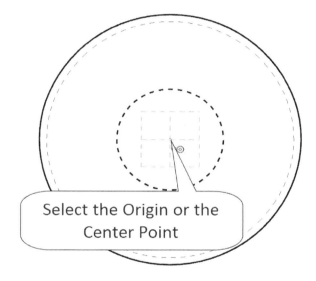

Select the Origin or the
Center Point

♦ Press **Enter** or select the **OK and Create New Operation** icon to continue in the same command.

2.2 Create Circles at known coordinates.

◆ Change the **Diameter** value to **0.25** as shown.

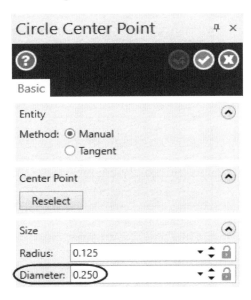

◆ [Enter the center point]: Select the **AutoCursor Fast Point** icon from the **General Selection Toolbar**.

◆ The coordinate field appears at the upper left corner of the graphics window.
◆ Enter the coordinates as shown.

1.375,0

◆ Hit **Enter** on your keyboard.

◆ Press **Enter** or select the **OK and Create New Operation** icon to continue in the same command.
◆ The geometry should look as shown.

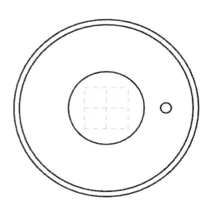

2.3 Create a Circle using the Arc Center of an existing entity.

♦ Change the **Diameter** value to **0.375**.

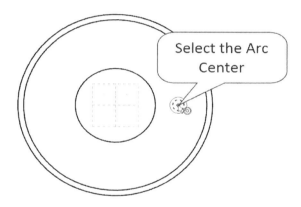

♦ [Enter the center point]: Select the **Arc Center** of the **0.25"** diameter circle as shown.

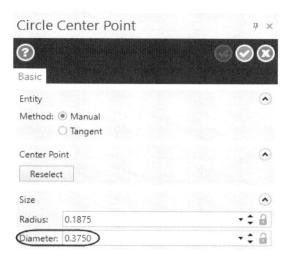

Select the Arc Center

♦ Choose the **OK** button to exit the command.
♦ The geometry should look as shown.

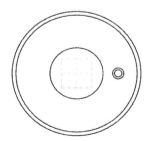

2.4 Change the Line Style and create circles

Home

♦ From the **Attributes** group, click on the arrow next to the **Line Style** options as shown.

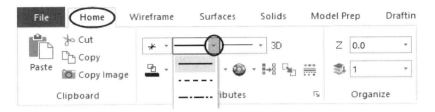

♦ Select from the list the **hidden line style** (2nd style in the list) as shown.

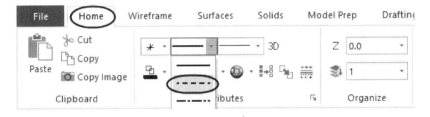

Wireframe

♦ From the **Arcs** group, select **Circle Center Point** as shown.

♦ In the **Circle Center Point** panel, change the **Diameter** to **2.00** and press **Enter**.

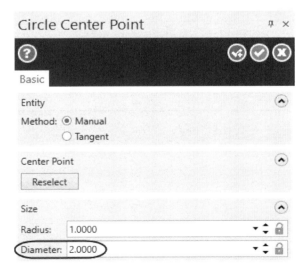

♦ [Enter the center point]: Select the **Origin**.

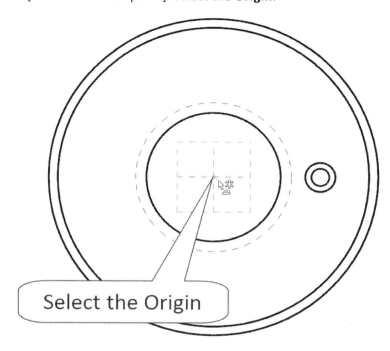

Select the Origin

♦ Press **Enter** or select the **OK and Create New Operation** icon to continue in the same command.
♦ Change the **Diameter** to **3.00** and press **Enter**.

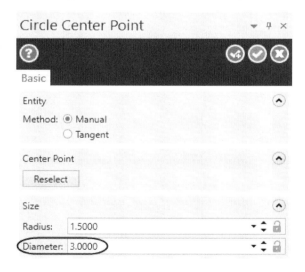

♦ [Enter the center point]: From the **General Selection** toolbar, click on the drop down arrow next to the **AutoCursor** as shown.

♦ From the fly-out menu, select **Origin**.

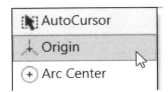

♦ Choose the **OK** button to exit the command.
♦ The geometry should look as shown.

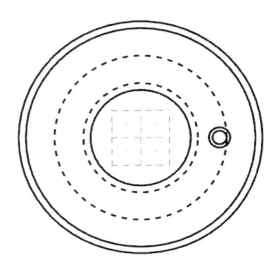

2.5 Change the Line Style back to Solid

♦ Right mouse click in the **Graphic Window**.
♦ From the **Mini Toolbar**, click on the arrow next to the **Line Style** options as shown.

♦ Select from the list the **solid line style** (1st style in the list) as shown.

STEP 3: CREATE VERTICAL LINES

In this step, you will use Line Endpoints command to create a vertical line.

Step Preview:

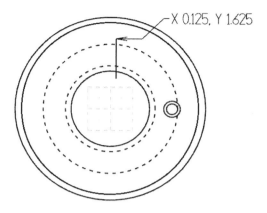

X 0.125, Y 1.625

Wireframe

♦ From the **Lines** group, select **Line Endpoints**.

♦ In the **Line Endpoints** panel, enable **Vertical** as shown.

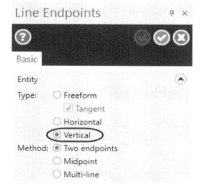

♦ [Specify the first endpoint]: Select **AutoCursor Fast Point** icon from the **General Selection** toolbar.

◆ The coordinate field appears at the upper left corner of the graphics window.

◆ Enter the coordinates as shown and hit **Enter** on your keyboard.

0.125, 1.625

◆ [Select second point]: Select a point below the first point as shown.

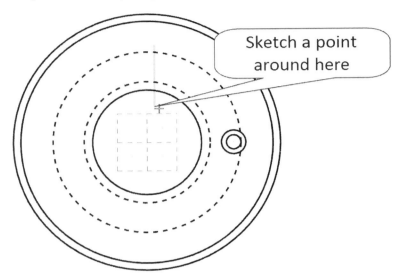

Sketch a point around here

◆ Select **OK** to exit the **Line Endpoints** panel.

◆ The geometry should look as shown.

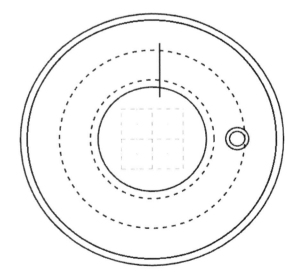

STEP 4: CREATE ARC USING ARC POLAR ENDPOINTS

In this step, you will use **Arc Polar Endpoints** to create an arc with a known diameter, start angle, end angle and start point.

Step Preview:

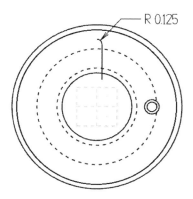

Wireframe

♦ From the **Arcs** group, select the dropdown arrow beside **Circle Edge Point** and select **Arc Polar Endpoints** as shown.

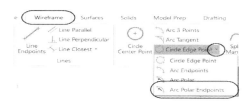

♦ In the **Arc Polar Endpoints** panel, set the **Diameter** to **0.25**, **Start Angle to 0** and **End Angle** to **90** as shown.

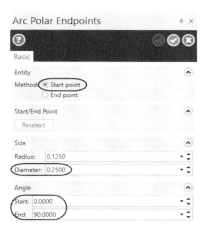

♦ [Enter the start point]: Select the upper endpoint of the vertical line as shown.

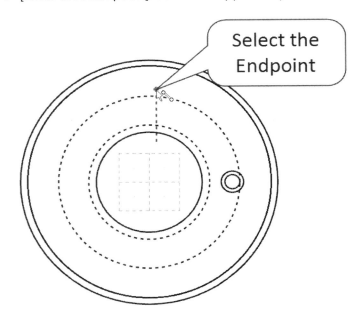

Select the Endpoint

♦ Select **OK** to close the **Arc Polar Endpoints** panel.

♦ The geometry should look as shown.

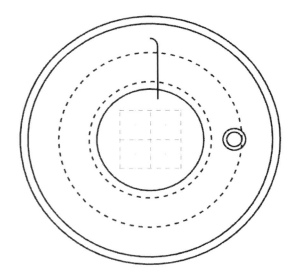

STEP 5: ROTATE GEOMETRY

In this step you will learn how to Rotate entities around a center point by a specified angle.

Step Preview:

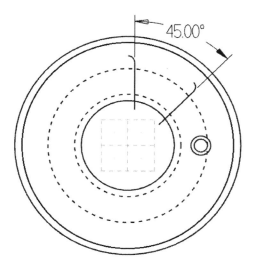

Transform

♦ From the **Position** group, select **Rotate**.

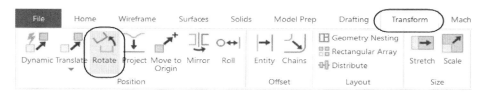

♦ Holding down the **Shift** key select the vertical line as shown.

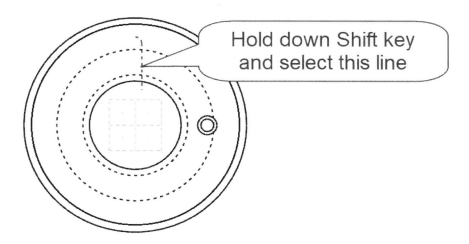

Hold down Shift key and select this line

♦ Select **End Selection** to complete the selection.

♦ In the **Rotate** panel, ensure that **Copy** is enabled. Set **Number** to **1** and **Angle** to **-45** as shown.

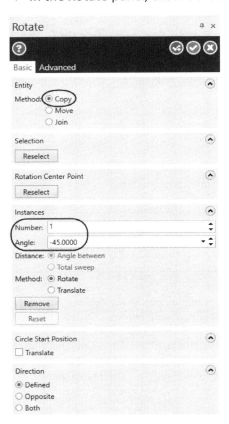

♦ Select **OK** to finish the command.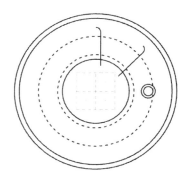

♦ Right mouse click in the graphics window and from the **Mini Toolbar**, select **Clear Colors** to return the colors to the original system colors.

♦ The geometry should look as shown.

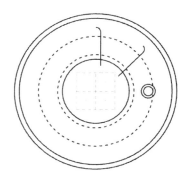

STEP 6: MIRROR GEOMETRY

In this step you will **Mirror** the inside geometry about an angle.

Step Preview:

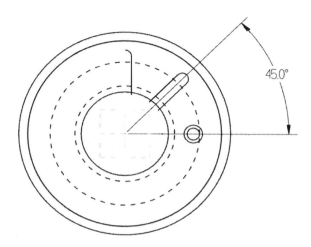

Transform

♦ From the **Position** group, select **Mirror** as shown.

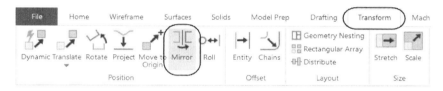

♦ Holding **Shift**, select the rotated geometry as shown.

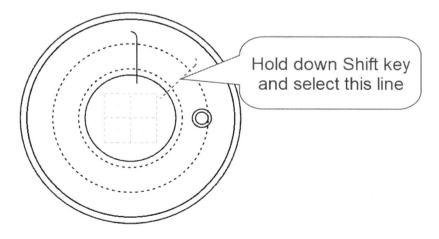

Hold down Shift key and select this line

♦ Press **Enter** to finish selection.

♦ In the **Mirror** panel, ensure that **Copy** is enabled. Enable the **Angle** radio button and change the **Angle** to **45**.

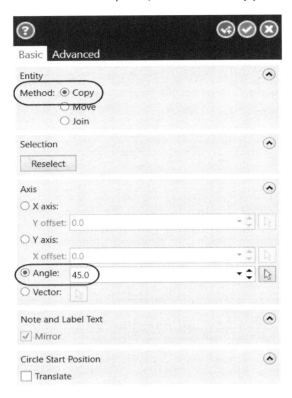

♦ Select **OK** to exit the command.

♦ Right mouse click in the graphics window and from the **Mini Toolbar**, select **Clear Colors** to return the colors to the original system colors.

♦ The geometry should look as shown.

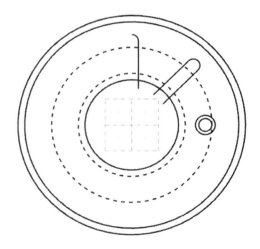

STEP 7: CREATE AN ARC TANGENT

In this step you will create an arc tangent to three entities.

Step Preview:

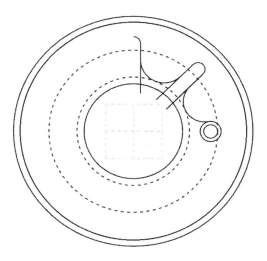

Wireframe

♦ From the **Arcs** group, select **Arc Tangent**.

♦ Set the method to **Arc three entities** as shown.

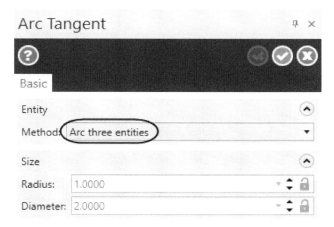

- ◆ Select **Entity A** as shown in Figure: 7.0.1.
- ◆ Select **Entity B** as shown in Figure: 7.0.1.
- ◆ Select **Entity C** as shown in Figure: 7.0.1.

Figure: 7.0.1

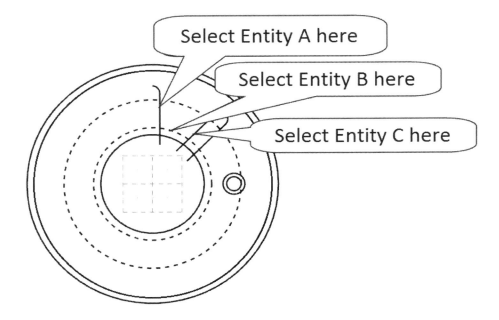

- ◆ Select **Entity D** as shown in Figure: 7.0.2.
- ◆ Select **Entity E** as shown in Figure: 7.0.2.
- ◆ Select **Entity F** as shown in Figure: 7.0.2.

Figure: 7.0.2

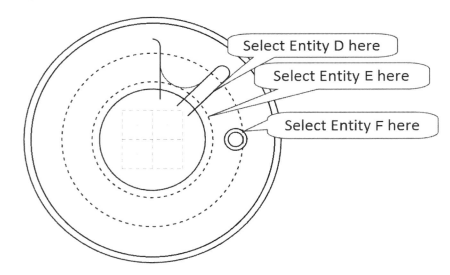

♦ Select **OK** to exit the command.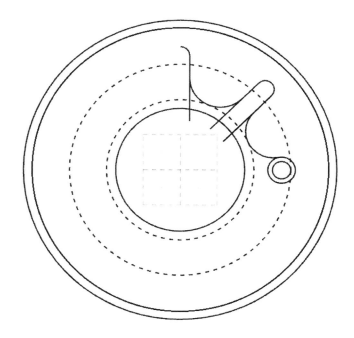

♦ The geometry should look as shown.

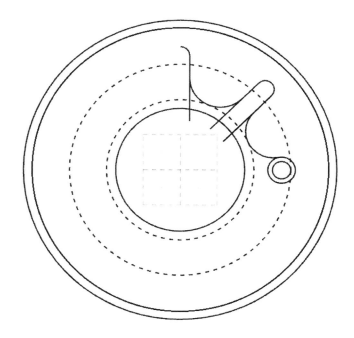

STEP 8: TRIM GEOMETRY

In this step you will use **Trim Break Extend** to clean up the geometry.

Step Preview:

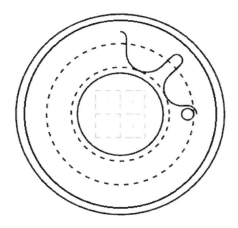

Wireframe

♦ From the **Modify** group, select **Trim Break Extend** icon as shown.

♦ In the **Trim To Entities** panel, ensure **Trim** is enabled and change **Method** to **Trim 3 entities.**

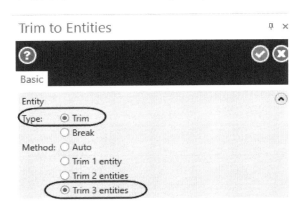

♦ Select **Entity A** as shown in Figure: 8.0.1.
♦ Select **Entity B** as shown in Figure: 8.0.1.
♦ Select **Entity C** as shown in Figure: 8.0.1.

Note: While trimming 3 entities, it is very important to select the entities in the order shown.

Figure: 8.0.1

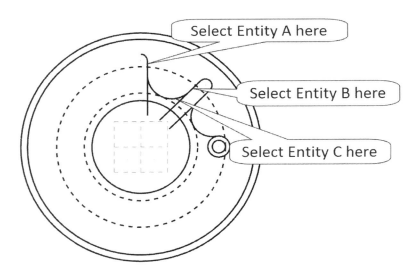

- ◆ Select **Entity D** as shown in Figure: 8.0.2.
- ◆ Select **Entity E** as shown in Figure: 8.0.2.
- ◆ Select **Entity F** as shown in Figure: 8.0.2.

Figure: 8.0.2

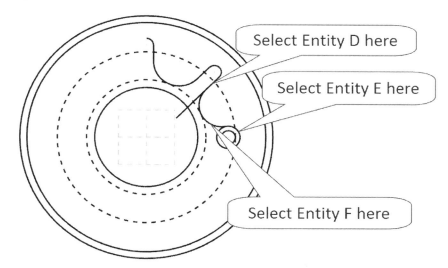

Select Entity D here

Select Entity E here

Select Entity F here

- ◆ Select **OK** to exit the command.
- ◆ The geometry should look as shown.

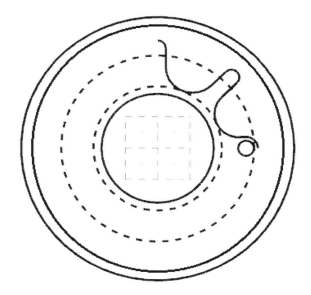

STEP 9: MIRROR GEOMETRY TO COMPLETE ARMS

In this step you will **Mirror** geometry over the **X axis** and **Y axis** to complete the arms.

Step Preview:

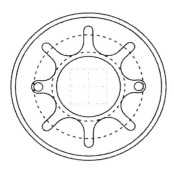

9.1 Mirror geometry over the Y axis

Transform

♦ From the **Position** group, select **Mirror**.

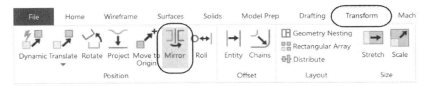

♦ Select the entities as shown.

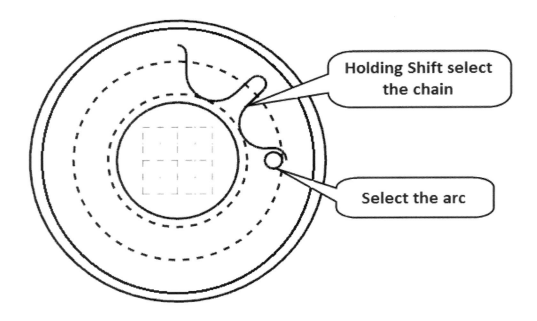

- ◆ Press **Enter** to finish selection.
- ◆ In the **Mirror** panel, enable the **Y Axis** radio button.

- ◆ Select **OK and Create New Operation** to remain in the command.

9.2 Mirror geometry over the X axis

- ◆ Holding **Shift** select the chain as shown.

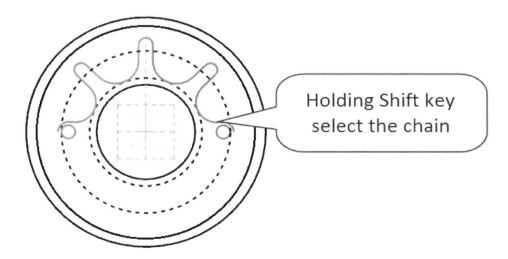

Holding Shift key select the chain

- ◆ Press **Enter** to finish selection.

♦ In the **Mirror** panel, enable the **X Axis** radio button.

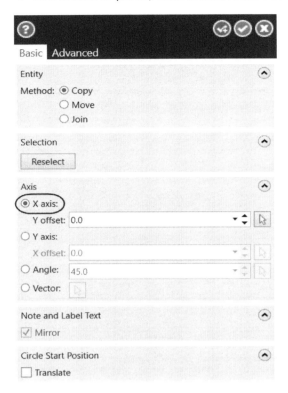

♦ Select **OK** to exit the command.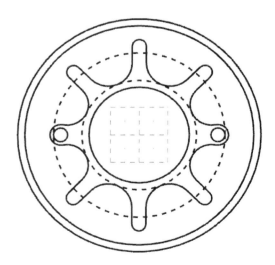

♦ Right mouse click in the graphics window and from the **Mini Toolbar**, select **Clear Colors** to return the colors

to the original system colors.

♦ The geometry should look as shown.

STEP 10: CREATE A CONSTRUCTION LINE

In this step you will use **Line Endpoints** to draw a construction line for creating the pocket.

Step Preview:

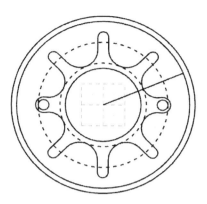

Wireframe

♦ From the **Lines** group, select **Line Endpoints**.

♦ In the **Line Endpoints** panel, enable **Freeform** and change **Length** and **Angle** as shown.

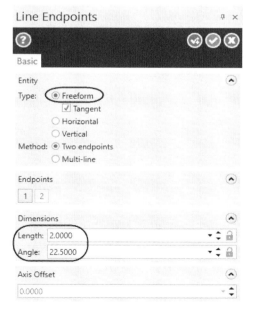

◆ [Specify the first endpoint]: Select the **Origin**.

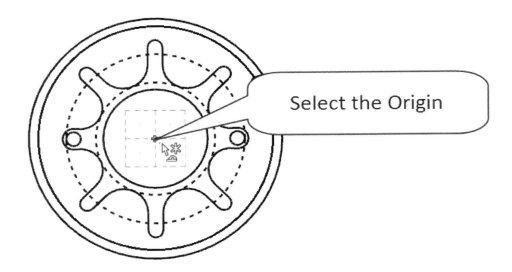

◆ Select **OK** to exit the command.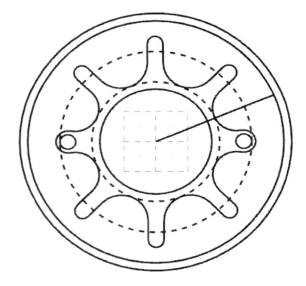
◆ The geometry should look as shown.

STEP 11: CREATE A 0.5" DIAMETER CIRCLE

In this step you will use **Circle Center Point** to draw a **0.5"** diameter circle.

Step Preview:

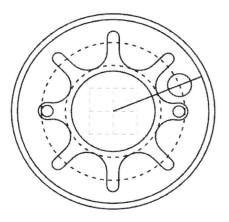

Wireframe

♦ From the **Arcs** group, select **Circle Center Point**.

♦ In the **Circle Center Point** panel, type the **Diameter** of **0.5**. Press **Enter**.

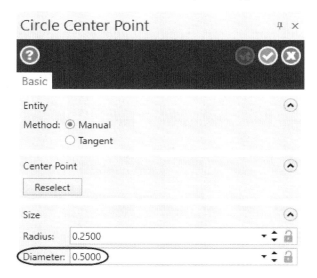

♦ [Enter the center point]: Select the intersection of the **3"** circle and **22.5** degree angled line as shown.

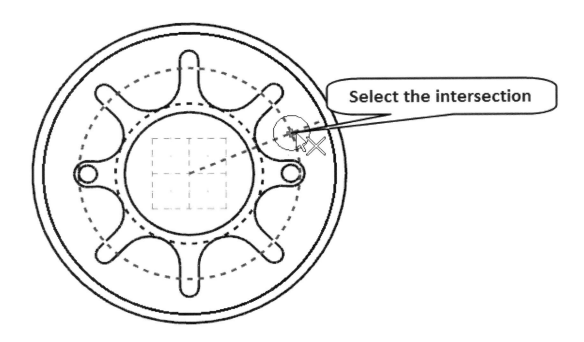

♦ Select **OK** to exit the command.

♦ The geometry should look as shown.

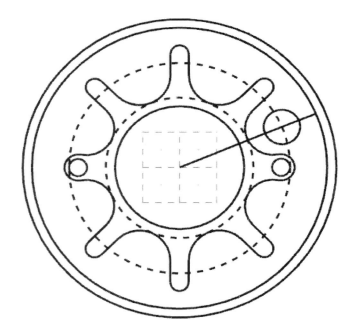

STEP 12: DELETE CONSTRUCTION GEOMETRY

In this step you will delete the construction geometry from the drawing.

Step Preview:

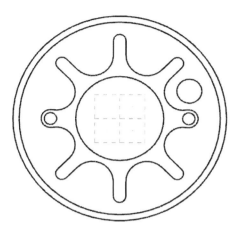

♦ Select the entities as shown.

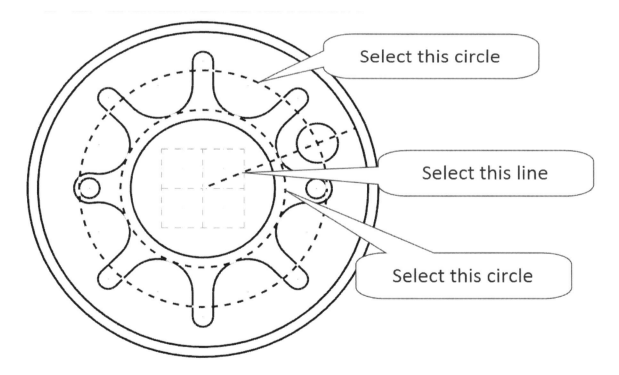

♦ Press **Delete** button from the keyboard.

STEP 13: CREATE TANGENT LINES

In this step you will learn how to create tangent lines given the angle of the lines.

Step Preview:

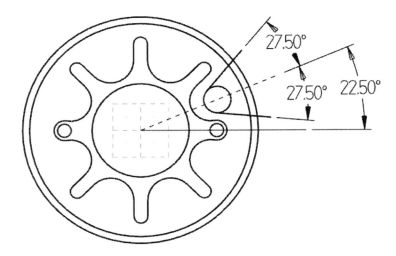

Wireframe

♦ From the **Lines** group, select **Line Endpoints** as shown.

♦ In the **Line Endpoints** panel, ensure the **Tangent** option is enabled as shown.

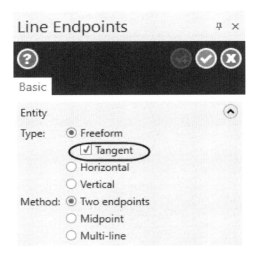

◆ Move the cursor to the right of the origin and scroll up the mouse wheel to zoom in as shown in Figure: 13.0.1.
◆ Select the arc as shown in Figure: 13.0.1.

Note: Make sure that you are not selecting any endpoints, midpoints or quadrants from the arc. If you select one of these points, Mastercam snaps to the points and disregards the tangent attribute.

Figure: 13.0.1

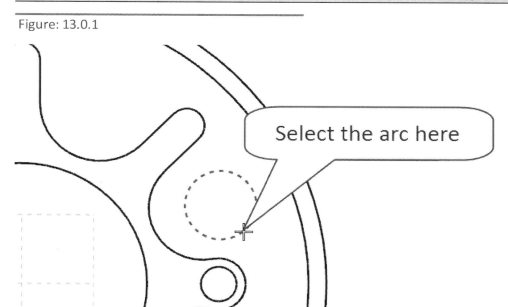

◆ Sketch a line at any angle to the point as shown.

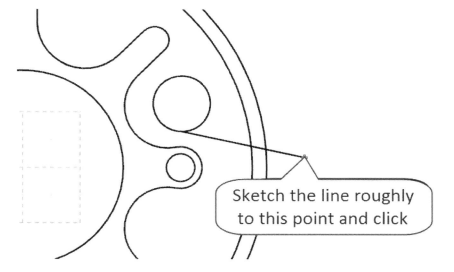

♦ In the **Line Endpoints** panel, enter a **Length** of **1.0** and an **Angle** of **22.5-27.5**.

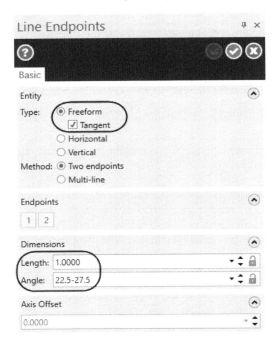

♦ Hit **Enter** on your keyboard to preview this line.
♦ Press again **Enter** to continue making lines.
♦ Select the arc as shown.

Note: Make sure that you are not selecting any endpoints, midpoints or quadrants from the arc. If you select one of these points, Mastercam snaps to the points and disregards the tangent attribute.

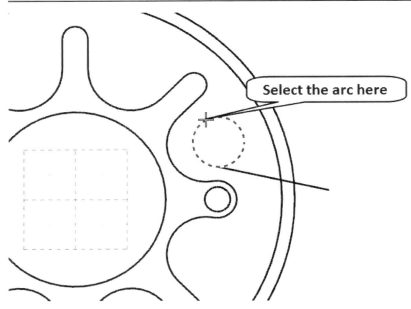

Select the arc here

♦ Sketch a line at any angle to the point as shown.

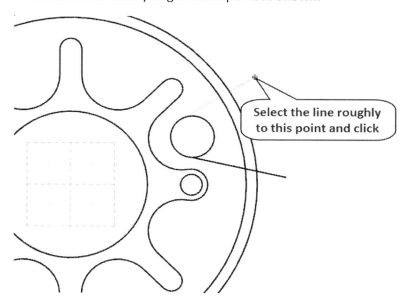

Select the line roughly to this point and click

♦ In the **Line Endpoints** panel, enter a **Length** of **1.0** and an Angle of **22.5+27.5** as shown.

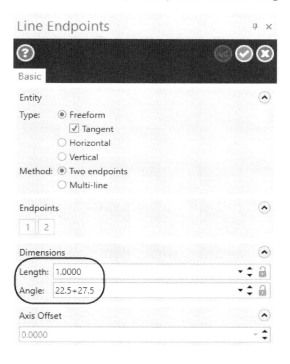

♦ Hit **Enter** to preview this line.

- ◆ Choose the **OK** button to exit the command.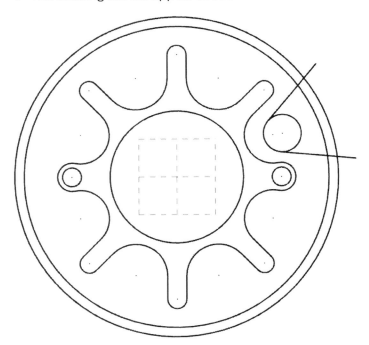
- ◆ Press **Alt + F1** to fit the geometry in the graphics window.
- ◆ The drawing should appear as shown.

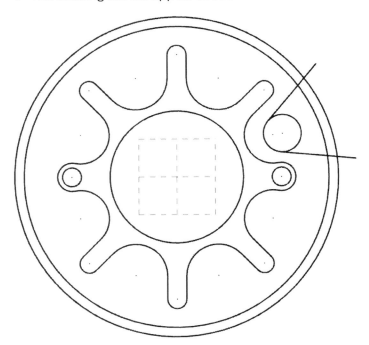

STEP 14: CREATE ARC POLAR

In this step you will learn how to create an arc polar, given the center point, radius, start angle, and end angle.

Step Preview:

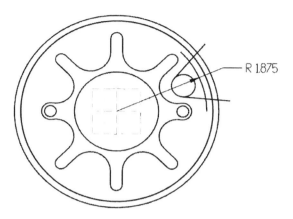

Wireframe

♦ From the **Arcs** group, click on the drop down arrow of the **Circle Edge Point** icon and select **Arc Polar** as shown.

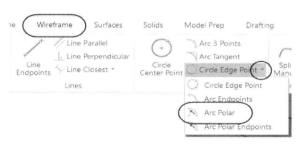

♦ [Enter center point]: Select the **Origin**.

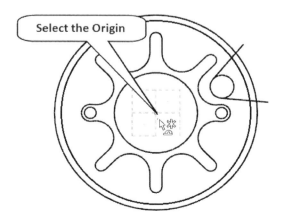

♦ Change the arc **Radius** to **1.875**, the **Start Angle** to **0.0** degrees and the **End Angle** to **45.0**. Press **Enter** after each value.

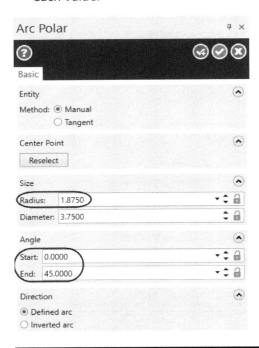

Note: Make sure that you enter the **Start Angle** even if it is by default set to 0.0.

♦ Select the **OK** button to exit the command.

♦ The geometry should look as shown.

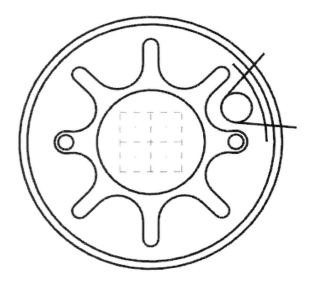

STEP 15: CREATE FILLETS

In this step you will learn how to create filleted corners. Filleted corners apply round corners to sharp corners.

Step Preview:

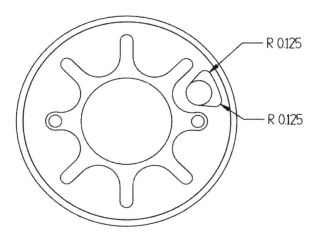

Wireframe

♦ From the **Modify** group, select **Fillet Entities**.

♦ In the **Fillet Entities** panel, input a **Radius** value of **0.125** as shown.

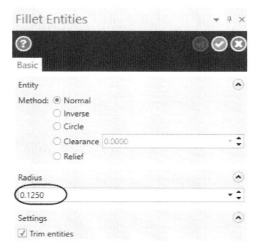

♦ Select the entities as shown.

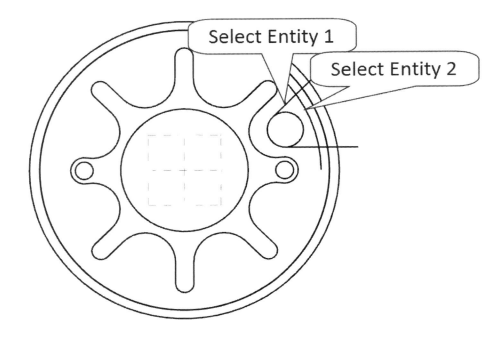

♦ Pick the entities as shown.

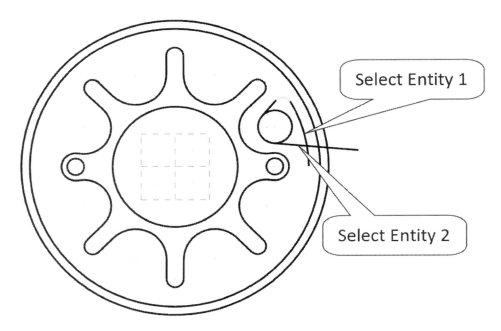

♦ Select the **OK** button to exit the command.

♦ The geometry should look as shown.

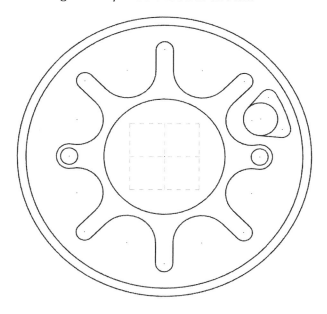

STEP 16: TRIM THE ARC

In this step you will learn how to use the **Divide** function.

Step Preview:

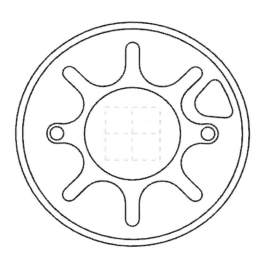

Wireframe

♦ From the **Modify** group, select **Divide** icon as shown.

♦ In the **Divide** panel, enable **Trim** as shown.

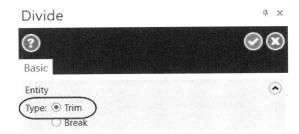

♦ Pick the arcs as shown.

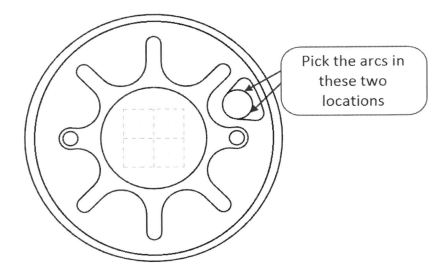

Pick the arcs in these two locations

♦ Once the arcs have been selected choose the **OK** button to exit the command.

♦ Your part up to this point will appear as shown.

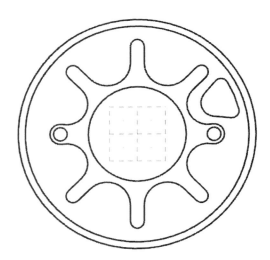

STEP 17: ROTATE

In this step you will rotate entities around a center point by a specified angle.

Step Preview:

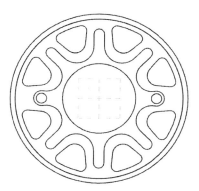

Transform

♦ From the **Position** group, select **Rotate**.

♦ Hold the **Shift** key and pick the shape as shown.

Note: By holding down the Shift key and selecting one entity of a chain, Mastercam selects the whole chain.

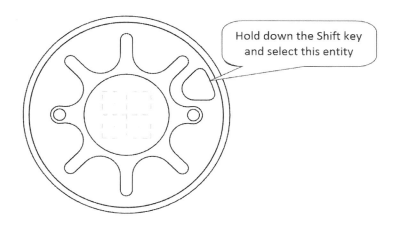

Hold down the Shift key and select this entity

♦ Click on the **End Selection** button or press **Enter** to finish the selection.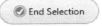

♦ When the **Rotate** panel appears, ensure that **Copy** is enabled, set the **Number** of instances to **7** and **Angle** to **360/8** as shown.

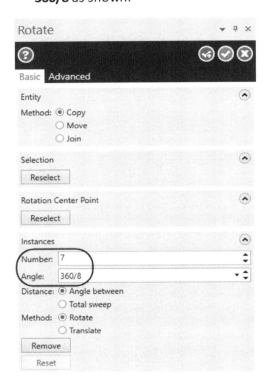

♦ Select **OK** to accept these parameters. ⊙⊘⊗

♦ Right click in the graphics window and from the **Mini Toolbar**, select the **Clear Colors** icon to reset the colors back to the original colors.

♦ The geometry will appear as shown.

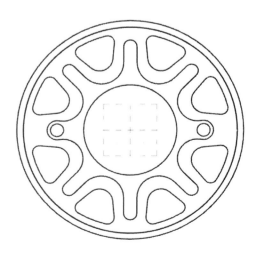

STEP 18: TRANSLATE

In this step you will learn how to translate entities to a different Z depth. This geometry will be used when creating the solid and the toolpaths.

Step Preview:

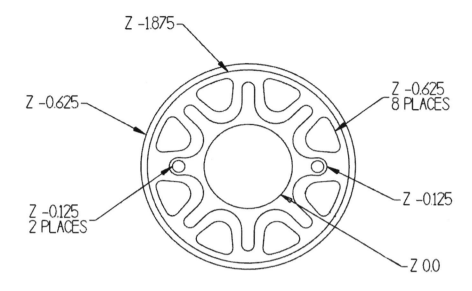

Transform

♦ From the **Position** group, select **Translate** as shown.

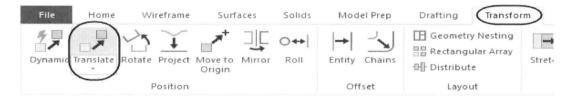

♦ [Translate: select entities to translate]: Select the arc as shown.

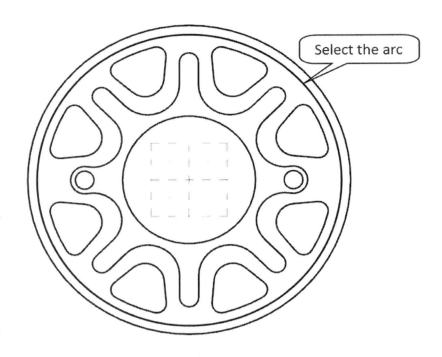

Select the arc

♦ Click on the **End Selection** button or press **Enter**.
♦ Right click in the graphics area, and select the graphic view **Isometric** as shown.

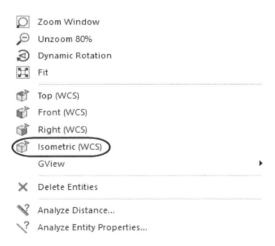

♦ When the **Translate** panel appears, ensure **Move** is enabled and input a **Z depth** of **-1.875**.

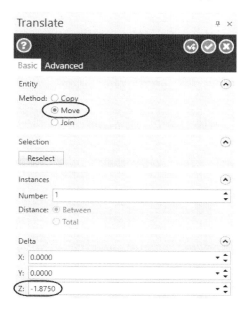

♦ Select **OK and Create New Operation** or press **Enter** to remain in the command.
♦ Press **Alt + F1** to fit the geometry in the graphics window.
♦ [Translate: select entities to translate]: Hold down the **Shift** key and click on all of the pockets and the outer circle as shown.

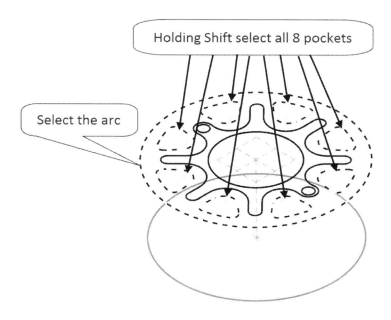

Holding Shift select all 8 pockets

Select the arc

♦ Click on the **End Selection** button or press **Enter**.

♦ Enable **Move** and change the **Z depth** to **-0.625** and press **Enter**.

♦ Select **OK and Create New Operation** or press **Enter** to remain in the command.
♦ [Translate: select entities to translate]: Select the entities as shown.

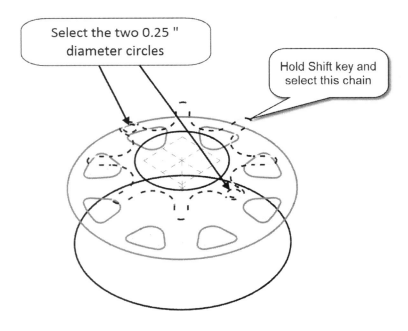

Select the two 0.25 "
diameter circles

Hold Shift key and
select this chain

♦ Click on the **End Selection** button or press **Enter**.   End Selection
♦ Change the **Z depth** to **-0.125**.

♦ Select **OK** to exit the command.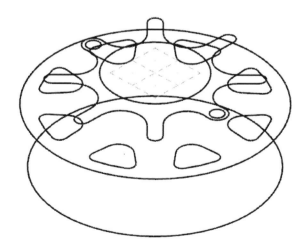
♦ Right mouse click in the graphics window and from the **Mini Toolbar**, select the **Clear Colors** icon to reset the

colors back to the original colors.

♦ Press **Alt + F1** to fit the entire geometry in the graphics window.
♦ The geometry should look as shown.

STEP 19: CHANGE THE MAIN LEVEL TO 2

Levels are a primary organizational tool in Mastercam. A Mastercam file can contain separate levels for wireframe, surfaces, drafting entities, solids, and toolpaths. By organizing your files into levels, you can easily control which areas of the drawing are visible at any time and which parts are selectable. By doing so, you will not inadvertently make changes to areas of the drawing you do not want to change.

In this step we will change the **Main Level** to **2**, to create the solid on **Level 2**.

♦ Right mouse click in the graphics area and in the **Mini Toolbar**, change the **Level** number to **2** as shown.

♦ Press the **Enter** key on your keyboard.

STEP 20: CREATE THE SOLID BODY BY EXTRUDING A CLOSED CHAIN

20.1 Extrude the 4.25" diameter cylinder

Solid Extrude: Uses planar chains to create one or more solid bodies, create cuts in an existing solid or create bosses to an existing solid. Mastercam extrudes entities by driving the shapes of the entity along a linear path using a specified direction, distance, and other parameters that further define the results.

Step Preview:

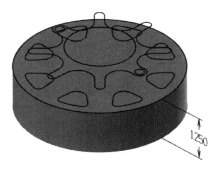

Solids

♦ From the **Create** group, select **Extrude** as shown.

♦ Leave the default settings in the **Chaining** dialog box and select outside circle to create the chain as shown.

Chaining is the process of selecting and linking geometry entities such that they form the foundation of a toolpath, a surface, or a solid. When you chain the geometry, you can select one or more sets of curves (lines, arcs, and splines) that have adjoining endpoints.

Chaining differs from other selection methods because it assigns order and direction to the selected curves. Chaining order and direction determine how surfaces, solids, and toolpaths are generated.

♦ [Select chain(s) to extrude 1]: Select the rectangle as shown.

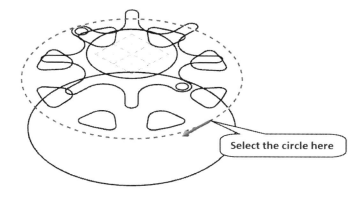

Select the circle here

Note: If you did not select the chain correctly, you can use the **Unselect** button ⊘ from the Chaining dialog box to undo the previous selection.

♦ Select the **OK** button to exit the **Chaining** dialog box.

♦ The **Solid Extrude** panel will display. An arrow will appear on the geometry. This arrow indicates the direction of the extrusion.

*Note: Make sure that the arrow points downwards. Otherwise, in the Solid Extrude panel, click on the **Reverse all** button.*

♦ In the **Solid Extrude** panel, set the **Distance** to **1.25** as shown.

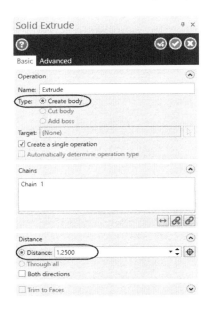

Extrusion Operation is used to create a solid body, cut a solid body, or add a boss to another solid.

Reverse Direction extrudes the solid in the opposite direction from the arrow on the chain indicating the extrusion direction.

Distance allows you to control the length of extrusion, by specifying a **Distance**, extending **Through all**, extending in **Both directions**, or trimming to selected faces.

Both Directions allows you to extrude in both directions from the chain.

♦ Select the **OK** button to exit the **Extrude** panel.
♦ The part, in the unshade mode, should appear as shown below.

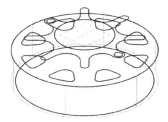

♦ To display the part in the shaded/unshade mode, press **Alt + S**.

♦ Click on the **Solids** tab at the bottom of the **Toolpaths Manager** or at the right side of the graphics window.
♦ If the **Solids Manager** is not yet in the display, select the **View** tab, then from the **Managers** group, click on **Solids** as shown.

♦ In the **Solids Manager**, you should see one **Solid** as shown.

♦ To see the solid history with all the operations listed, click on the plus sign (+) in front of the **Solid**.

*Note: To modify any of the solids operation, first make sure the **Solids** panel is locked, then double click on the operation. The corresponding panel will appear on the screen, and hence the parameters can be modified. To update the solid after modifying the parameters, click on the **Regen all** button from the **Solids Manager**.*

20.2 Add boss for the arms

Step Preview:

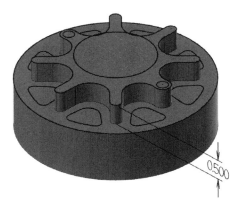

Solids

♦ From the **Create** group, select **Extrude**.

♦ Leave the default settings in the **Chaining** dialog box and select the chain as shown.

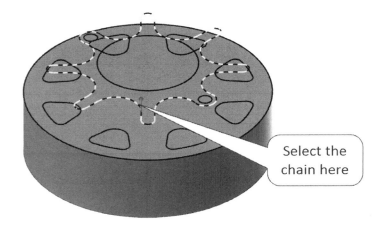

Select the chain here

♦ Select the **OK** button to exit the **Chaining** dialog box.

*Note: Make sure that the arrow points downwards. Otherwise, in the Solid Extrude panel, click on the **Reverse all** button.*

♦ The **Solid Extrude** panel will appear. Change the **Type** to **Add boss** and enter the **Distance 0.5** as shown.

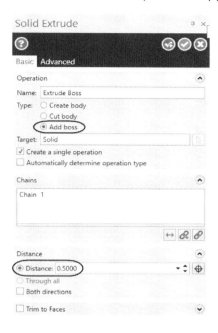

♦ Select the **OK and Create New Operation** button or press **Enter** to remain in the command.
♦ The part should appear as shown in the **Isometric** view.

♦ To display the part in the unshaded mode, press **Alt + S**.

20.3 Add boss for the 1.75" diameter circle

Step Preview:

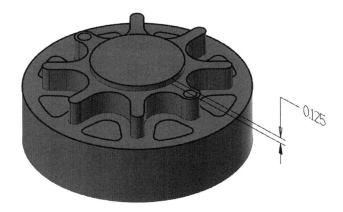

◆ Leave the default settings in the **Chaining** dialog box and select the arc as shown.

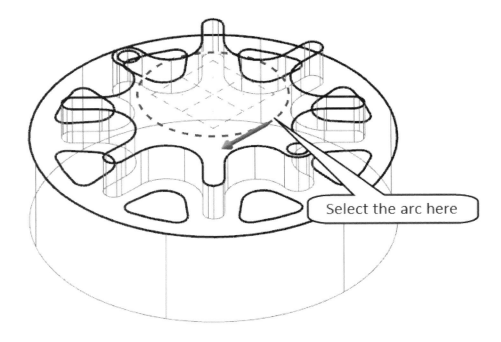

Select the arc here

◆ Select the **OK** button to exit the **Chaining** dialog box.

*Note: Make sure that the arrow points downwards. Otherwise, in the Solid Extrude panel, click on the **Reverse all** button.*

♦ The **Solid Extrude** panel will appear. Leave the **Type** as **Add boss** and enter the **Distance 0.125** as shown.

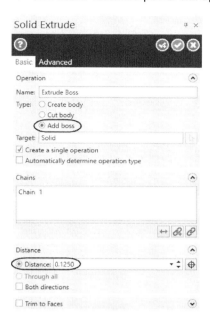

♦ Select the **OK and Create New Operation** button or press **Enter** to remain in the command.
♦ The part should appear as shown below.

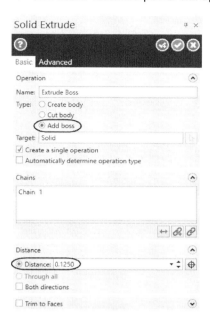

♦ To display the part in the shaded mode, press **Alt + S**.

STEP 21: EXTRUDE CUT THE PART POCKETS AND THE HOLES

In this step another extrusion operation will be performed to cut the pockets and through holes from the solid body to a specific depth.

Step Preview:

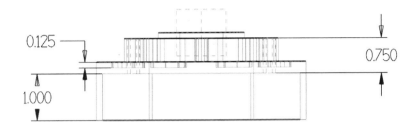

♦ Leave the default settings in the **Chaining** dialog box and select a pocket as shown.

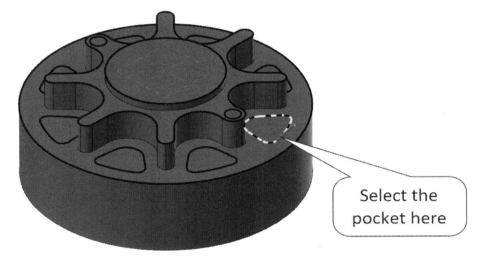

Select the pocket here

♦ In the **Chaining** dialog box, select **Chain Similar**.

♦ All eight pockets should be chained now.

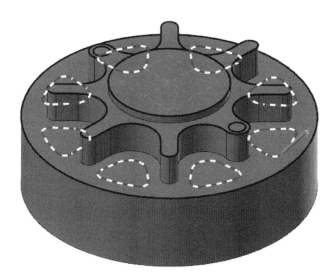

♦ Select **OK** to exit the **Chaining** dialog box.
♦ Ensure the arrow points downwards. Click on the **Reverse All** button, if needed, to change the arrow direction as shown. ⟨↔⟩ ⫰ ⫰

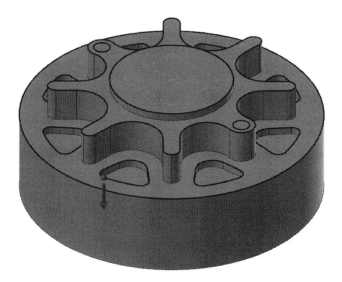

♦ In the **Solid Extrude** panel, ensure **Cut body** is enabled and set **Distance** to **0.125**.

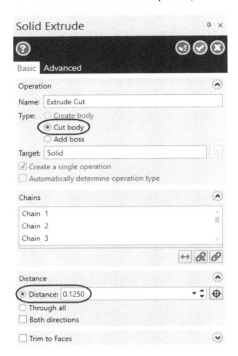

♦ Select **OK and Create New Operation** button or press **Enter** to remain in the command.
♦ Leave the default settings in the **Chaining** dialog box and select the circle as shown.

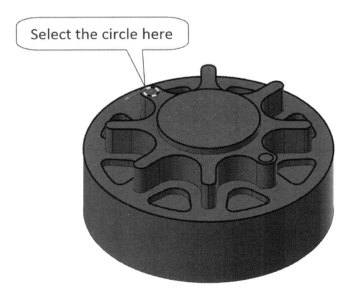

Select the circle here

♦ In the **Chaining** dialog box, select **Chain Similar**.

♦ Both circles should be chained now.

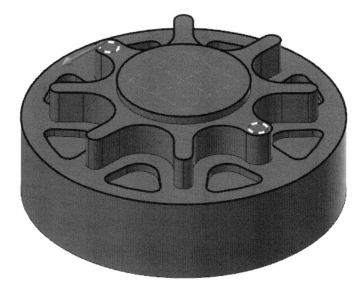

♦ Select **OK** to close the dialog box.

◆ Ensure the arrow is pointing down. If not, select **Reverse All**.

◆ In the **Solid Extrude** panel, ensure **Cut body** is selected and change **Distance** to **Through all**.

◆ Select **OK and Create New Operation** button or press **Enter** to remain in the command.

◆ Click somewhere in the middle of the part using the mouse wheel, and while holding down the wheel move the cursor to rotate the part to check the cuts through as shown.

♦ Right mouse click in the graphics window and select the **Isometric** view.

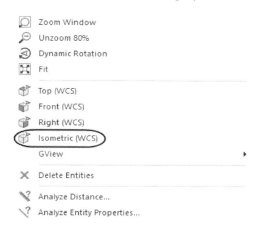

♦ Press **Alt + S** to unshade the part.
♦ Leave the default settings in the **Chaining** dialog box and select the bottom circle as shown.

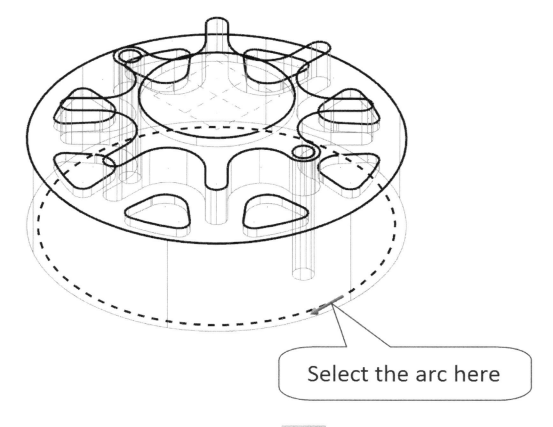

Select the arc here

♦ Select **OK** to close the **Chaining** dialog box.

♦ If necessary, select **Reverse All** to match the arrow as shown.

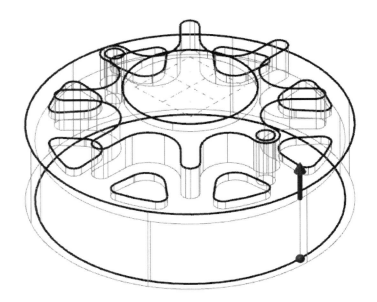

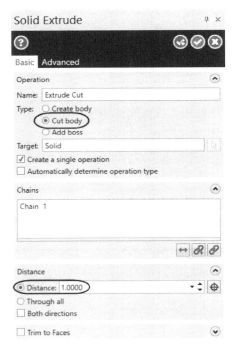

♦ In the **Solid Extrude** panel, ensure **Cut body** and Distance are enabled and set **Distance** to **1.0**.

- Select **OK** to exit the command.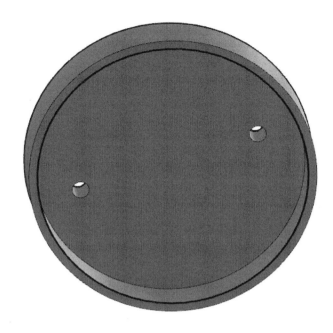
- Press **Alt + S** to shade the part.
- Use the mouse wheel and rotate the part to check the cut from the solid bottom as shown.

- Right mouse click in the graphics window and select the **Isometric** view.

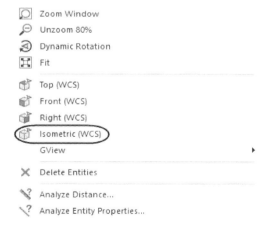

	Zoom Window
	Unzoom 80%
	Dynamic Rotation
	Fit
	Top (WCS)
	Front (WCS)
	Right (WCS)
	Isometric (WCS)
	GView
	Delete Entities
	Analyze Distance...
	Analyze Entity Properties...

STEP 22: CHAMFER THE PART

One-Distance Chamfer uses edge blending to create a symmetrical beveled edge with the same chamfer distance for both edge faces.

22.1 Add a 0.025" X 45° chamfer

In this step you will apply a 0.025" X 45°chamfer to the pockets and the holes.

Step Preview:

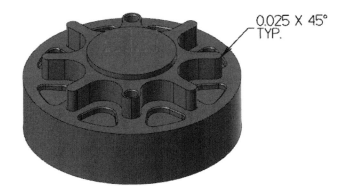

♦ To un-hide the **Levels** panel, from the left side of the graphics window click on the **Levels** tab as shown.

♦ Make **Level 1** invisible by clicking on the X under Visible column next to Level 1 as shown. (The X indicates the selected level is visible.)

Solids

♦ From the **Modify** group, select **One Distance Chamfer** as shown.

♦ In the **Solid Selection** panel, enable only the **Edge** button, and make sure that **Face**, **Body** and other buttons are disabled, as shown in the figure.

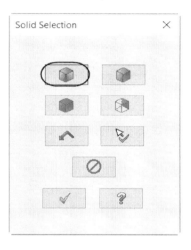

♦ [Select entities to chamfer]: Select one of the top edges from each pocket as shown.

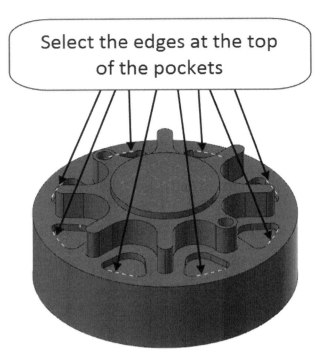

♦ [Select entities to chamfer]: Select all the edges of the holes as shown.

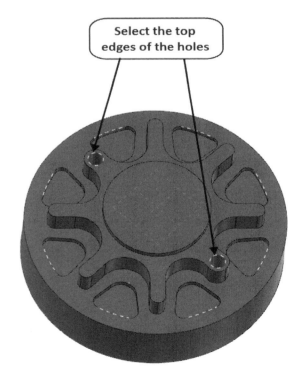

♦ Select the **OK** button to exit the **Solid Selection** panel.

♦ The **One-Distance Chamfer** panel will appear. Enable **Propagate along tangencies** and set the **Distance** as shown.

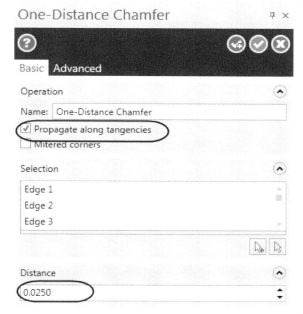

Distance sets the distance of the chamfer from the selected edge on the adjacent faces.

Mitered Corners will extend each chamfer to the extent of the edge. Use this feature where three or more chamfered edges meet at a vertex. With this option disabled, a smooth face at the vertex where the chamfers meet will be created.

Propagate Along Tangencies extends the chamfer along all tangent edges until a non-tangent edge is reached.

♦ Select the **OK and Create New Operation** button or press **Enter** to continue in the command.

22.2 Create a 0.125" X 45° chamfer

In this step you will add a 0.125" X 45° chamfer around the edge of the large circle.

Step Preview:

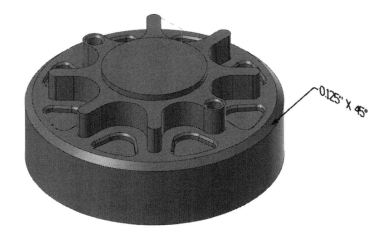

♦ Leaving **Edge Selection** enabled, select the edge as shown.

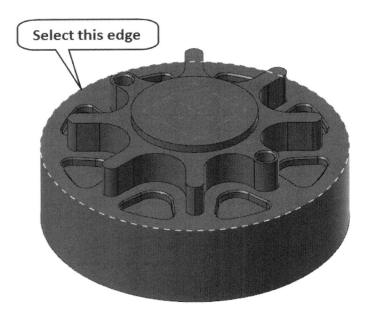

♦ Select the **OK** button to exit the **Solid Selection** panel.

♦ Change the **Distance** to **0.125**.

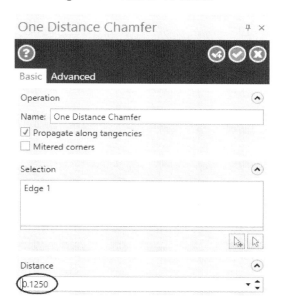

♦ Select **OK** to close the panel.

♦ The part should look as shown.

STEP 23: SAVE THE FILE

File

♦ **Save As.**

♦ Click on the **Browse** icon as shown.

♦ Find a location on the computer to save your file.

♦ File name: "Your Name_4".

TUTORIAL #4 REVIEW EXERCISE

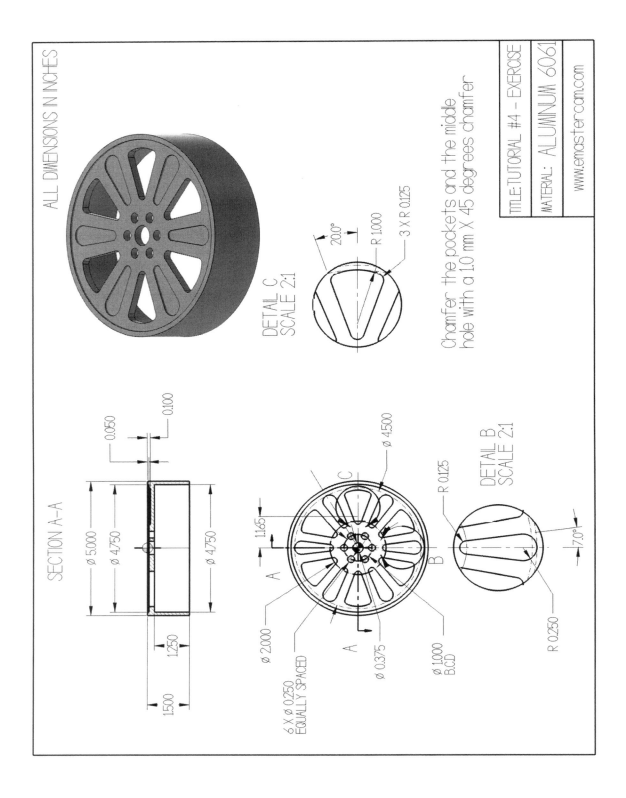

CREATE THE GEOMETRY FOR TUTORIAL #4 EXERCISE

Use these commands to create the geometry.

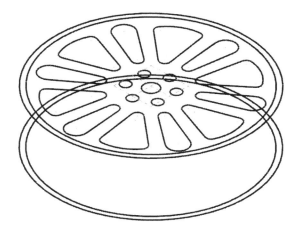

- ◆ Circle Center Point.
- ◆ Tangent Lines.
- ◆ Mirror.
- ◆ Arc Tangent.
- ◆ Arc Polar.
- ◆ Trim Break Extend.
- ◆ Fillets.
- ◆ Delete Entities.
- ◆ Rotate.
- ◆ Translate.

CREATE THE SOLID GEOMETRY FOR TUTORIAL #4 EXERCISE

Change the Main Level to Level 2

Use these commands to create the geometry:

- ◆ Solid Extrude Create body.
- ◆ Solid Extrude Cut body.
- ◆ Solid One Distance Chamfer.

TUTORIAL #4 GEOMETRY CREATION QUIZ

♦ What are levels and why do we need to change the main level to 2?

♦ What does Translate do?

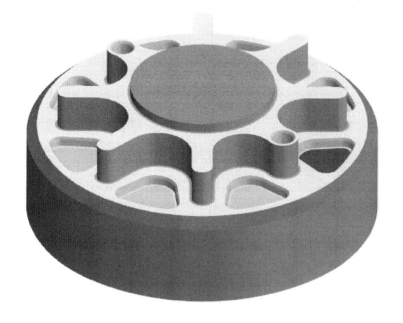

OVERVIEW OF STEPS TAKEN TO CREATE THE FINAL PART:

Create the necessary Toolpaths to machine the part:

♦ The student will set up the stock size and the clamping method used. Two setups will be used to machine the part from the top and then from the bottom.
♦ A 2D High Speed Dynamic Mill toolpath will be created to remove the material from the two steps.
♦ A Contour toolpath will be created to finish the walls.
♦ A 2D High Speed Area Mill toolpath will be created to remove the material inside of one pocket.
♦ A Transform-Rotate toolpath will be created to machine the rest of the smaller pockets.
♦ A Contour toolpath will be created to finish all the pockets.
♦ Two Drill toolpaths will be created to machine the holes.
♦ A Contour-Chamfer toolpath will be created to chamfer the edge.
♦ A 2D High Speed Dynamic Mill toolpath will be created to remove the material inside of the part from the bottom.
♦ A Contour toolpath will be created to finish the walls.

Backplot and Verify the file:

♦ Backplot will be used to simulate a step-by-step process of the tool's movements.
♦ Verify will be used to watch a tool machine the part out of a solid model.

Post Process the file to generate the G-code:

♦ The student will then post process the file to obtain an NC file containing the necessary code for the machine.

SUGGESTED FIXTURE

Note: In order to machine this part, we will have 2 setups and output 2 NC files.

SETUP SHEET

TOOL LIST

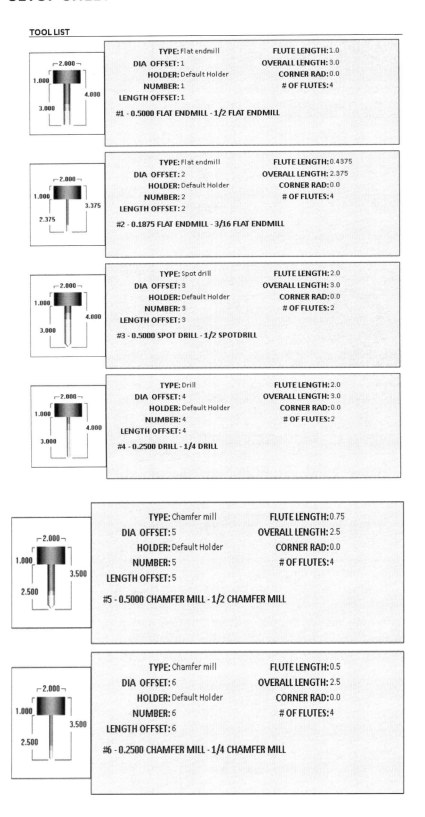

TYPE: Flat endmill   **FLUTE LENGTH:** 1.0
DIA OFFSET: 1   **OVERALL LENGTH:** 3.0
HOLDER: Default Holder   **CORNER RAD:** 0.0
NUMBER: 1   **# OF FLUTES:** 4
LENGTH OFFSET: 1

#1 - 0.5000 FLAT ENDMILL - 1/2 FLAT ENDMILL

TYPE: Flat endmill   **FLUTE LENGTH:** 0.4375
DIA OFFSET: 2   **OVERALL LENGTH:** 2.375
HOLDER: Default Holder   **CORNER RAD:** 0.0
NUMBER: 2   **# OF FLUTES:** 4
LENGTH OFFSET: 2

#2 - 0.1875 FLAT ENDMILL - 3/16 FLAT ENDMILL

TYPE: Spot drill   **FLUTE LENGTH:** 2.0
DIA OFFSET: 3   **OVERALL LENGTH:** 3.0
HOLDER: Default Holder   **CORNER RAD:** 0.0
NUMBER: 3   **# OF FLUTES:** 2
LENGTH OFFSET: 3

#3 - 0.5000 SPOT DRILL - 1/2 SPOTDRILL

TYPE: Drill   **FLUTE LENGTH:** 2.0
DIA OFFSET: 4   **OVERALL LENGTH:** 3.0
HOLDER: Default Holder   **CORNER RAD:** 0.0
NUMBER: 4   **# OF FLUTES:** 2
LENGTH OFFSET: 4

#4 - 0.2500 DRILL - 1/4 DRILL

TYPE: Chamfer mill   **FLUTE LENGTH:** 0.75
DIA OFFSET: 5   **OVERALL LENGTH:** 2.5
HOLDER: Default Holder   **CORNER RAD:** 0.0
NUMBER: 5   **# OF FLUTES:** 4
LENGTH OFFSET: 5

#5 - 0.5000 CHAMFER MILL - 1/2 CHAMFER MILL

TYPE: Chamfer mill   **FLUTE LENGTH:** 0.5
DIA OFFSET: 6   **OVERALL LENGTH:** 2.5
HOLDER: Default Holder   **CORNER RAD:** 0.0
NUMBER: 6   **# OF FLUTES:** 4
LENGTH OFFSET: 6

#6 - 0.2500 CHAMFER MILL - 1/4 CHAMFER MILL

STEP 1: SELECT THE MACHINE AND SET UP THE STOCK

In Mastercam, you select a **Machine Definition** before creating any toolpath. The **Machine Definition** is a model of your machine's capabilities and features. It acts like a template for setting up your machine. The machine definition ties together three main components: the schematic model of your machine's components, the control definition that models your control capabilities, and the post processor that will generate the required machine code (G-code). For a Mill Essentials exercise (2D toolpaths), we need just a basic machine definition.

*Note: For the purpose of this tutorial, we will be using the **Default Mill** machine.*

1.1 Unhide the Toolpaths Manager panel

♦ From the left side of the graphics window, click on the **Toolpaths** tab as shown.

♦ Pin the **Toolpaths Manager** by clicking on the **Auto Hide** icon as shown.

1.2 Select the machine

*Note: Select the **Mill Default** only if there is no **Machine Group** in the **Toolpaths Manager.***

Machine

♦ From the **Machine Type** group, select the drop down arrow below **Mill**.
♦ Select the **Default**.

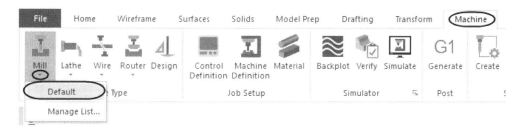

*Note: Once you select the **Mill Default**, the **Ribbon bar** changes to reflect the toolpaths that could be used with **Mill Default**.*

♦ Select the plus sign (**+**) in front of **Properties** in the **Toolpaths Manager** to expand the **Toolpaths Group Properties**.

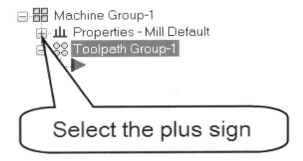

♦ Select **Tool settings** to set the tool parameters.

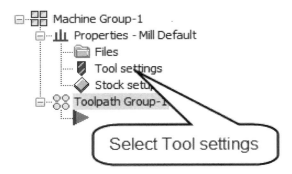

♦ Change the parameters to match the screen shot as shown.

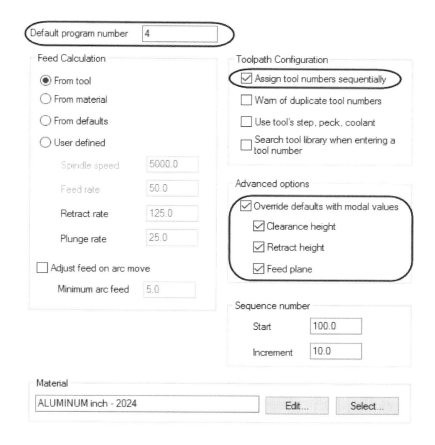

Default program number is used to enter a number if your machine requires a number for a program name.

Assign tool numbers sequentially allows you to overwrite the tool number from the library with the next available tool number. (First operation tool number 1; second operation tool number 2, etc.).

Warn of duplicate tool numbers allows you to get a warning if you enter two tools with the same number.

Override defaults with modal values enables the system to keep the values that you enter.

Feed Calculation set to **From tool** uses feed rate, plunge rate, retract rate, and spindle speed from the tool definition.

- Select the **Stock Setup** tab to define the stock.
- Select the **Cylindrical Shape** and select **All Entities** as shown.

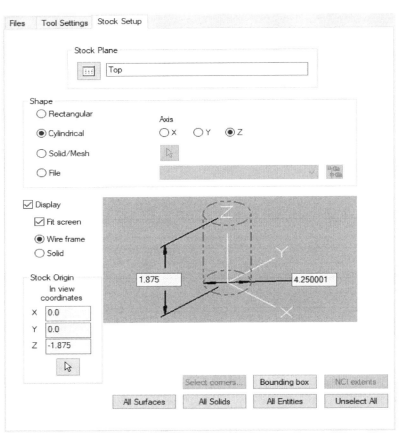

The **Stock Origin** values adjust the positioning of the stock, ensuring that you have an equal amount of extra stock around the finished part.

Display options allow you to set the stock as Wireframe and to fit the stock to the screen. (Fit Screen)

*Note: The **stock** model that you create can be displayed with the part geometry when viewing the file or the toolpaths, during backplot, or while verifying toolpaths.*

- Select the **OK** button to exit **Machine Group Properties**.

- The stock model will appear as shown.

Note: The stock is not geometry and cannot be selected. There will not be a facing toolpath because the stock is already to size.

STEP 2: 2D HIGH SPEED DYNAMIC MILL

2D High Speed Dynamic Mill utilizes the entire flute length of cutting tools to produce the smoothest, most efficient tool motion for high speed pocketing. The toolpath supports a custom entry method and many others. Micro lifts further refine the dynamic milling motion and avoid excessive heat build up. Custom feeds and speeds optimize and generate safe tool motion. Dynamic Mill machines pockets using one or more chains to drive the toolpath. The outside chain contains the toolpath; all inside chains are considered islands.

In this step you will machine the three steps of the part using **Island Facing**. You will have to make the wireframe geometry from Level 1 visible.

Toolpath Preview:

2.1 Chain selection

♦ To make **Level 1** visible, right mouse click in the graphics window and from the **Mini Toolbar**, select the drop down arrow next to **Level** and click on **Level 1** as shown.

♦ The wireframe geometry should now be visible in the graphics window.

Toolpaths

♦ From the **2D** group, select the **Dynamic Mill** icon.

♦ In the **Chain Options**, select **From outside** as the **Machining region strategy**. Choose **Select avoidance regions** as shown to chain the geometry for the islands.

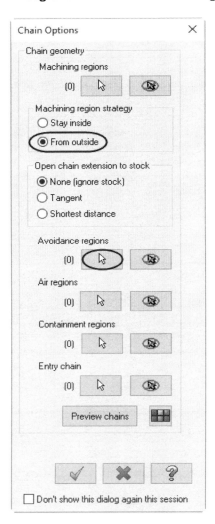

Note: If you do not select a Machining region, the stock is used as the machining region.

- In the **Chaining** dialog box, ensure the **Chaining** dialog box is set to **Wireframe** selection as shown.
- Leave the default setting in the **Chaining** dialog box.
- Pick the chains as shown.

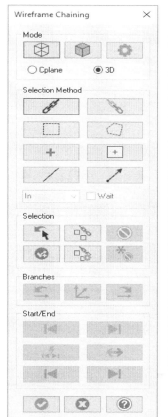

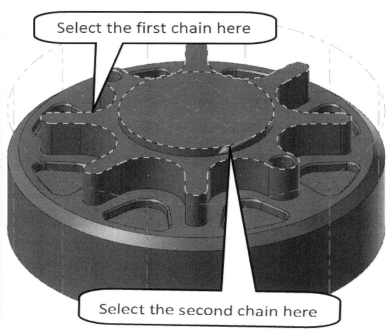

- Select the **OK** button to exit the **Chaining** dialog box.

- Select the **OK** button to exit the **Chain Options** dialog box.

- In the **Toolpath Type** page, **Dynamic Mill** will be already selected as shown.

 Dynamic Mill   Area Mill   Dynamic Contour   Peel Mill   Blend Mill

2.2 Preview Chains

The **Preview Chains** function is intended to give the user a quick visual representation of how Mastercam sees the various pieces of geometry that have been selected, how they interact with one another and a general overview of how the toolpath will be calculated with the selections presently made.

♦ Click on the **Color** icon to see the legend for **Preview chains** as shown.

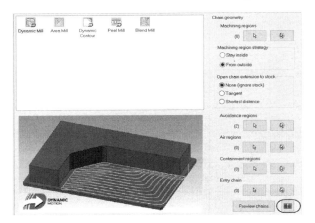

♦ The **Preview Chains Colors** dialog box should look as shown.

The **Material region** and **Material crosshatch** are the two colors that are used to define the material to be cut. The default colors are red for the background and black for the crosshatch.

The **Motion region** displays the area that Mastercam is making available to the toolpath for motion if it needs it. The color to represent it is dark blue. The primary reason for the display of the entire available (but not necessarily used) **Motion region** is to help the user visualize how the tool may move near or interact with any adjacent geometry.

The **Tool containment** is what you have selected as the containment region in the chain geometry. If you have not selected a containment region, it will default to the outside of the **Motion region** since that is currently the default area the toolpath is being contained to. The color used to represent the **Tool containment** is yellow.

♦ Select the **OK** button to exit **Preview Chains Colors**.

♦ Select the **Preview chains** button as shown.

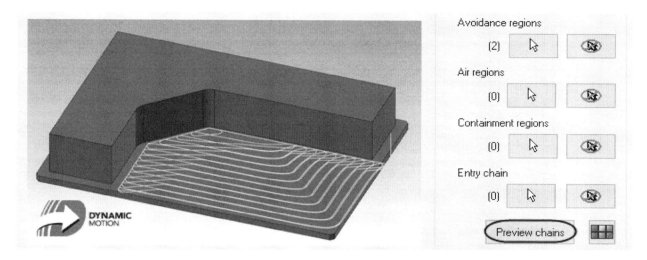

♦ Select the **Hide dialog** button to see the preview in the graphics window.
♦ The **Preview chains** should look as shown.

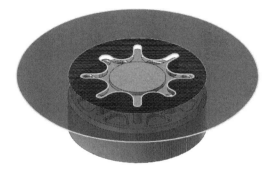

♦ Press **Esc** key to return to the toolpath parameters.
♦ Click on the **Preview chains** button again to clear the **Preview chains** display.

2.3 Select a 1/2" Flat Endmill from the library and set the Tool Parameters

♦ From the **Tree View list**, select **Tool**.

♦ Click on the **Select library tool** button.

♦ Select the **Filter** button.

♦ Select the **None** button and then under **Tool Types**, choose the **Flat Endmill** icon.
♦ Under **Tool Diameter**, pick **Equal** and input a value of **0.5**as shown.

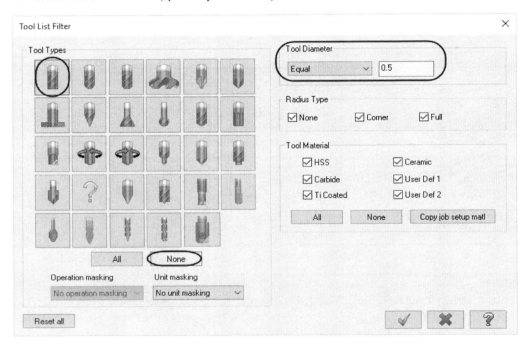

♦ Select the **OK** button to exit the **Tool List Filter**.
♦ In the **Tool Selection** panel you should only see a **1/2" Flat Endmill**.

#	Assembly...	Tool Name	Holder N...	Dia.	Cor. r...	Length	# Flut...	Type	Rad....
290	—	1/2 FLAT ...	—	0.5	0.0	1.0	4	End...	None

♦ Select the **1/2" Flat Endmill** in the **Tool Selection** page and then select the **OK** button to exit.

♦ Make all the necessary changes as shown.

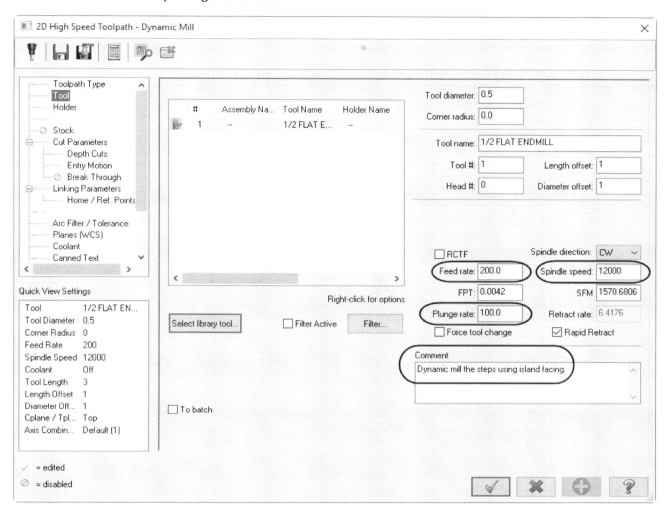

2.4 Set the Cut Parameters

♦ From the **Tree View list**, select **Cut Parameters**.

♦ Change the settings as shown.

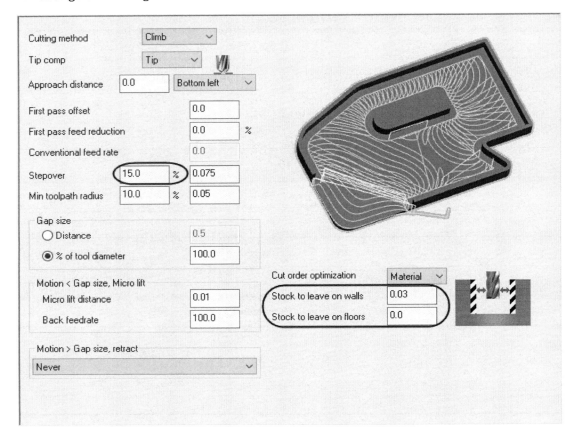

Stepover sets the distance between cutting passes in the X and Y axes.

Toolpath radius reduces sharp corner motion between cut passes.

Micro lift distance enters the distance the tool lifts off the part on the back moves. Microlifts are slight lifts that help clear chips and minimize excessive tool heating.

Back feedrate controls the speed of the backfeed movement of the tool.

Motion > Gap Size, retract controls retracts in the toolpath when making a non-cutting move within an area where the tool can be kept down or microlifted.

Cut order optimization defines the cut order Mastercam applies to different cutting passes in the dynamic mill toolpath.

Stock to leave on walls sets the stock left on the walls that has to be removed by another operation.

2.5 Enable Island Facing

♦ Select **Depth Cuts** from the **Tree View List**.
♦ Enable **Island facing** and set **Overlap** to **20%** as shown.

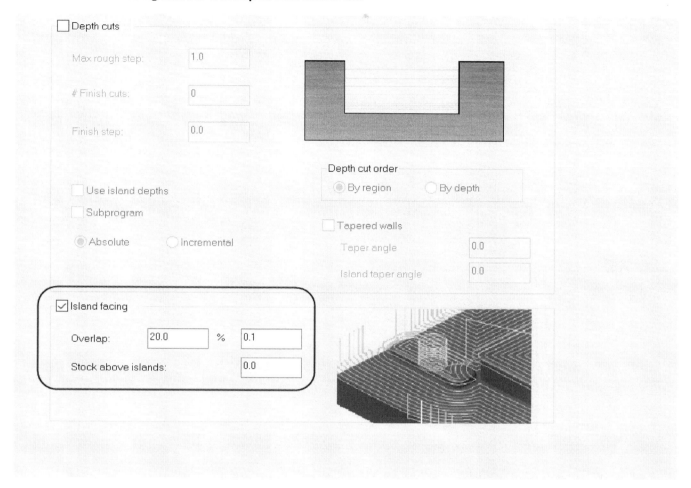

2.6 Set the Entry Motion

Entry motion configures an entry method for the dynamic mill toolpath which determines not only how and where the tool enters the part, but the cutting method/machining strategy used by the toolpath.

*Note: This toolpath uses **From Outside** as the **Machining region strategy** therefore it will automatically plunge outside of the part.*

2.7 Set the Linking Parameters

♦ Select **Linking Parameters** and enable **Clearance**, change the **Clearance** value to **1.0**. Change the **Top of Stock** value to **0.0**, **Absolute** and the **Depth** to **-0.625**, **Absolute** as shown.

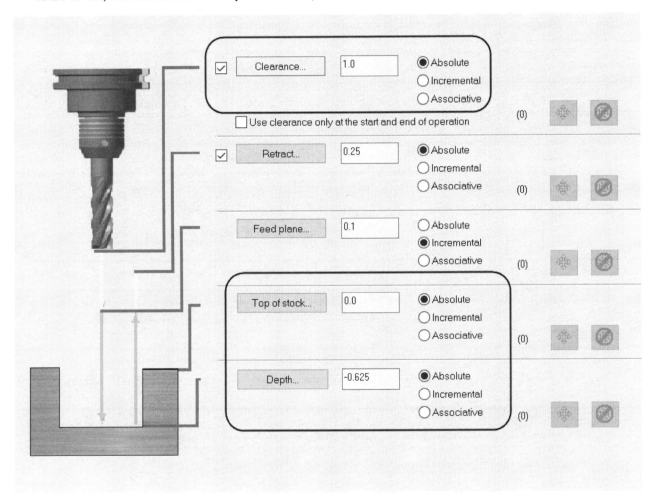

2.8 Set the Arc Filter / Tolerance

Use this page to control the toolpath tolerances. When you activate line and arc filtering, Mastercam replaces very small moves within the defined line/arc filter tolerance with larger ones wherever possible.

♦ From the **Tree view List**, select the **Arc Filter/Tolerance** and enable **Line/Arc Filtering Settings**.
♦ Set the **Tolerance Distribution** for **Cut tolerance** to **30%** and the **Line/Arc tolerance** to **70%** as shown.

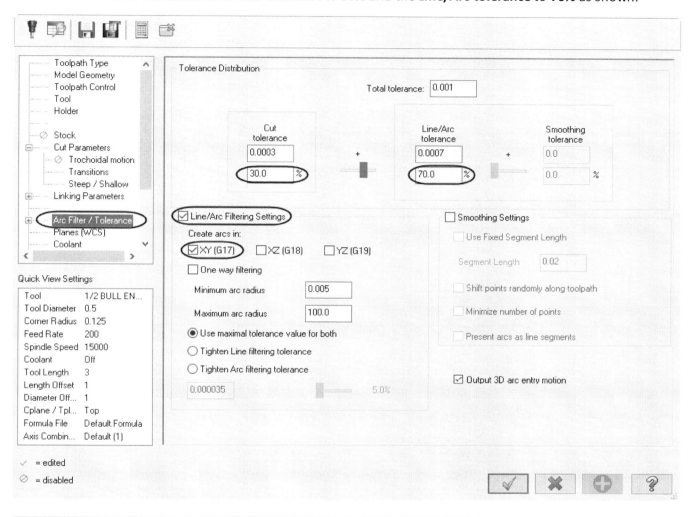

Line/Arc Filtering Settings replaces very small moves within the defined line/arc filter tolerance with larger ones wherever possible.

Line/arc filtering significantly reduces the number of NC blocks in the post, and may improve the machined precision of the part as well as its surface quality.

2.9 Preview the Toolpath

♦ To quickly check how the toolpath will be generated, select the **Preview toolpath** icon as shown.

♦ To hide the dialog box, click on the **Hide dialog** icon as shown.

♦ To see the part from an **Isometric** view, right mouse click in the graphics window and select **Isometric** as shown.

⌕	Zoom Window
⌕	Unzoom 80%
⟳	Dynamic Rotation
⤢	Fit
⬢	Top (WCS)
⬢	Front (WCS)
⬢	Right (WCS)
⬢	Isometric (WCS)
	GView ▸
✕	Delete Entities
⌖	Analyze Distance...
⌖	Analyze Entity Properties...

♦ The toolpath should look as shown.

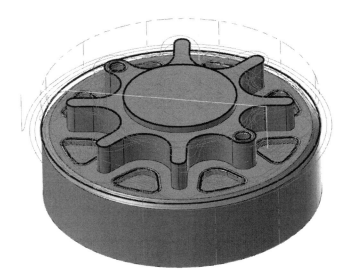

♦ Press **Esc** key to exit the preview.

Note: If the toolpath does not look as shown in the preview, check your parameters again.

♦ Select the **OK** button to generate the toolpath.

STEP 3: BACKPLOT THE TOOLPATHS

◆ Make sure that the toolpaths are selected (signified by the green check mark on the folder icon). If the operation is not selected, choose the **Select all operations** icon.

◆ Select the **Backplot selected operations** button.

◆ In the **Backplot** dialog box, enable **Display with color codes, Display tool** and **Display rapid moves** icons as shown.

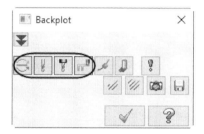

◆ To see the part from an **Isometric view**, right mouse click in the graphics window and select **Isometric** as shown.

◆ To fit the workpiece to the screen, if needed, right mouse click in the graphics window again and select **Fit**.

◆ You can step through the **Backplot** by using the **Step forward** or **Step back** buttons.

◆ You can adjust the speed of the backplot.

◆ Select the **Play** button to run **Backplot**.

♦ After **Backplot** is completed, the toolpath should look as shown.

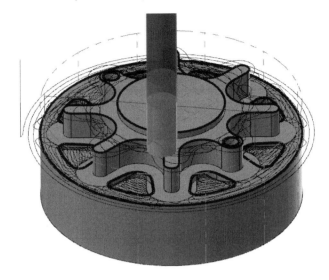

♦ Select the **OK** button to exit **Backplot** dialog box.

STEP 4: SIMULATE THE TOOLPATH IN VERIFY

♦ From the **Toolpaths Manager**, select **Verify selected operations** icon as shown.

Toolpaths

Verify selected operations

---

*Note: Mastercam launches a new window that allows you to check the part using **Backplot** or **Verify**.*

♦ From **Home** tab, change the settings for the **Visibility** as shown in Figure: 4.0.1.
♦ In the **Visibility** group, click on **Workpiece** twice to display it translucent as shown in Figure: 4.0.1.

Figure: 4.0.1

♦ Select the **Play** button to run **Verify**.

♦ The part should appear as shown.

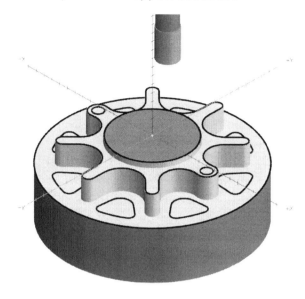

♦ To go back to the Mastercam window, minimize the **Mastercam Simulator** window as shown.
♦ Press **Alt + T** to remove the toolpath display.

STEP 5: FINISH THE WALLS USING CONTOUR TOOLPATH

In this step we will utilize the **Contour** toolpath to finish the walls of the part. You will remove the 0.03" stock from the walls.

Toolpath Preview:

5.1 Chain Selection

Toolpaths

♦ In the **2D** group, select the **Contour** icon as shown.

♦ In the **Chaining** dialog box, select **Solids selection** and enable only **Loop** as shown.
♦ Select the base of the arms as shown.

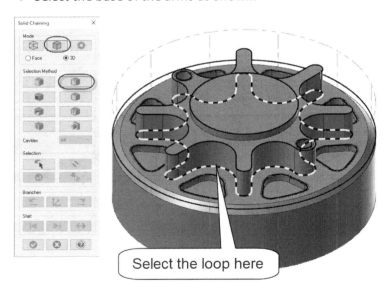

Select the loop here

♦ The **Pick Reference Face** dialog appears, make sure that the bottom edge is selected and click on the **OK** button to continue.

♦ The arrow should be pointing in the clockwise direction as shown. If it is not, select **Reverse**.

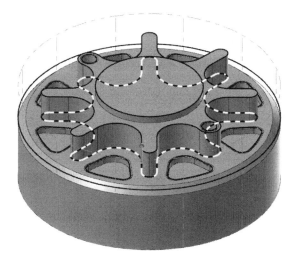

♦ Select the base of the small cylinder as the final chain.

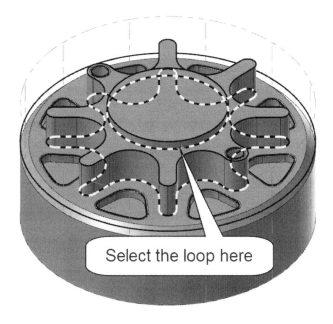

Select the loop here

♦ Ensure the bottom edge is selected and click **OK** to confirm the **Reference Face**.

♦ The arrow should be pointing in the clockwise direction. If it is not, select **Reverse**.

♦ Select the **OK** button to exit the **Chaining** dialog box.

♦ In the **Toolpath Type** page, **Contour** will be selected.

Contour　　Pocket　　Facing　　Slot mill　　Model Chamfer

5.2 Select a 1/2" Flat Endmill from Tool list window

♦ Select **Tool** from the **Tree View list**.
♦ Select the **1/2" Flat Endmill** in the **Tool list** window. Make all the necessary changes as shown.

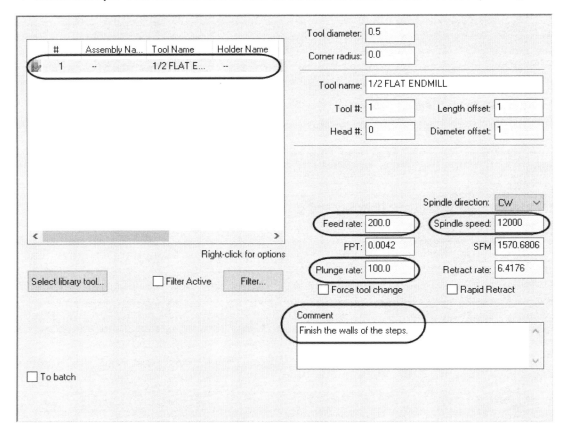

5.3 Set the Cut Parameters

♦ From the **Tree View list**, select **Cut Parameters** and make sure that the parameters are set as shown.

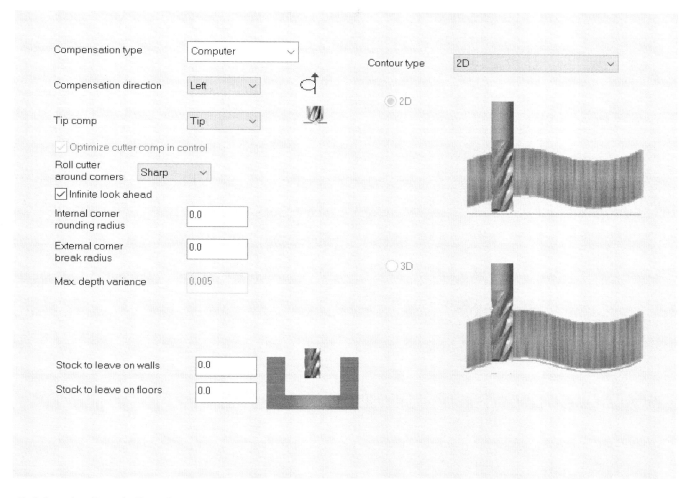

5.4 Set the Depth Cuts Parameters

♦ From the **Tree View list**, disable the **Depth Cuts** if needed as shown.

5.5 Set the Lead In/Out parameters

♦ Make sure that the parameters are set as shown. Click the circled arrow button near the center of the window to copy appropriate fields from the **Entry** section to the **Exit** section.

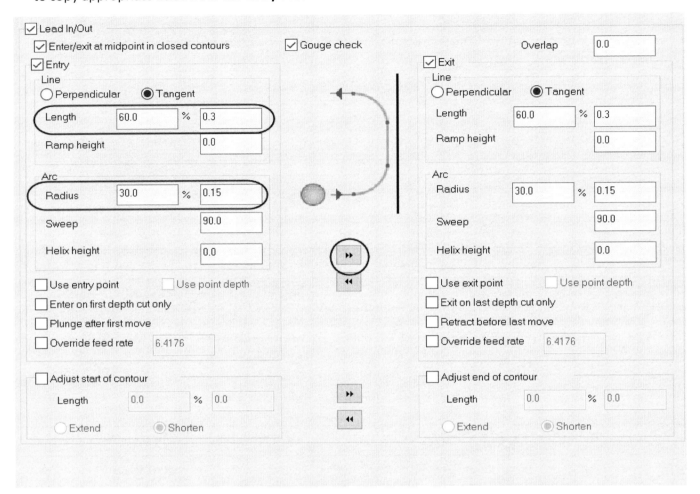

5.6 Set the Linking Parameters

♦ Select **Linking Parameters** and enable **Clearance**. Ensure the the **Clearance** value is set to **1.0, Absolute**. Set the **Depth** to **0.0** and **Incremental** as shown.

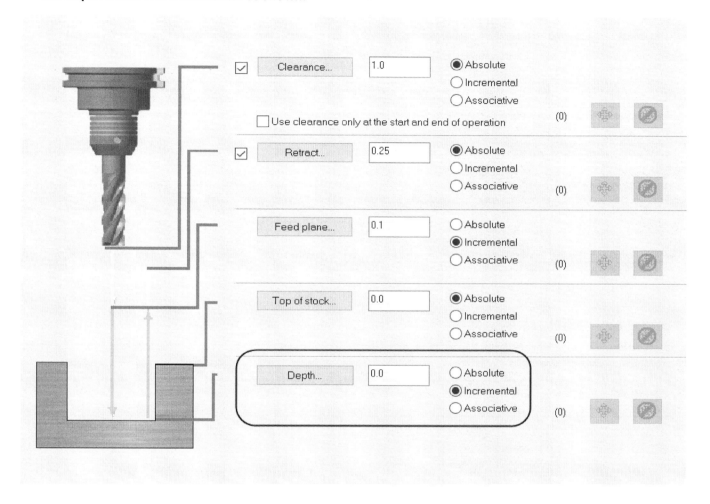

5.7 Preview the Toolpath

♦ To quickly check how the toolpath will be generated, select the **Preview toolpath** icon as shown.

♦ See**"Preview the Toolpath" on page 438** to review the procedure.
♦ The toolpath should look as shown.

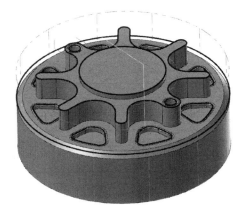

♦ Press **Esc** key to exit the preview.

Note: If the toolpath does not look as shown in the preview, check your parameters again.

♦ Select the **OK** button to exit the toolpath parameters.
♦ **Backplot** and **Verify** your toolpath. See **"Backplot The Toolpaths" on page 439** and **"Simulate the toolpath in Verify" on page 440** to review these procedures.
♦ The part will appear as shown.

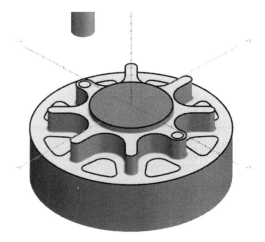

♦ To go back to the Mastercam window, minimize the **Mastercam Simulator** window as shown.
♦ Press **Alt + T** to remove the toolpath display if needed.

STEP 6: AREA MILL TOOLPATH

6.1 2D High Speed Area Mill the pocket

2D High Speed Area Mill toolpath allows you to machine pockets, material that other toolpaths left behind, and standing bosses or cores using a smooth clean motion. Helical entries and tangent stepovers create efficient motion for your machine tools. Cut parameters let you control corner rounding to create the best toolpath, avoiding sharp corners or direction changes. You will machine the pocket keeping the tool inside the machining region by selecting Stay inside as your machining region strategy.

Toolpath Preview:

Toolpaths

♦ From the **2D** group, select the **Expand gallery** arrow as shown.

♦ Select the **Area Mill** icon.

♦ In the **Chain Options**, make sure that **Stay inside** is enabled and click on the **Select Machining Chains** button in the **Machining regions** as shown.

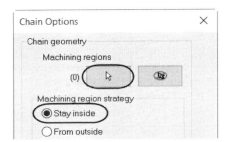

♦ In the **Chaining** dialog box, switch to **Solids** selection as shown.

♦ Make sure that only the **Loop** button is enabled as shown.

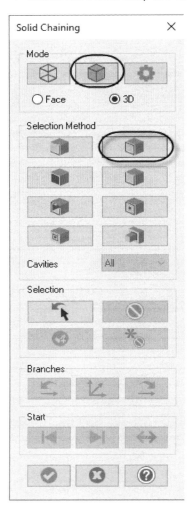

♦ Select the bottom of the pocket edge as shown.

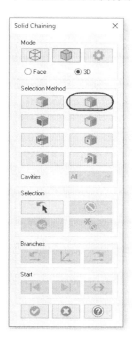

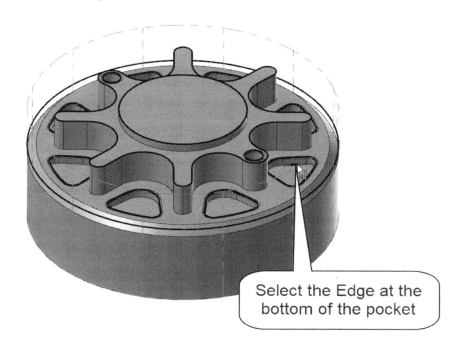

Select the Edge at the bottom of the pocket

♦ The pocket bottom loop should be selected as shown.

♦ The **Pick Reference Face** dialog appears, make sure that the bottom edge is selected and click on the **OK** button to continue.

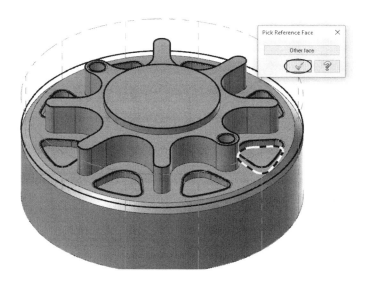

- Select the **OK** button to exit the **Chaining** dialog box.
- Select the **OK** button to exit the **Chain Options** dialog box.
- In the **Toolpath Type** page, **Area Mill** should be already selected as shown.

Dynamic Mill   Area Mill   Dynamic Contour   Peel Mill   Blend Mill

6.2 Preview Chains

- Select the **Preview chains** button as shown.
- See "Preview Chains" on page 430 to review the procedure.
- The **Preview chains** should look as shown.

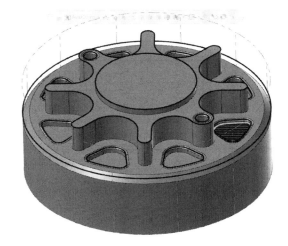

- Click on the **Hide dialog** button.
- Press **Esc** key to return to the toolpath parameters.

- Click on the **Preview chains** button again to clear the Preview chains display.

6.3 Select a 3/16" Flat Endmill from the Library and set the Tool Parameters

- Select **Tool** from the **Tree View list**.

- Click on the **Select library tool** button.  Select library tool...
- Select the **Filter** button.

Filter...
☑ Filter Active
1 of 427 tools

- Select the **None** button and then under **Tool Types** choose the **Endmill Flat** icon as shown.
- Under **Tool Diameter**, pick **Equal** and input a value of **0.1875** as shown.

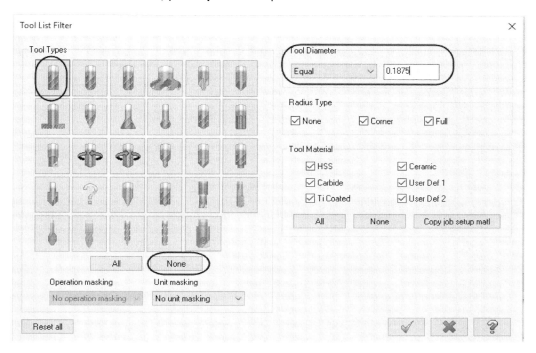

- Select the **OK** button to exit the **Tool List Filter**.
- In the **Tool Selection** panel you should only see a **3/16" Flat Endmill**.

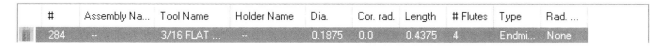

#	Assembly Na...	Tool Name	Holder Name	Dia.	Cor. rad.	Length	# Flutes	Type	Rad. ...
284	--	3/16 FLAT ...	--	0.1875	0.0	0.4375	4	Endmi...	None

- Select the **3/16" Flat Endmill** in the **Tool Selection** page and then select the **OK** button to continue.

♦ Make all the necessary changes as shown.

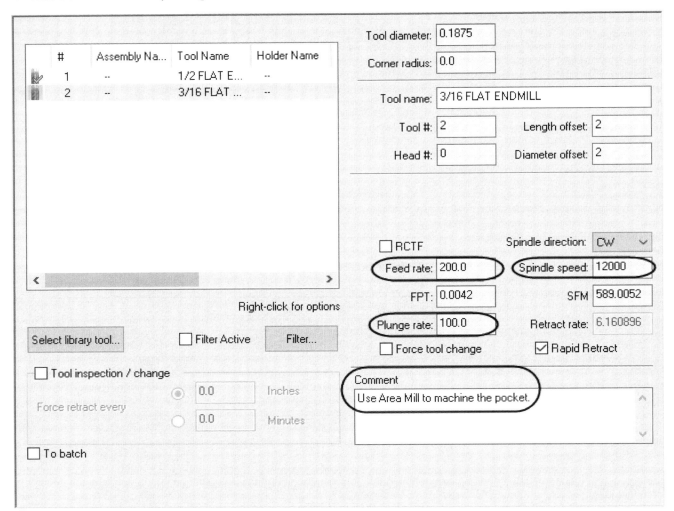

6.4 Set the Cut Parameters

♦ From the **Tree View list**, select **Cut Parameters**.
♦ Set the parameters as shown.

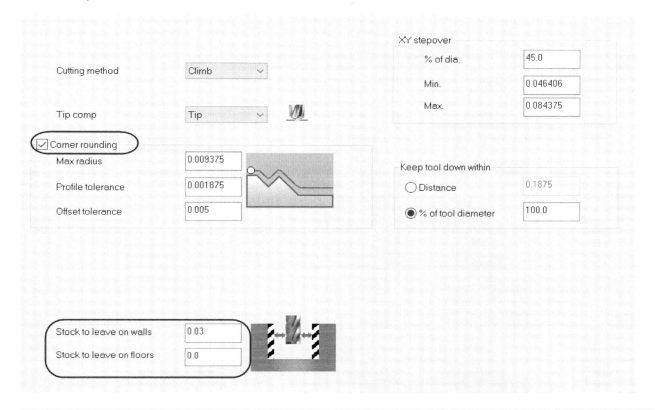

Cutting method set to Climb cuts in one direction with the tool rotating in the opposite direction of the tool motion.

XY stepover sets the distance between cutting passes in the X and Y axes.

% of tool dia expresses the maximum XY stepover as a percentage of the tool diameter. The Max. XY stepover field will update automatically when you enter a value in this field. The actual stepover is calculated by Mastercam between the Min. and Max. values.

Corner rounding activates toolpath corner rounding, which replaces sharp corners with arcs for faster and smoother transitions in tool direction.

Profile tolerance represents the maximum distance that the outermost profile of a toolpath created with corner rounding can deviate from the original toolpath.

Offset tolerance represents the maximum distance that a profile of a toolpath created with corner rounding can deviate from the original toolpath. This is the same measurement as the profile tolerance but is applied to all the profiles except the outermost one.

6.5 Set the Depth Cuts parameters

♦ From the **Tree View list**, select **Depth Cuts** and set the parameters as shown.

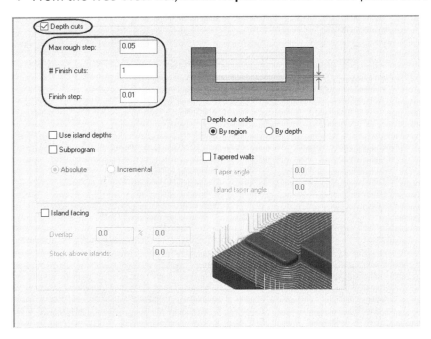

6.6 Set the Transitions

♦ From the **Tree View list**, select **Transitions** and leave the **Entry method** set to **Entry helix** as shown.

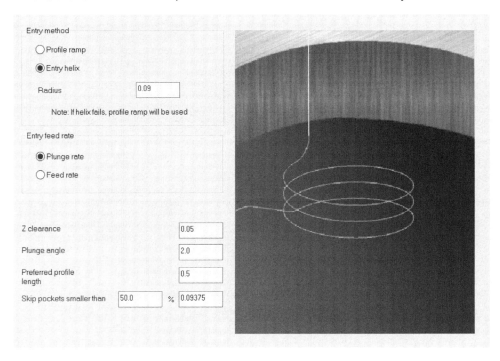

Entry method set to Helix only creates a helical entry into the part.

6.7 Set the Linking Parameters

♦ Select **Linking Parameters** from the tree view list and set the parameters as shown.

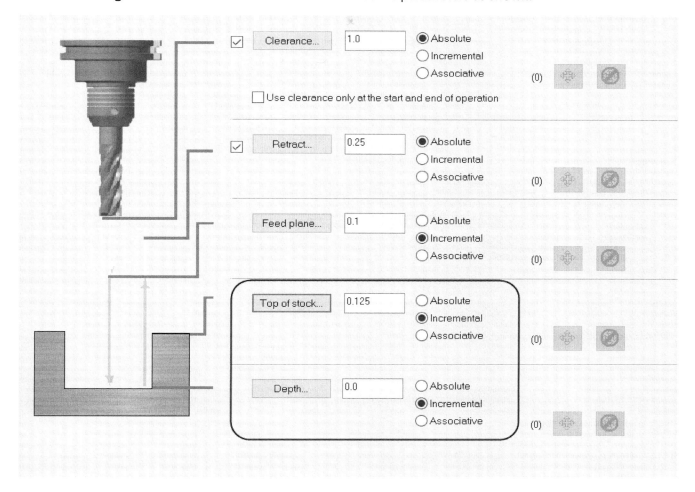

6.8 Preview the Toolpath

♦ To quickly check how the toolpath will be generated, select the **Preview toolpath** icon as shown.

♦ See **"Preview the Toolpath" on page 438** to review the procedure.
♦ The toolpath should look as shown.

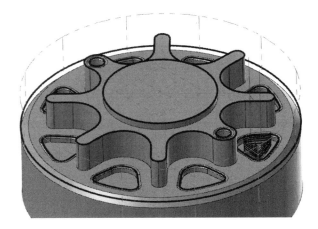

♦ Press **Esc** key to exit the preview.

Note: If the toolpath does not look as shown in the preview, check your parameters again.

♦ Select the **OK** button to exit the toolpath parameters.
♦ **Backplot** the toolpath as shown on **"Backplot The Toolpaths" on page 439**.

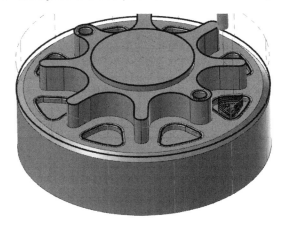

♦ Select the **OK** button to exit **Backplot**.

- ◆ To **Verify** the toolpaths, make sure all the operations are selected. To select all operations, click on the **Select all operations** icon.

- ◆ **Verify** the toolpaths as shown on **"Simulate the toolpath in Verify" on page 440**.

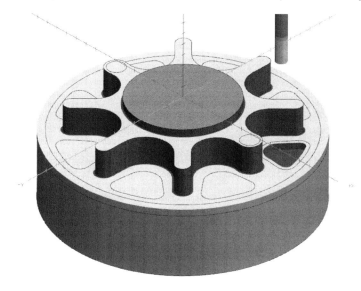

- ◆ To go back to the Mastercam window, minimize the **Mastercam Simulator** window as shown.

STEP 7: TRANSFORM-ROTATE TOOLPATH

Transform toolpaths are used when you want to run the same toolpath in different locations. You can transform a single toolpath or several at a time. In this step you will machine one of the smaller pockets using 2D HS Area Mill. Then, using the Transform Rotate toolpath, you will generate the toolpaths for the rest of the identical pockets.

Toolpath Preview:

Toolpaths

♦ From the **Utilities** group, select the **Toolpath Transform**.

- For the **Type**, select **Rotate**, and select **Coordinate** for **Method**.
- Select **Operation 3**.
- In the **Group NCI output by** area select **Operation order** as shown.

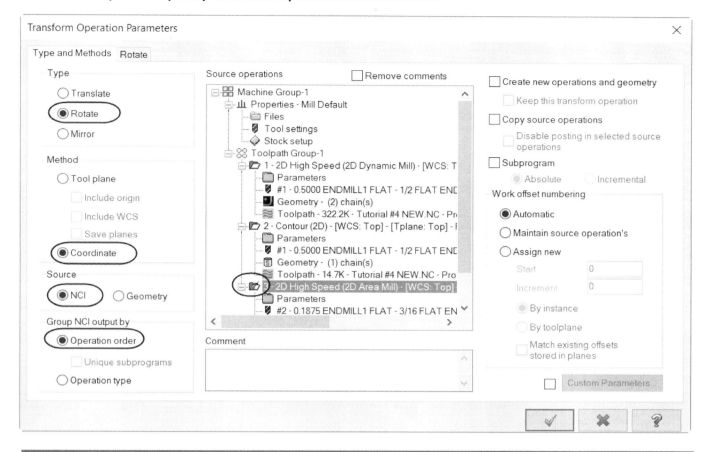

Rotate revolves the toolpath about the construction origin or a specified point. Activate the Rotate tab and you can set the rotation point and number of copies.

Coordinate creates new coordinate positions for the new toolpaths in the original tool plane.

NCI copies and transforms only the source operation's NCI lines to the transformed operations.

Operation order sorts the transformed operations by the order they were selected. For example, if we choose the large pocket then small pocket, it will execute them in that order (large pocket, small pocket, large pocket, small pocket, etc.).

♦ Choose the **Rotate** tab.

♦ Input a **# of instances of 7**, a **Start angle** of **45.0** degrees, and a **Rotation angle** of **45.0** degrees as shown.

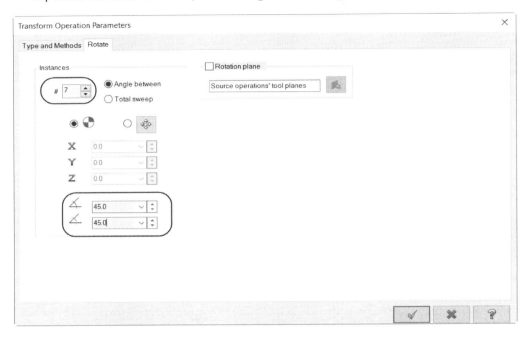

Number of instances is the number of times to rotate the toolpath.

Start angle sets the beginning angle for the rotate toolpath.

Rotation angle sets the angle of rotation for the transformed toolpath.

♦ Select the **OK** button to generate the toolpath.

♦ **Backplot** the toolpath as shown on **"Backplot The Toolpaths" on page 439**.

♦ Select the **OK** button to exit **Backplot**.

♦ Select all toolpaths to **Verify** them as shown on **"Simulate the toolpath in Verify" on page 440**.

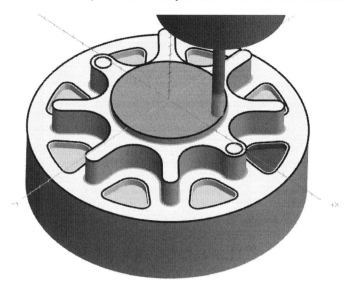

♦ To go back to the Mastercam window, minimize the **Mastercam Simulator** window as shown.
♦ Press **Alt + S** to shade the solid.
♦ Press **Alt + T** to remove the toolpath display.

STEP 8: FINISH THE POCKET WALLS USING CONTOUR TOOLPATH

In this step we will utilize the Contour toolpath to finish the walls of the part. You will remove the 0.03" stock from the walls.

Toolpath Preview:

8.1 Chain Selection

Toolpaths

♦ From the **2D** group, select the **Contour** icon as shown.

♦ In the **Chaining** dialog box, select **Solids selection** and enable only **Face** as shown.

- ◆ Right mouse click in the graphics window and select the **Top** view.
- ◆ Select the bottom pocket as shown. Use the **Reverse** button to change the direction to CCW if needed.

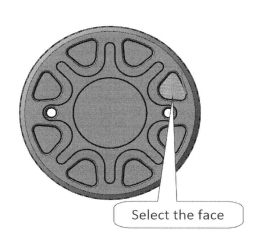

Select the face

- ◆ Select the rest of the pockets as shown. The arrow should be pointing in the Counterclockwise direction. If it is not, select **Reverse**.

- ◆ Select the **OK** button to exit the **Chaining** dialog box.
- ◆ In the **Toolpath Type** page, **Contour** will be selected.

Contour   Pocket   Facing   Slot mill   Model Chamfer

8.2 Select a 3/16" Flat Endmill from Tool list window

♦ Select **Tool** from the **Tree View list**.
♦ Select the **3/16" Flat Endmill** in the **Tool list** window. Make all the necessary changes as shown.

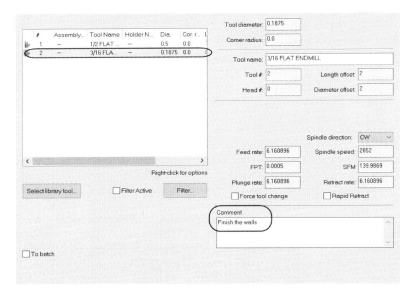

8.3 Set the Cut Parameters

♦ From the **Tree View list**, select **Cut Parameters** and make sure that the parameters are set as shown.

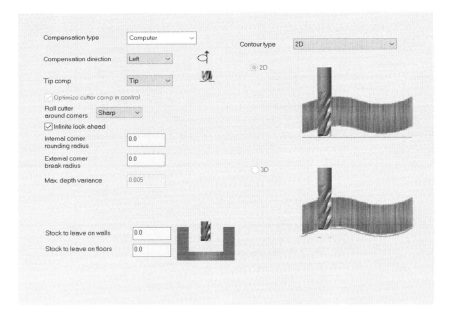

8.4 Set the Depth Cuts Parameters

♦ From the **Tree View list**, disable the **Depth Cuts** as shown, if needed.

8.5 Set the Lead In/Out parameters

♦ Make sure that the parameters are set as shown.

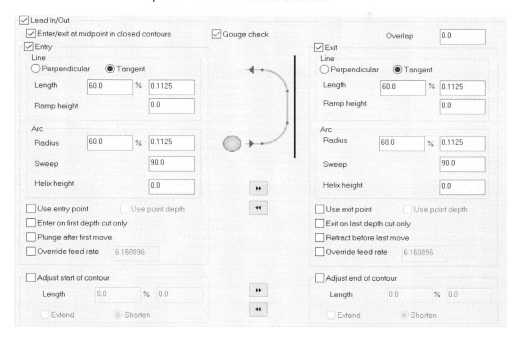

8.6 Set the Linking Parameters

♦ Select **Linking Parameters** and enable **Clearance**. Set the **Clearance** value to **1.0, Absolute**. Set the parameters as shown.

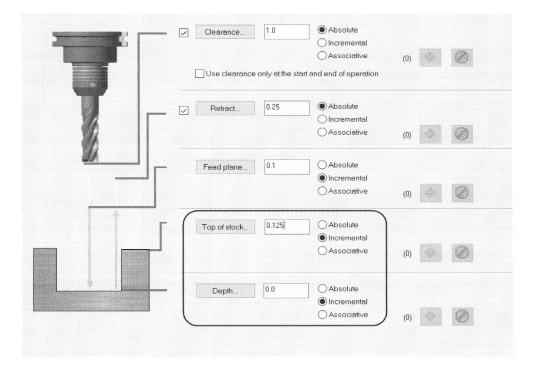

8.7 Preview the Toolpath

♦ To quickly check how the toolpath will be generated, select the **Preview toolpath** icon as shown.

♦ See **"Preview the Toolpath" on page 438** to review the procedure.
♦ The toolpath should look as shown.

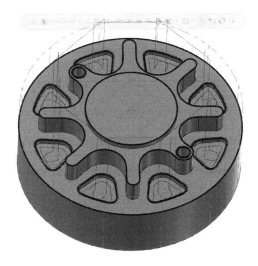

♦ Press **Esc** key to exit the preview.

Note: If the toolpath does not look as shown in the preview, check your parameters again.

♦ Select the **OK** button to exit the toolpath parameters.
♦ **Backplot** and **Verify** your toolpath. See **"Backplot The Toolpaths" on page 439** and **"Simulate the toolpath in Verify" on page 440** to review these procedures.
♦ The part will appear as shown.

STEP 9: SPOT DRILL THE HOLES

Spot Drilling the holes allows you to start the hole. In this operation, we will use the spot drill to chamfer the hole before drilling it.

Toolpath Preview:

Toolpaths

♦ From the **2D** group, select the **Drill** icon.

♦ The **Toolpath Hole Definition** panel opens.
♦ Right mouse click in the graphics window and select the **Top** view.

- Zoom Window
- Unzoom 80%
- Dynamic Rotation
- Fit
- Top (WCS)
- Front (WCS)   Top (WCS)
- Right (WCS)
- Isometric (WCS)

♦ [Select one or more entities to add or remove from the features list. Select an arc or edge]: Select the center points of the circles as shown.

Note: Make sure that if you select a point you select the center point of the circles. Otherwise you can select the circles or the edges of the solid holes.

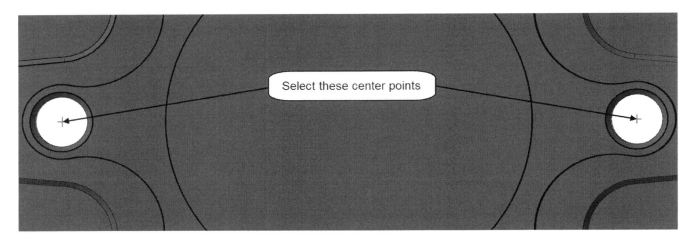

Select these center points

♦ Select the **OK** button to exit the **Toolpath Hole Definition** dialog box.
♦ In the **Toolpath Type** page, the **Drill** toolpath will be selected.

Drill   Circle Mill   Point   Helix Bore   Thread Mill

9.1 Select a 1/2" Spot Drill from the Library and set the Tool Parameters

♦ Select **Tool** from the **Tree view list**.

♦ Click on the **Select library tool** button. Select library tool...

♦ To be able to see just the spot drill, select the Filter button.

Filter...

☑ Filter Active

1 of 427 tools

♦ Under **Tool Types**, select the **None** button and then choose the **Spot drill** icon as shown.

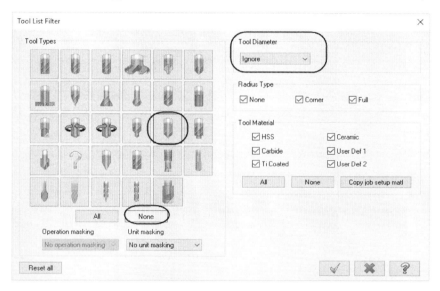

♦ Select **OK** button to exit the **Tool List Filter** dialog box. ✓

♦ At this point you should only see **Spot Drills**.

♦ From that list select the **1/2" Spot Drill**.

#	Assembly Name	Tool Name	Holder Name	Dia.	Cor. rad.	Length	Type	Ra...	# Flutes
21	--	1/8 SPOTDRILL	--	0....	0.0	2.0	Sp...	No...	2
22	--	1/4 SPOTDRILL	--	0....	0.0	2.0	Sp...	No...	2
23	--	3/8 SPOTDRILL	--	0....	0.0	2.0	Sp...	No...	4
24	--	1/2 SPOTDRILL	--	0.5	0.0	2.0	Sp...	No...	2
25	--	3/4 SPOTDRILL	--	0....	0.0	2.0	Sp...	No...	4
26	--	1. SPOTDRILL	--	1.0	0.0	2.0	Sp...	No...	4

♦ Select the tool in the **Tool Selection** page and then select the **OK** button to exit. ✓

♦ Make the necessary changes to the **Tool** page as shown.

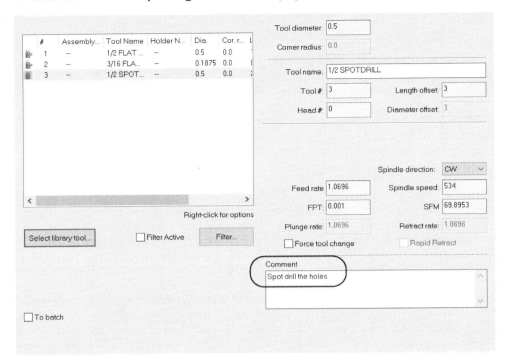

9.2 Set the Cut Parameters

♦ From the **Tree View list**, select **Cut Parameters** and make the necessary changes as shown.

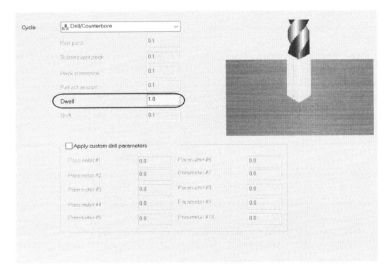

Drill/Counterbore is recommended for drilling holes with depths of less than three times the tool's diameter.

Dwell sets the amount of time in seconds that the tool remains at the bottom of a drilled hole.

9.3 Set the Linking Parameters

◆ Choose **Linking Parameters**, ensure **Clearance** is enabled and set to **Absolute** and **1.0** and the **Top of stock** and **Depth** are set to **Incremental** and **0.0**.

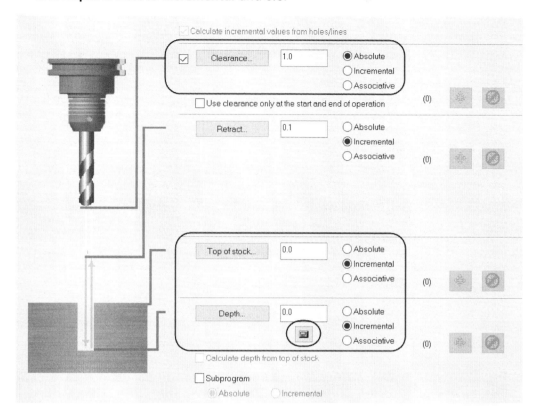

◆ Select the **Calculator** icon.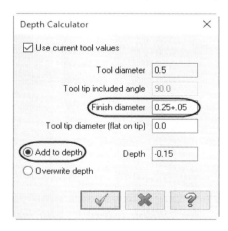
◆ To calculate the **Depth** of the spot drill, in the **Finish diameter** area, enter **0.25+0.05** as shown.

◆ Select the **OK** button to exit the **Depth Calculator**.

◆ You will now see the depth we calculated for the spot drilling operation set in the **Depth** field as shown.

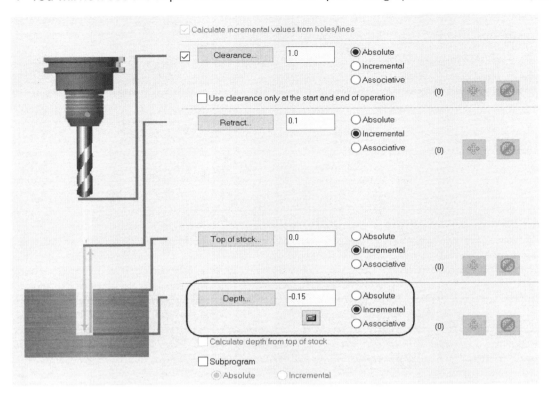

◆ Select the **OK** button to exit the **2D Toolpaths - Drill/Circles Simple drill - no peck** parameters.
◆ **Verify** the toolpaths. See **"Simulate the toolpath in Verify" on page 440** to review this procedure.

STEP 10: DRILL ALL HOLES

In this example, we will drill the 1/4" holes to a specified depth.

Toolpath Preview:

Toolpaths

♦ From the **2D** group, select **Drill** icon.

♦ [Select one or more entities to add or remove from the features list. Select an arc or edge]: Select the center points of the circlesas shown.

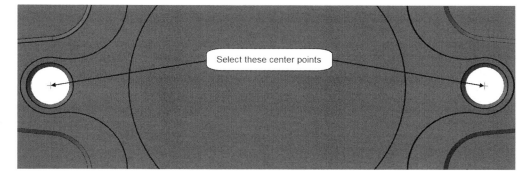

♦ Select the **OK** button to exit the **ToolpathHole Definition** dialog box.

♦ In the **Toolpath Type** page, the **Drill** toolpath will be selected.

Drill

Circle Mill

Point

Helix Bore

Thread Mill

10.1 Select a 1/4" Drill from the Library and set the Tool Parameters

♦ Select **Tool** from the **Tree View list**.

♦ Click on the **Select library tool** button. [Select library tool...]

♦ To be able to see just the drill, select the **Filter** button.

♦ Under **Tool Types**, select the **None** button and then choose the **Drill icon**.
♦ Under **Tool Diameter**, select **Equal** and enter **0.25** as shown.

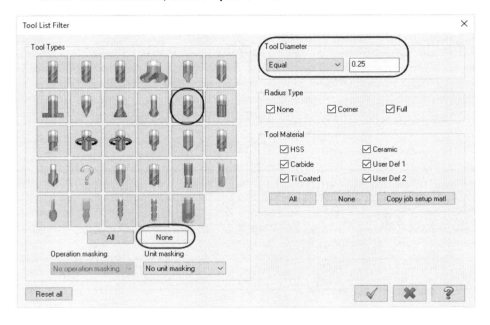

♦ Select the **OK** button to exit the **Tool List Filter** panel.
♦ From that list, select the **1/4" Drill**.

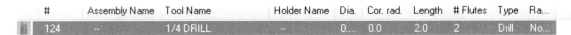

#	Assembly Name	Tool Name	Holder Name	Dia.	Cor. rad.	Length	# Flutes	Type	Ra...
124	--	1/4 DRILL	--	0....	0.0	2.0	2	Drill	No...

♦ Select the tool in the **Tool Selection** page and then choose the **OK** button to exit. [✓]

♦ Make the necessary changes to the **Tool** page as shown.

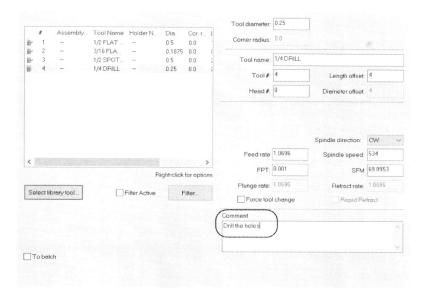

10.2 Set the Cut Parameters

♦ Select **Cut Parameters**, change the drill **Cycle** to **Chip Break** and input a **Peck** value of **0.1** as shown.

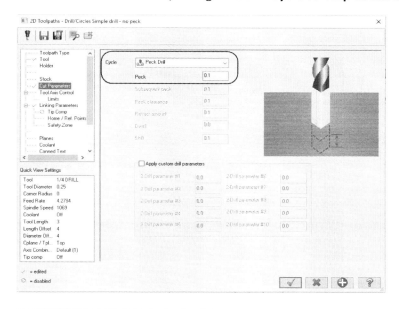

Chip Break drills holes with depths of more than three times the tool diameter. The tool retracts partially out of the drilled hole to break material chips.

Peck sets the depth for the first peck move which plunges in and out of the material to clear and break chips.

10.3 Set the Linking Parameters

♦ Choose **Linking Parameters** and input a **Top of stock** value of **Incremental 0.0** and a **Depth** value of **Incremental -0.75** as shown.

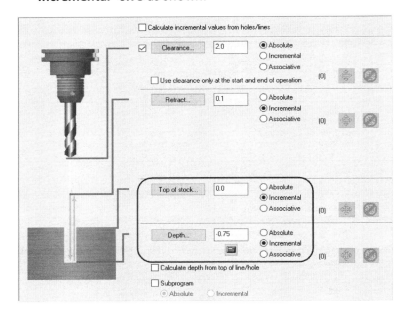

10.4 Set the Tip Compensation page

♦ Select **Tip Comp** and enable it.
♦ Set the **Breakthrough amount** to **0.1** as shown.

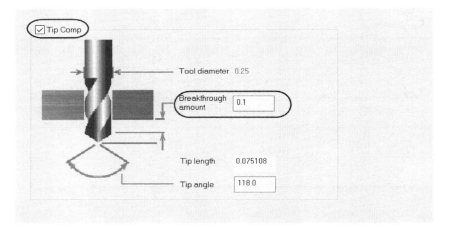

♦ Select the **OK** button to exit the **2D Toolpaths - Drill/Circles Peck drill - no peck** parameters. ✓
♦ **Backplot** and **Verify** your toolpath. See **"Backplot The Toolpaths" on page 439** and **"Simulate the toolpath in Verify" on page 440** to review these procedures.

STEP 11: CHAMFER THE OUTSIDE DIAMETER

Contour - Chamfer toolpath automatically cuts a chamfer around a contour using a chamfer mill. The chamfer size you are machining in this step is 0.1" X 45 degrees.

Toolpath Preview:

Toolpaths

♦ From the **2D** group, select the **Contour** icon.

♦ In the **Chaining** dialog box, make sure that **Wireframe** selection is enabled and leave the defaults as shown. Select the outside circle in **Clockwise** direction as shown.

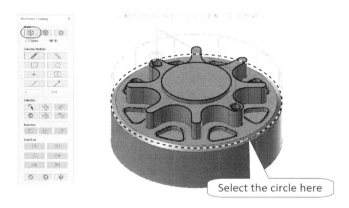

Select the circle here

*Note: Use the **Reverse** button to change the direction of the chain if needed.*

♦ Select the **OK** button to exit the **Chaining** dialog box.

♦ In the **Toolpath Type** page, the **Contour** toolpath will be selected.

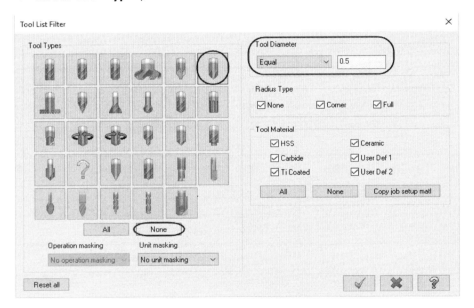

Contour   Pocket   Facing   Slot mill   Model Chamfer

11.1 Select a 1/2" Chamfer Mill from the Library and set the Tool Parameters

♦ Select **Tool** from the **Tree View list**.

♦ Click on the **Select library tool** button.   Select library tool...

♦ To be able to see just the chamfer mill, select the **Filter** button.

Filter...

☑ Filter Active

1 of 427 tools

♦ Under **Tool Types**, select the **None** button and then choose the **Chamfer Mill** icon as shown.

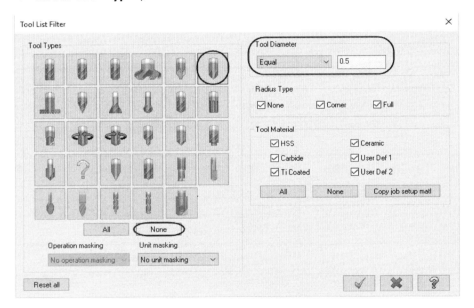

♦ Select the **OK** button to exit the **Tool List Filter** panel.

♦ From that list select the **1/2" Chamfer Mill**.

#	Assembly...	Tool Name	Holder N...	Dia.	Cor. r...	Length	# Flut...	Type	Rad....
319	—	1/2 CHA...	—	0.5-45	0.0	0.75	4	Cha...	None

- ◆ Select the tool in the **Tool Selection** page and then choose the **OK** button to exit. ✓
- ◆ Make all the necessary changes as shown.

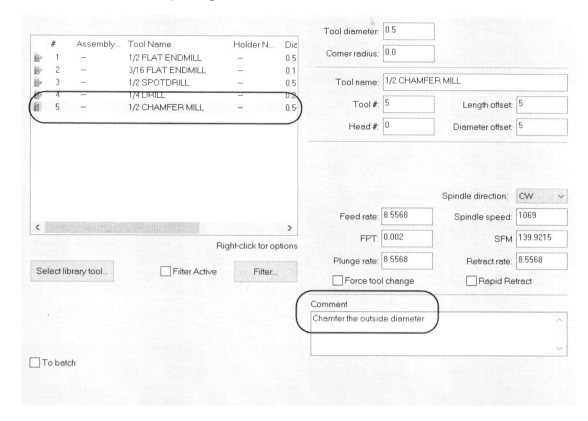

#	Assembly...	Tool Name	Holder N...	Dia
1	–	1/2 FLAT ENDMILL	–	0.5
2	–	3/16 FLAT ENDMILL	–	0.1
3	–	1/2 SPOTDRILL	–	0.5
4	–	1/4 DRILL	–	0.2
5	–	1/2 CHAMFER MILL	–	0.5

Right-click for options

Select library tool...   ☐ Filter Active   Filter...

☐ To batch

Tool diameter: 0.5
Corner radius: 0.0

Tool name: 1/2 CHAMFER MILL

Tool #: 5   Length offset: 5
Head #: 0   Diameter offset: 5

Spindle direction: CW

Feed rate: 8.5568   Spindle speed: 1069
FPT: 0.002   SFM 139.9215
Plunge rate: 8.5568   Retract rate: 8.5568
☐ Force tool change   ☐ Rapid Retract

Comment
Chamfer the outside diameter

11.2 Set the Cut Parameters

- ◆ Select the **Cut Parameters** page and change the **Contour type** to **2D chamfer**.
- ◆ Input a **Chamfer Width** of **0.125** and a **Bottom offset** of **0.02** as shown.

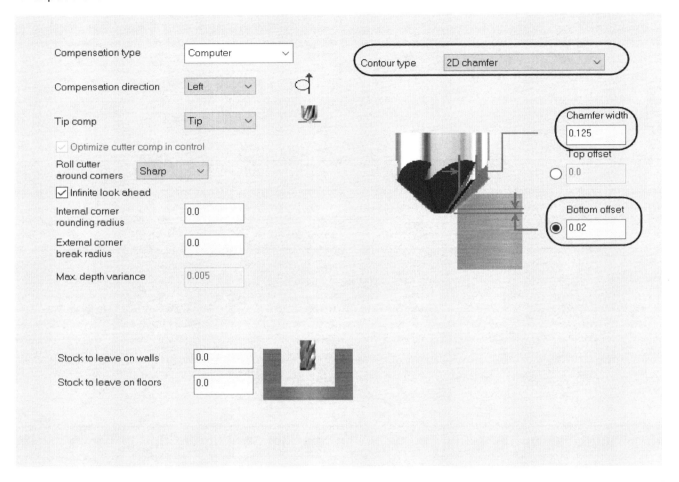

2D chamfer cuts chamfers around a contour.

Chamfer Width sets the chamfer width. Mastercam measures the width from the chained geometry adjusted by the cut depths defined on the linking parameters page.

Bottom offset is an amount to ensure that the tip of the tool clears the bottom of the chamfer.

11.3 Set the Depth Cuts Parameters

♦ From the **Tree View list**, disable the **Depth Cuts** as shown, if needed.

11.4 Set the Lead In/Out Parameters

♦ Choose the option **Lead In/Out**.
♦ Make any other necessary changes as shown.

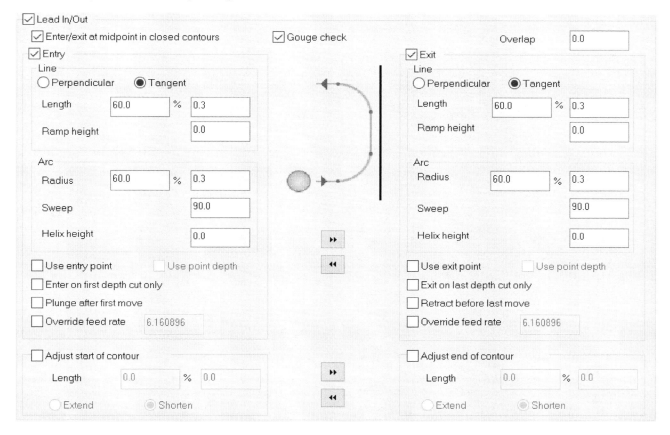

Lead In/Out allows you to create either entry moves, exit moves, or both. **Lead In/Out** moves can include both lines and arcs.

Enter/exit at midpoint in closed contours starts and ends a toolpath with closed chains at the midpoint of the first chained entity.

Gouge check ensures that the entry/exit moves do not gouge the part. If the entry/exit moves cause a gouge, they are removed from the toolpath.

11.5 Set the Linking Parameters

♦ Select the **Linking Parameters** from the **Tree View list**. Set the **Top of stock** to **0.0 Incremental** and the **Depth** to **0.0 Incremental** as shown.

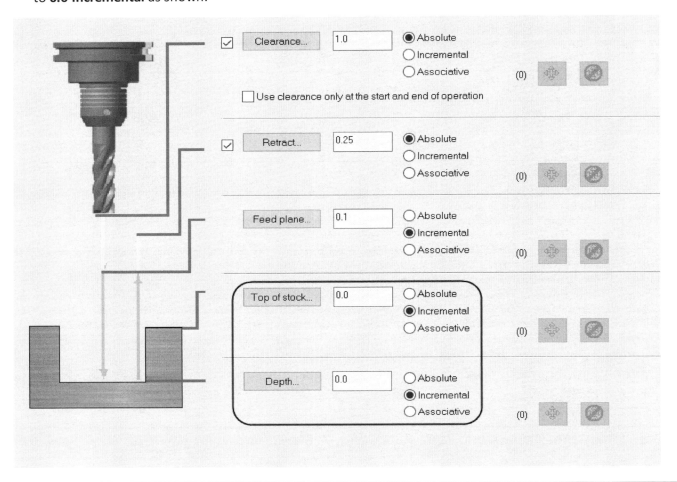

> Note: The depth of the chamfer is based on the width and tip offset set in the **Cut Parameters** page. This is why we set the depth here to zero.

11.6 Preview the Toolpath

◆ To quickly check how the toolpath will be generated, select the **Preview toolpath** icon as shown.

◆ See **"Preview the Toolpath" on page 438** to review the procedure.
◆ The toolpath should look as shown.

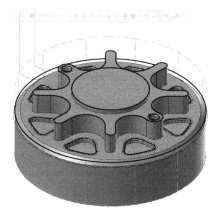

◆ Press **Esc** key to exit the preview.

Note: If the toolpath does not look as shown in the preview, check your parameters again.

◆ Select the **OK** button to exit the toolpath parameters.

11.7 Backplot and Verify

◆ **Verify** the toolpath. See **"Simulate the toolpath in Verify" on page 440** to review the procedures. To see the chamfer better, in the **Visibility** group, disable **Wireframe**.
◆ Your part will appear as shown.

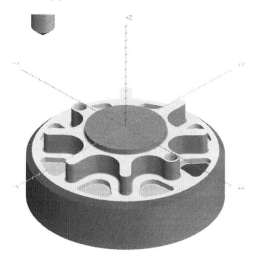

STEP 12: CHAMFER THE POCKETS

Contour - Chamfer toolpath automatically cuts a chamfer around a contour using a chamfer mill. The chamfer size you are machining in this step is 0.025" X 45 degrees.

Toolpath Preview:

Toolpaths

♦ From the **2D** group, select the **Contour** icon.

♦ Right mouse click in the graphic view and change the graphic view to **Top**.

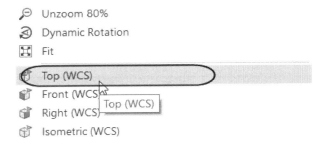

♦ In the **Chaining** dialog box, make sure that **Wireframe** selection is enabled and leave the defaults as shown. Select the pockets in the **Counterclockwise** direction as shown.

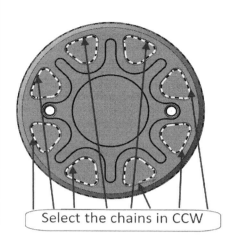

Select the chains in CCW

Note: Use the **Reverse** button to change the direction of the chain if needed.

♦ Select the **OK** button to exit the **Chaining** dialog box.
♦ In the **Toolpath Type** page, the **Contour** toolpath will be selected.

 Contour   Pocket   Facing   Slot mill   Model Chamfer

12.1 Select a 1/4" Chamfer Mill from the Library and set the Tool Parameters

♦ Select **Tool** from the **Tree View list**.

♦ Click on the **Select library tool** button. Select library tool...

♦ To be able to see just the chamfer mill, select the **Filter** button.

♦ Under **Tool Types**, select the **None** button and then choose the **Chamfer Mill** icon as shown.

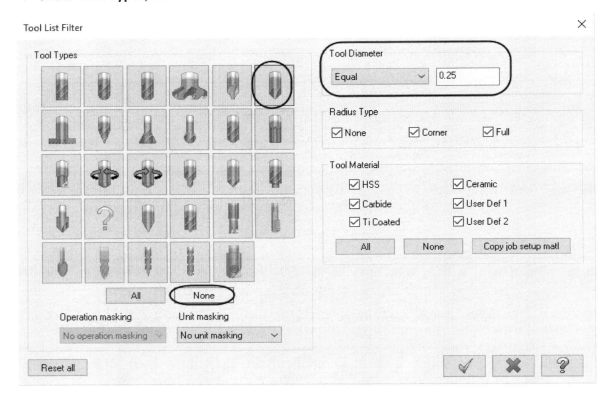

♦ Select the **OK** button to exit the **Tool List Filter** panel. ✓

♦ Select the tool in the **Tool Selection** page and then choose the **OK** button to exit. ✓

#	Assembly...	Tool Name	Holder N...	Dia.	Cor. r...	Length	# Flut...	Type	Rad....
318	—	1/4 CHAMFER MILL	—	0.25-45	0.0	0.5	4	Cha...	None

♦ Make all the necessary changes as shown.

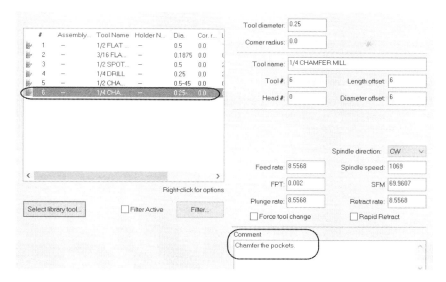

12.2 Set the Cut Parameters

♦ Select the **Cut Parameters** page and change the **Contour type** to **2D chamfer**.
♦ Input a **Width** of **0.025** and a **Bottom offset** of **0.025** as shown.

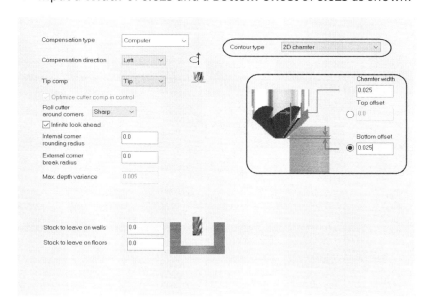

2D chamfer cuts chamfers around a contour.

Width sets the chamfer width. Mastercam measures the width from the chained geometry adjusted by the cut depths defined on the linking parameters page.

Bottom offset is an amount to ensure that the tip of the tool clears the bottom of the chamfer.

12.3 Set the Depth Cuts Parameters

♦ From the **Tree View list**, disable the **Depth Cuts** as shown, if needed.

12.4 Set the Lead In/Out Parameters

♦ Choose the option **Lead In/Out**.
♦ Make any other necessary changes as shown.

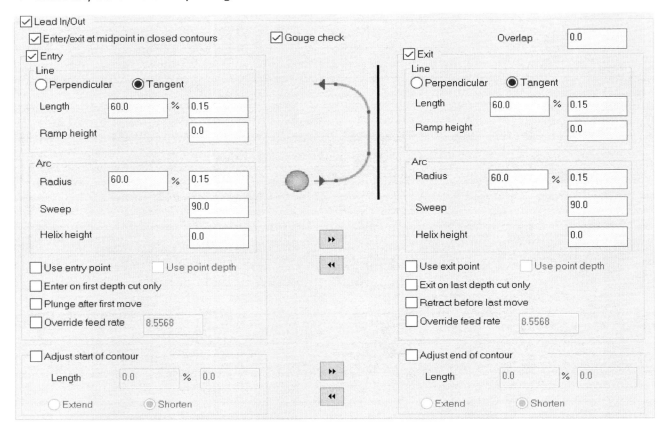

Lead In/Out allows you to create either entry moves, exit moves, or both. Lead In/Out moves can include both lines and arcs.

Enter/exit at midpoint in closed contours starts and ends a toolpath with closed chains at the midpoint of the first chained entity.

Gouge check ensures that the entry/exit moves do not gouge the part. If the entry/exit moves cause a gouge, they are removed from the toolpath.

12.5 Set the Linking Parameters

♦ Select the **Linking Parameters** from the **Tree View list**. Set the **Top of stock** to **0.0 Incremental** and the **Depth** to **0.0 Incremental** as shown.

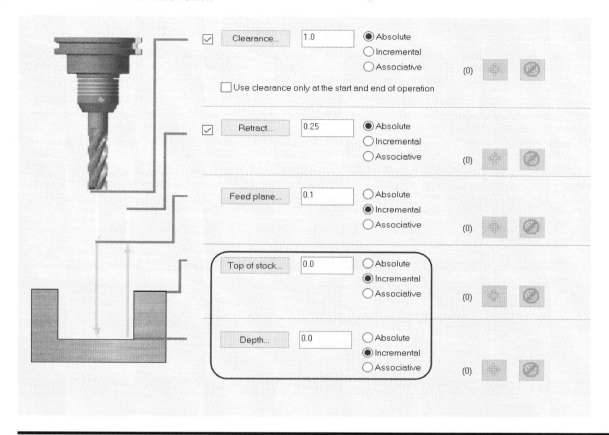

Note: The depth of the chamfer is based on the width and tip offset set in the **Cut Parameters** page. This is why we set the depth here to zero.

12.6 Preview the Toolpath

♦ To quickly check how the toolpath will be generated, select the **Preview toolpath** icon as shown.

♦ See **"Preview the Toolpath" on page 438** to review the procedure.

◆ The toolpath should look as shown.

◆ Press **Esc** key to exit the preview.

Note: If the toolpath does not look as shown in the preview, check your parameters again.

◆ Select the **OK** button to exit the toolpath parameters.

12.7 Backplot and Verify

◆ **Verify** the toolpath. See **"Simulate the toolpath in Verify" on page 440** to review the procedures. To see the chamfer better, in the **Visibility** group, disable **Wireframe**.
◆ Your part will appear as shown.

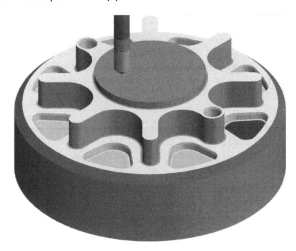

Toolpath Creation - Setup 2

SUGGESTED FIXTURE 2:

Note: The part is now flipped over and we will machine the part from the bottom.

SETUP SHEET 2:

TOOL LIST

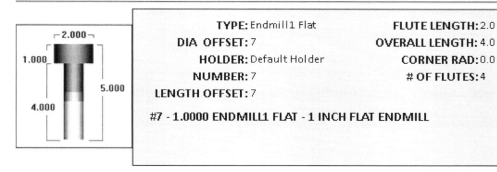

TYPE: Endmill1 Flat	**FLUTE LENGTH:** 2.0
DIA OFFSET: 7	**OVERALL LENGTH:** 4.0
HOLDER: Default Holder	**CORNER RAD:** 0.0
NUMBER: 7	**# OF FLUTES:** 4
LENGTH OFFSET: 7	

#7 - 1.0000 ENDMILL1 FLAT - 1 INCH FLAT ENDMILL

STEP 13: CREATING AND RENAMING TOOLPATH GROUPS

To machine the part in two different setups, we will need to have two separate programs. To be able to post process the operations of each setup separately, we will create them under different toolpath groups with different NC names.

13.1 Rename the current Toolpath Group - 1 and NC file

♦ Click on the **Toolpath Group - 1** to highlight and then click again on it and rename it **"Setup #1**."

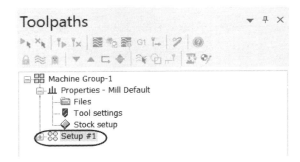

♦ Right mouse click on the toolpath group and select **Edit selected operations** and then select **Change NC file name** as shown.

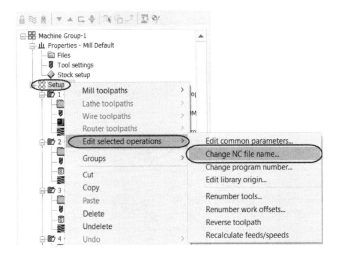

♦ Enter the new NC name: **Setup #1**.

♦ Select the **OK** button to accept the new **NC** name.

13.2 Create a New Toolpath Group

♦ Right mouse click on the **Machine Group-1** and select Groups and then the **New Toolpath group**.

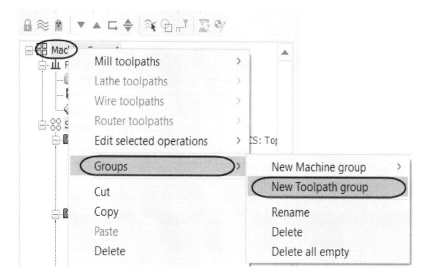

♦ Rename the toolpath group "**Setup #2**" as shown.

♦ Make sure that the **Insert arrow** is below the **Setup #2**, otherwise click on the **Move the insert arrow down an item** icon until the arrow is below the **Setup #2** group.

Note: The next operation is going to be generated at the insert arrow location.

STEP 14: SET THE WCS TO BOTTOM

Work coordinate system (WCS) is the active coordinate system in use by Mastercam at any given time. The **WCS** contains the orientation of the **X, Y, Z** axes plus the location of the zero point (the origin). This tells Mastercam how your part is positioned or oriented in the machine.

Construction plane (Cplane) is the plane in which the geometry is created.

Tool plane (Tplane) is the plane normal to Z or to the vertical tool axis in which the tool moves. When creating a toolpath, both Cplane and Tplane should be set to the same plane. If the **Tplane** is different then the **WCS**, the post will produce a rotary motion code. By setting the **Cplane**, **Tplane** and **WCS** to one plane, no rotary move will be generated in the code, which is what you want when machining parts with multiple setups.

In this step you are going to create a copy of the **Bottom** plane. This allows you to set a new origin for the plane and set Z0 to the top of the flipped part.

♦ Select **Planes** tab located at the bottom left corner.

♦ To create a new plane based on an existing plane, click on the + sign as shown.

♦ To create a copy of the **Bottom** plane, select **Relative to WCS** and select **Bottom** as shown.

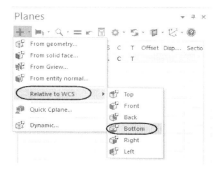

♦ Enter the **Name** and change the **Z Origin** value to **-1.875** and enable **Set As WCS, Tplane** and **Cplane** as shown.

♦ Select the **OK** button to exit the **New Plane** panel.

◆ Right mouse click in the graphics window and select the **Isometric** view.

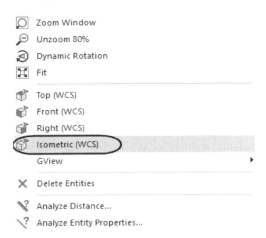

◆ Press **F9** on your keyboard to display the coordinate axes.

Note: The dark blue axes are the original axes and the light blue axes are the current axes.

◆ Your part will appear as shown up to this point.

◆ Press **F9** to remove the axes display.
◆ Press **Alt + S** to unshade the model.
◆ Hide the **Plane** panel and open the **Toolpaths** panel.

STEP 15: 2D HS DYNAMIC MILL

In this step we will utilize the 2D High Speed Dynamic Mill toolpath to remove the material in the middle of the part with the part now flipped over.

Toolpath Preview:

15.1 Chain Selection

Toolpaths

♦ In the **2D** group, select the **Dynamic Mill** icon as shown.

♦ From the **Chain Options,** make sure that the **Stay inside** is enabled and then click on the **Select machining chains** button as shown.

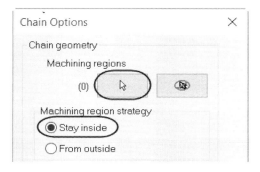

♦ Leave the default settings in the **Chaining** dialog box and pick the inner circle as shown.

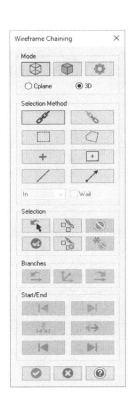

♦ Select the **OK** button to exit the **Chaining** dialog box.

♦ Select the **OK** button to exit the **Chain Options** dialog box.

♦ In the **Toolpath Type** page, the **Dynamic Mill** should already be selected as shown.

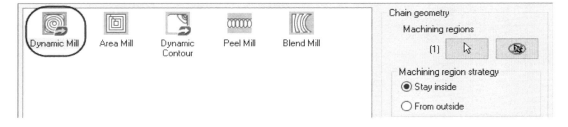

15.2 Preview Chains

♦ Select the **Preview chains** button as shown.

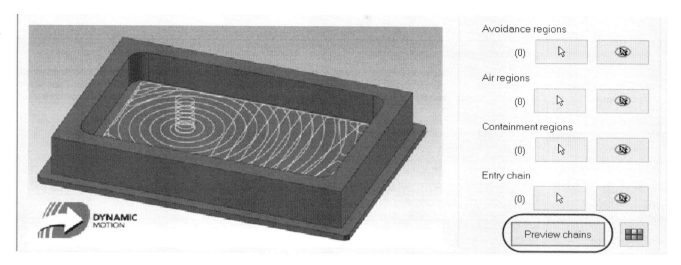

♦ See **"Preview Chains" on page 430** to review the procedure.
♦ The **Preview chains** should look as shown.

♦ Press **Esc** key to return to the toolpath parameters.
♦ Click on the **Preview chains** button again to clear the **Preview chains** display.

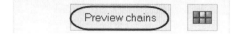

15.3 Select a 1.0" Flat Endmill from the library and set the Tool Parameters

♦ Select **Tool** from the **Tree View list**.

♦ Click on the **Select library tool** button.

♦ Select the **Filter** button as shown.

♦ Select the **None** button and then under **Tool Types** choose the **Flat Endmill** icon.

♦ Under tool diameter, pick **Equal** and input a value of **1.0** as shown.

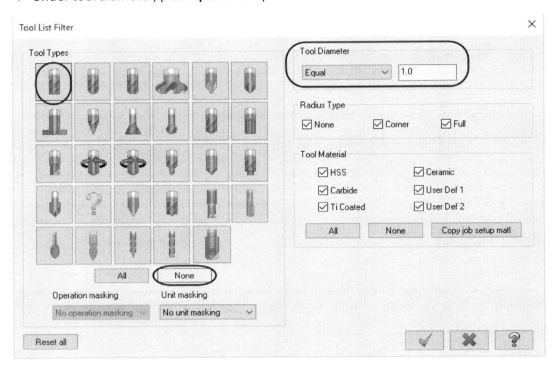

♦ Select the **OK** button to exit the **Tool List Filter**.

♦ In the **Tool Selection** panel you should only see **a 1.0" Flat Endmill**.

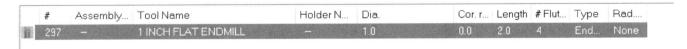

#	Assembly...	Tool Name	Holder N...	Dia.	Cor. r...	Length	# Flut...	Type	Rad....
297	–	1 INCH FLAT ENDMILL	–	1.0	0.0	2.0	4	End...	None

♦ Select the **1.0" Flat Endmill** in the **Tool Selection** page.

♦ Select the **OK** button to exit.

♦ Make all the necessary changes as shown.

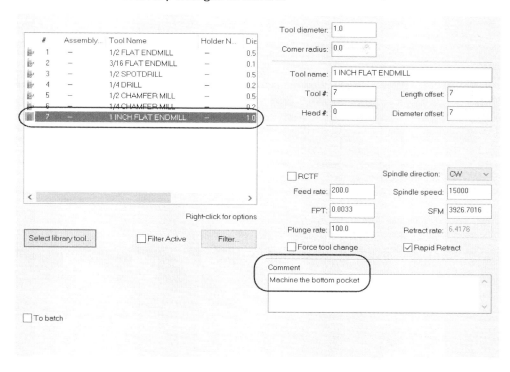

15.4 Set the Cut Parameters

♦ From the **Tree View list**, select **Cut Parameters**. Make sure that the parameters are set as shown.

Note: For more information on these settings, see "Set the Cut Parameters" on page 434.

15.5 Set the Depth cuts parameters

♦ From the **Tree View list**, disable the **Depth Cuts** if needed as shown. Island facing was on in the previous Dynamic Mill toolpath. Ensure it is disabled for this operation.

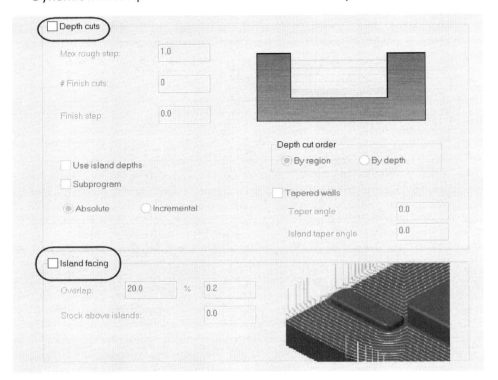

15.6 Set the Entry Motion

- Set the **Entry** method to **Helix** only.
- Set the **Helix radius** to **0.5"** and the rest of the parameters as shown in Figure: 15.6.1.
- Enable **Entry feeds / speeds** and set a **Ramp feed rate** of **10.0** Inches per minute, a **Ramp spindle speed** of **800** RPM and **Dwell before cut** of **3.0** seconds as shown in Figure: 15.6.1.

Figure: 15.6.1

Note: For more information on these settings, see **"Set the Entry Motion" on page 436**.

15.7 Set the Linking Parameters

♦ Select **Linking Parameters** and input the **Depth of -1.0** as shown in Figure: 15.7.1.
♦ Change any other parameters to match what is shown in Figure: 15.7.1 if necessary.

Figure: 15.7.1

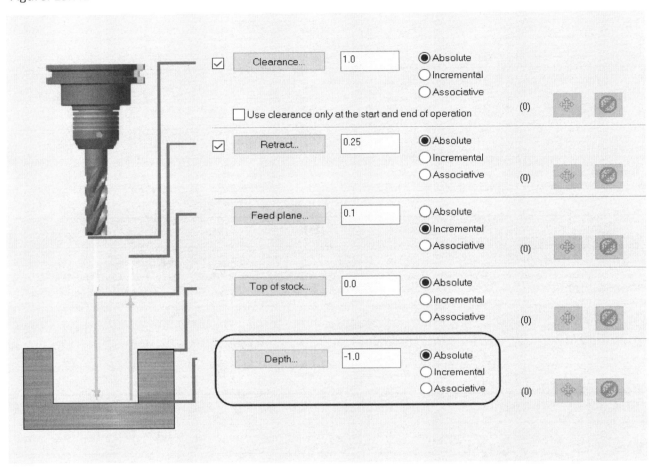

15.8 Preview the Toolpath

♦ To quickly check how the toolpath will be generated, select the **Preview toolpath** icon as shown.

♦ See **"Preview the Toolpath" on page 438** to review the procedure.

♦ The toolpath should look as shown.

♦ Press **Esc** key to exit the preview.

Note: If the toolpath does not look as shown in the preview, check your parameters again.

♦ Select the **OK** button to exit the toolpath parameters.
♦ Select the **Toolpaths** tab in the bottom left of the toolpaths manager.
♦ **Backplot** and **Verify** your toolpath. See **"Backplot The Toolpaths" on page 439** and **"Simulate the toolpath in Verify" on page 440** to review these procedures.

Note: The High Speed toolpaths do not have a finish wall option inside of their parameters. You need to finish the walls using a Contour toolpath.

STEP 16: FINISH THE POCKET WALL USING CONTOUR TOOLPATH

In this step we will utilize the Contour toolpath to finish the middle of the part with the part now flipped over. You will remove the 0.03" stock from the walls.

Toolpath Preview:

16.1 Chain Selection

Toolpaths

♦ From the **2D** group, select the **Contour** icon as shown.

♦ Leave the default settings in the **Chaining** dialog box and pick the inner circle as shown. Ensure the chain is going in a counter clockwise direction.

Select the circle here

♦ Select the **OK** button to exit the **Chaining** dialog box.
♦ In the **Toolpath Type** page, **Contour** will be selected.

16.2 Select the 1.0" Flat Endmill from Tool list window

♦ Select **Tool** from the **Tree View list**.

♦ Select the **1.0" Flat Endmill** in the **Tool list** window. Make all the necessary changes as shown.

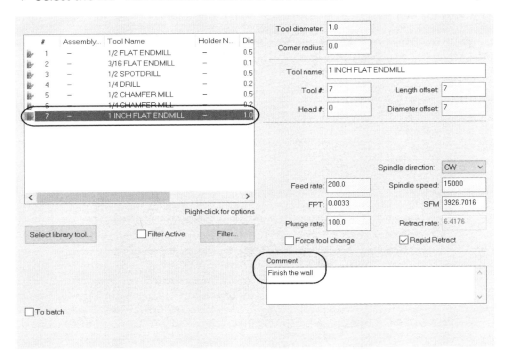

16.3 Set the Cut Parameters

♦ From the **Tree View list**, select **Cut Parameters** and make sure that the parameters are set as shown.

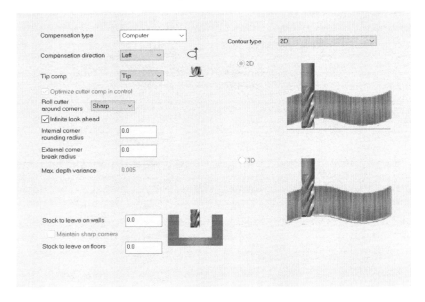

16.4 Set the Depth Cuts Parameters

♦ From the **Tree View list**, disable the **Depth Cuts** if needed as shown.

16.5 Set the Lead In/Out parameters

♦ Make sure that the parameters are set as shown.

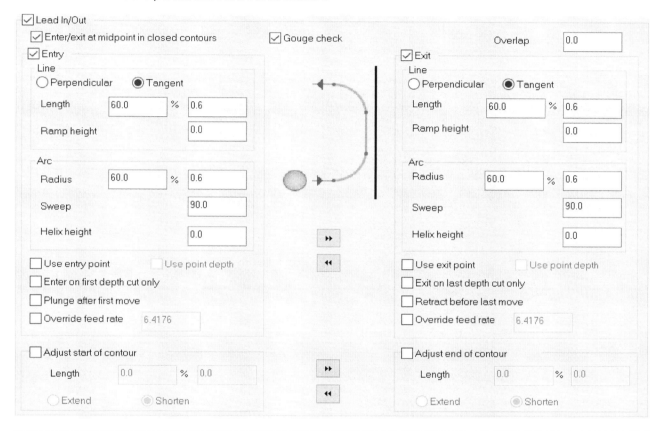

Note: For more information on these settings, see **"Set the Lead In/Out parameters" on page 467**.

16.6 Set the Linking Parameters

◆ Select **Linking Parameters** and input the **Depth** of **-1.0** as shown.

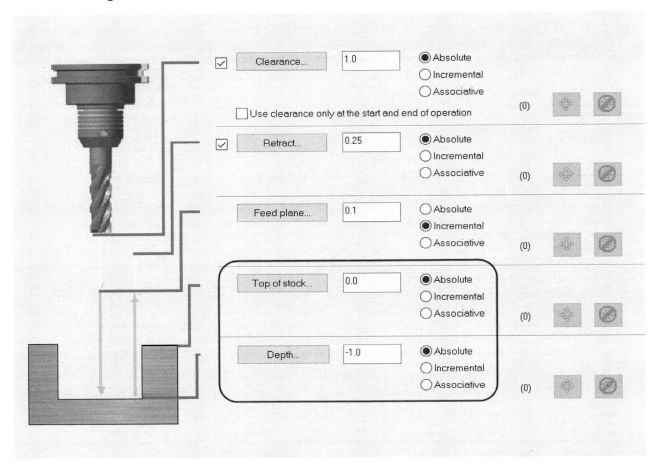

16.7 Preview the Toolpath

◆ To quickly check how the toolpath will be generated, select the **Preview toolpath** icon as shown.

◆ See **"Preview the Toolpath" on page 438** to review the procedure.

♦ The toolpath should look as shown.

♦ Press **Esc** key to exit the preview.

Note: If the toolpath does not look as shown in the preview, check your parameters again.

♦ Select the **OK** button to exit the toolpath parameters.
♦ **Backplot** and **Verify** your toolpath. See"Backplot The Toolpaths" on page 439and **"Simulate the toolpath in Verify" on page 440**on**"Simulate the toolpath in Verify" on page 440** to review these procedures.
♦ The part will appear as shown.

♦ To exit the Mastercam Simulator, click on the **Close** icon.

STEP 17: RENAME THE NC FILE

The **2D High Speed Dynamic mill** operation in Setup #2 kept the NC name from Setup #1. We need to rename this operation so it will create 2 separate programs.

♦ Click on the **Setup #2** group to select only operation **#10** and operation **#11**.
♦ Right click on **Setup #2**, choose the option **Edit selected operations** and then pick **Change NC file name**.

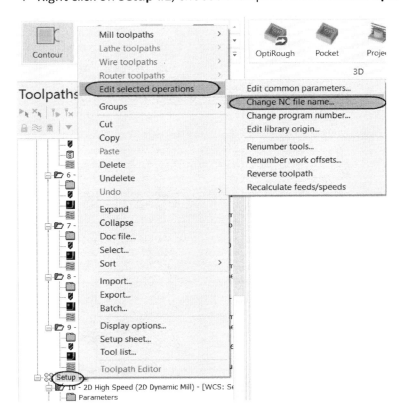

♦ When the **Enter new NC name** panel appears enter **Setup #2**.

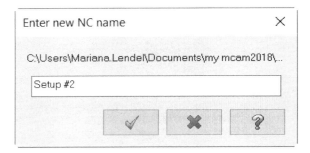

♦ Select the **OK** button to apply the changed **NC** name to operation **10** and **11**.

- As a result, you should see **Setup #2.NC** in the last item of text for operation **#10** and **#11**.

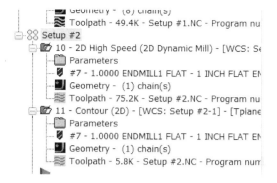

STEP 18: POST THE FILE

- Ensure all operations are selected. If not, use the button **Select all operations** in the **Toolpaths Manager**.
- Select the **Post selected operations** icon from the **Toolpaths Manager** as shown.

- In the **Post processing** window, make necessary changes as shown.

NC file enabled allows you to keep the NC file and to assign the same name as the MCAM file.

Edit enabled allows you to automatically launch the default.

- Select the **OK** button to continue.

- Save Setup #1 NC file.

- Save Setup #2 NC file.

◆ A window with **Mastercam Code Expert** will be launched and the NC program will appear as shown.

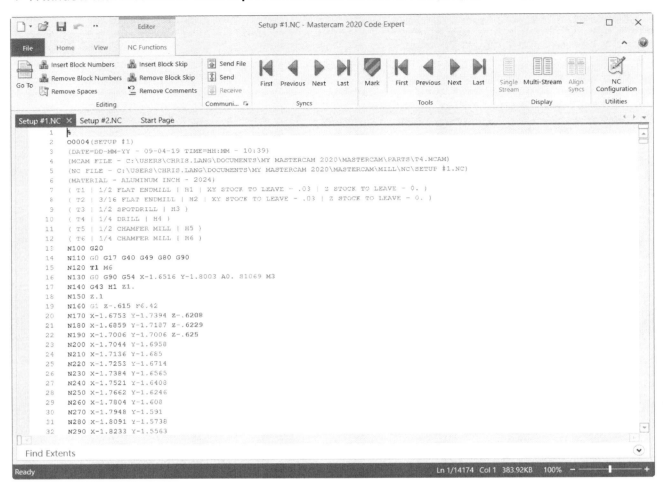

◆ Select the "**X**" box at the upper right corner to exit the editor.

STEP 19: SAVE THE UPDATED MCAM FILE

CREATE THE TOOLPATHS FOR TUTORIAL #4 EXERCISE

Create the Toolpaths for Tutorial #4 Exercise as per the instructions below.

Set the machine properties including the stock setup.

Area Mill the center of the part.

- ◆ Use a **1/2" Flat Endmill**.
- ◆ **Stock to leave on the walls = 0.0**.
- ◆ Disable **Depth Cuts**.
- ◆ Set the **Transitions** to **Entry helix**.
- ◆ Make sure the **Skip pockets smaller than** is set to **110%**.
- ◆ Set the **Depth** according to the drawing.

Dynamic Mill the large pockets.

- ◆ Chain 6 larger pockets and enable **Stay inside**.
- ◆ Use a **3/16" Flat Endmill**.
- ◆ **Stock to leave on the walls = 0.03**.
- ◆ Set the **Entry Motion** to **Profile**.
- ◆ Set the **Top of Stock** and **Depth** according to the drawing.

Area Mill one of the small pockets.

- ◆ Select one of the smaller pockets.
- ◆ Use a **3/16" Flat Endmill**.
- ◆ **Stock to leave on the walls = 0.03**.
- ◆ Enable **Depth Cuts**.
- ◆ Set **Max rough step = 0.05**, **# Finish cuts = 1** and **Finish step = 0.01**.
- ◆ Set the **Transitions** to **Entry helix**.
- ◆ Make sure the **Skip pockets smaller than** is set to **55%**.
- ◆ Set the **Top of Stock** and **Depth** according to the drawing.

Transform Toolpaths.

- ◆ Choose **Rotate** and select **Operation #3**.
- ◆ Select **Coordinate** and **Operation order**.
- ◆ Select the **Rotate** tab.
- ◆ Input the number of steps **# = 5**.
- ◆ **Start angle** = **60.0**.
- ◆ **Rotation angle** = **60.0**.

Use a pocket toolpath to finish the walls.

- ◆ Select the bottom of the pockets using **Solid** selections **Loop** and **Face**.
- ◆ Use the existing **3/16" Flat Endmill**.
- ◆ **Stock to leave on walls/floors** = **0.0**.
- ◆ Disable **Roughing**.
- ◆ Turn **Off** the **Entry motion**.
- ◆ Set **Finishing Spacing** to **0.03**.
- ◆ In the **Lead In/Out** set the **Length** and the **Radius** to **60%** of the tool diameter.
- ◆ **Depth** to **Incremental** and **0.0**.

Spot Drill the holes.

- ◆ Use a **1/2" Spot Drill**.
- ◆ Set the **Cycle** and **Dwell**.
- ◆ Set the **Top of Stock** and **Depth** using the depth calculator.

Drill the holes.

- ◆ Use a **1/4" Drill**.
- ◆ Set the **Cycle** to **Chip Break** and input your increments.
- ◆ Set the **Top of Stock** and **Depth** according to the drawing.

Circle Mill the Center Hole.

(For more instruction on **Circle Mill**, refer to **"Select a 3/4" Flat Endmill from the library and set the Tool parameters"** on page **71**.)

- ◆ Use the **3/16" Flat Endmill**.
- ◆ **Stock to leave** = **0.0**.
- ◆ Disable **Roughing**.
- ◆ Enable **Finishing**.
- ◆ Enable **Finish** and set **1 Finish** at a **Spacing** of **0.03**.
- ◆ Enable **Final depth** and **Keep tool down**.
- ◆ Set the depth to the appropriate depth.

Chamfer the sharp edges using Contour toolpath.

- ◆ Use **Wireframe** mode selection and select all the tops of the pockets and the center hole.
- ◆ Select all the chains in CCW direction.
- ◆ Use a **1/4" Chamfer Mill**.
- ◆ **Contour type** set to **2D Chamfer**; **Width** = **0.025**; **Tip offset** = **0.02**.
- ◆ In the **Lead In/Out** set the **Length** and the **Radius** to **60%** of the tool diameter.
- ◆ **Top of stock and Depth** set to the depth of the top of the pockets.

Flip the part over - Setup #2.

Create a new plane Relative to WCS Bottom, set to appropriate depth and set as WCS

- ◆ Use **Dynamic Mill** and enable **Stay inside** to remove the material starting from the center.
- ◆ Use the **1-1/2" Flat Endmill**.
- ◆ **Stock to leave on walls = 0.03**.
- ◆ Disable **Depth Cuts**.
- ◆ Set the **Entry Motion**.
- ◆ Set the **Depth** according to the drawing.

Use a contour toolpath to finish the walls.

- ◆ Select the inner circle in CCW direction.
- ◆ Use the existing **1-1/2" Flat Endmill**.
- ◆ Set **Contour type** to **2D**.
- ◆ **Stock to leave on walls/floors = 0.0**.
- ◆ Disable **Depth cuts**.
- ◆ In the **Lead In/Out** set the **Length** and the **Radius** to **60%** of the tool diameter.
- ◆ Set **Top of stock** and **Depth** according to the drawing.

- ◆ Your part should appear as shown once complete.

TUTORIAL #4 TOOLPATH CREATION QUIZ

♦ What does the Solid Extrude command do?

♦ What does a "Dwell before cut spindle speed" do?

♦ What does a Transform toolpath operation do?

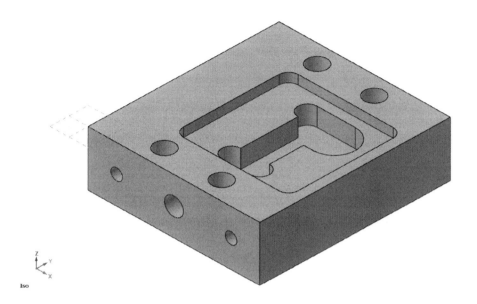

OVERVIEW OF STEPS TAKEN TO CREATE THE PART GEOMETRY:

Import the 2D CAD Model and prepare it to generate Toolpaths from:

♦ The student will open the Solidworks file in Mastercam.

STEP 1: SETTING UP THE GRAPHICAL USER INTERFACE

Please refer to the **Getting Started** section to set up the graphical user interface.

STEP 2: IMPORTING THE SOLIDWORKS FILE GEOMETRY

Mastercam lets you read (import) a variety of CAD file types into the Mastercam database. You can also write (export) Mastercam files to a variety of different file formats.

To import a SolidWorks file in Mastercam, you have to use the Open function and then select SolidWorks files from the File type list.

File

♦ **Open**.
♦ In the file name extension, click on the drop down arrow as shown.

♦ From the file type list, select SOLIDWORKS Files (*.sldprt;*sldasm;*.slddrw) as shown.

```
Mastercam Files (*.mcam)
Mastercam X Files (*.mcx*)
Mastercam Edu X Files (*.emcx*)
All Mastercam Files (*.mc*;*.emc*)
IGES Files (*.igs;*.iges)
AutoCAD Files (*.dwg;*.dxf;*.dwf;*.dwfx)
Parasolid Files (*.x_t;*.x_b;*.xmt_txt)
ProE/Creo Files (*.prt;*.asm;*.prt.*;*.asm.*)
ACIS Kernel SAT Files (*.sat;*.sab)
STEP Files (*.stp;*.step)
VDA Files (*.vda)
Rhino 3D Files (*.3dm)
SOLIDWORKS Files (*.sldprt;*.sldasm;*.slddrw)
Solid Edge Files (*.par;*.psm;*.asm)
Autodesk Inventor Files (*.ipt;*.iam;*.idw)
KeyCreator Files (*.ckd)
Unigraphics/NX Files (*.prt)
ASCII Files (*.txt;*.csv)
StereoLithography Files (*.stl)
Catia Files (*.model;*.exp;*.catpart;*.CATProduct)
SpaceClaim Files (*.scdoc)
Alibre/Geomagic Design Files (*.ad_prt;*.ad_smp)
HPGL Plotter files (*.plt)
PostScript Files (*.eps;*.ai;*.ps)
All Files (*.*)
```

- Find and select **TUTORIAL #5.SLDPRT**. Note that you do not double-click on the file.
- Click on the **Options** button.

- Leave the **Solids** enabled to import the file as a solid and enable **Edge curves** for Mastercam to automatically create curves at the edges of the solid as shown.

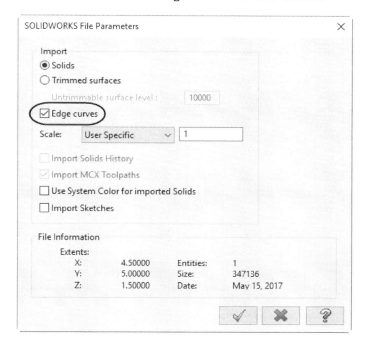

- Select the **OK** button to exit the **SolidWorks File Parameters** dialog box.
- Open the file.
- Press **Alt + S** to see the solid in a shaded mode, if needed.
- Right mouse click in the graphics area and select the graphic view **Isometric** as shown.

- Press **Alt + F1** to fit the geometry to the screen.
- Scroll the mouse wheel to zoom or unzoom as needed.
- The geometry should look as shown.

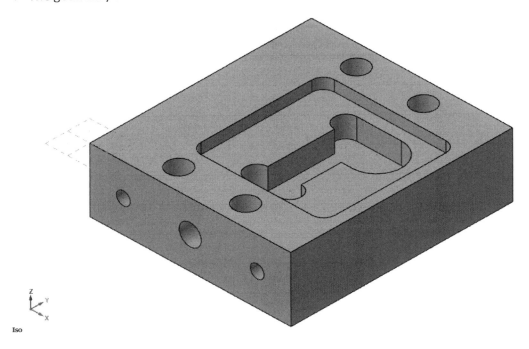

STEP 3: SAVE THE FILE

File

- **Save As.**

- Click on the **Browse** icon as shown.
- Find a location on the computer to save your file.
- File name: "Your Name_5".

TUTORIAL #5 REVIEW EXERCISE

Download the file from www.emastercam.com/trainingfiles.

♦ Save the file to a known location.

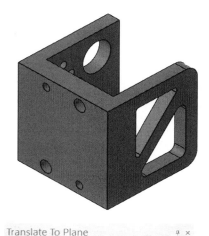

Use File/Open.

♦ Set the extension to SOLIDWORKS (*.sldprt; *.sldasm;*.slddrw).
♦ Select Tutorial #5 Exercise.SLDPRT.
♦ In Options enable **Solids, Edge curves, and Use System Color for imported Solids**.
♦ Open the file.
♦ The geometry should look as shown.

Use Transform/Translate to Plane to rotate the part for machining.

♦ Make a Window around the entire part.
♦ **Transform**.
♦ **Translate to Plane**.
♦ Set the parameters and set the **Source** to **Back** and the **Destination** to **Top** view in the new layout, as shown below.

♦ The part should look as shown.

Save the file.

♦ Save the file as "Your Name_5 Exercise".

TUTORIAL #5 GEOMETRY IMPORT QUIZ

♦ What function does Alt+F1 short cut perform?

♦ What function does Alt+S short cut perform?

♦ What does Transform to Plane command allows you to do?

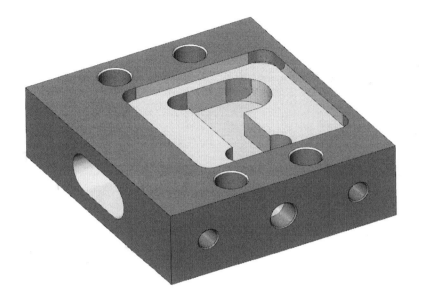

OVERVIEW OF STEPS TAKEN TO CREATE THE FINAL PART:

Create the necessary Toolpaths to machine the part:

♦ The student will set up the stock size and the clamping method. Three setups will be used to machine the part from the top and then from the bottom.
♦ A 2D High Speed Area Mill toolpath will be created to remove the material inside of the step.
♦ Two 2D High Speed Area Mill toolpaths will be created to remove the material inside of the pockets.
♦ Drill toolpaths will be created to machine the three holes in the front view.
♦ A Slot Mill toolpath will be created to remove the material inside of the slot from the left side view.

Backplot and Verify the file:

♦ Backplot will be used to simulate a step-by-step process of the tool's movements.
♦ Verify will be used to watch a tool machine the part out of a solid model.

Post Process the file to generate the G-code:

♦ The student will then post process the file to obtain an NC file containing the necessary code for the machine.

SUGGESTED FIXTURE

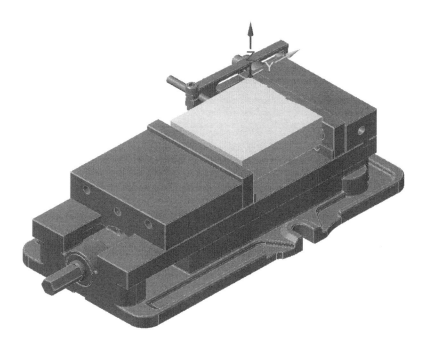

Note: In order to machine this part, we will have 3 setups and output 3 NC files. To view the second setup, see **"toolpath Creation - Setup 2" on page 593** and to view the third setup, see "toolpath Creation - Setup 3" on page 634.

SETUP SHEET

TOOL LIST

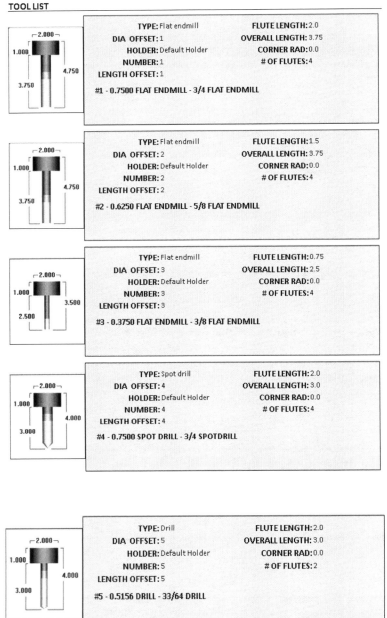

TYPE: Flat endmill	**FLUTE LENGTH:** 2.0
DIA OFFSET: 1	**OVERALL LENGTH:** 3.75
HOLDER: Default Holder	**CORNER RAD:** 0.0
NUMBER: 1	**# OF FLUTES:** 4
LENGTH OFFSET: 1	

#1 - 0.7500 FLAT ENDMILL - 3/4 FLAT ENDMILL

TYPE: Flat endmill	**FLUTE LENGTH:** 1.5
DIA OFFSET: 2	**OVERALL LENGTH:** 3.75
HOLDER: Default Holder	**CORNER RAD:** 0.0
NUMBER: 2	**# OF FLUTES:** 4
LENGTH OFFSET: 2	

#2 - 0.6250 FLAT ENDMILL - 5/8 FLAT ENDMILL

TYPE: Flat endmill	**FLUTE LENGTH:** 0.75
DIA OFFSET: 3	**OVERALL LENGTH:** 2.5
HOLDER: Default Holder	**CORNER RAD:** 0.0
NUMBER: 3	**# OF FLUTES:** 4
LENGTH OFFSET: 3	

#3 - 0.3750 FLAT ENDMILL - 3/8 FLAT ENDMILL

TYPE: Spot drill	**FLUTE LENGTH:** 2.0
DIA OFFSET: 4	**OVERALL LENGTH:** 3.0
HOLDER: Default Holder	**CORNER RAD:** 0.0
NUMBER: 4	**# OF FLUTES:** 4
LENGTH OFFSET: 4	

#4 - 0.7500 SPOT DRILL - 3/4 SPOTDRILL

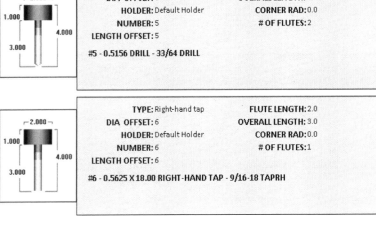

TYPE: Drill	**FLUTE LENGTH:** 2.0
DIA OFFSET: 5	**OVERALL LENGTH:** 3.0
HOLDER: Default Holder	**CORNER RAD:** 0.0
NUMBER: 5	**# OF FLUTES:** 2
LENGTH OFFSET: 5	

#5 - 0.5156 DRILL - 33/64 DRILL

TYPE: Right-hand tap	**FLUTE LENGTH:** 2.0
DIA OFFSET: 6	**OVERALL LENGTH:** 3.0
HOLDER: Default Holder	**CORNER RAD:** 0.0
NUMBER: 6	**# OF FLUTES:** 1
LENGTH OFFSET: 6	

#6 - 0.5625 X 18.00 RIGHT-HAND TAP - 9/16-18 TAPRH

STEP 1: SELECT THE MACHINE AND SET UP THE STOCK

In Mastercam, you select a **Machine Definition** before creating any toolpath. The **Machine Definition** is a model of your machine's capabilities and features. It acts like a template for setting up your machine. The machine definition ties together three main components: the schematic model of your machine's components, the control definition that models your control capabilities, and the post processor that will generate the required machine code (G-code). For a Mill Essentials exercise (2D toolpaths), we need just a basic machine definition.

Note: For the purpose of this tutorial, we will be using the Default milling machine.

1.1 Unhide the Toolpaths manager panel and lock it if needed

♦ From the left side of the graphics window, click on the **Toolpaths** tab as shown.

♦ Pin the **Toolpaths Manager** by clicking on the **Auto Hide** icon as shown.

1.2 Select the machine

*Note: Select the **Mill Default** only if there is no **Machine Group** in the **Toolpaths Manager**.*

Machine

♦ From the **Machine Type** group, select the drop down arrow below **Mill**. Select the **Default**.

*Note: Once you select the **Mill Default**, the **Ribbon bar** changes to reflect the toolpaths that could be used with **Mill Default**.*

♦ Select the plus sign (**+**) in front of **Properties** in the **Toolpaths Manager** to expand the **Toolpaths Group Properties**.

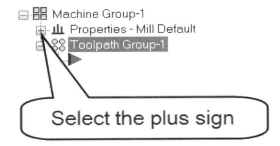

♦ Select **Tool settings** to set the tool parameters.

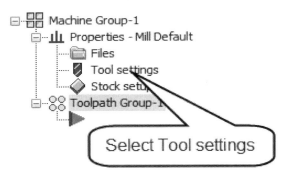

♦ Change the parameters to match the screen shot as shown.

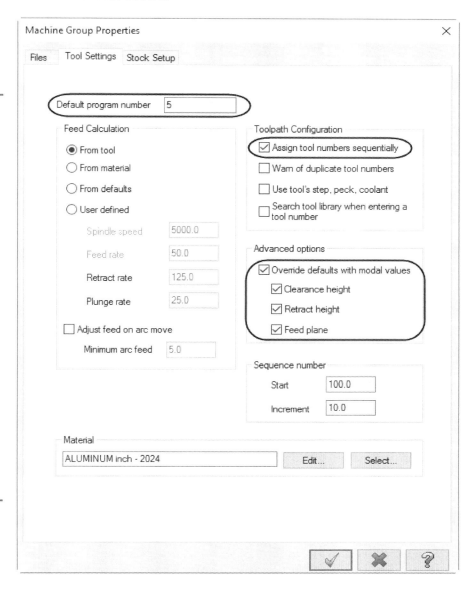

Default program number is used to enter a number if your machine requires a number for a program name.

Assign tool numbers sequentially allows you to overwrite the tool number from the library with the next available tool number. (First operation tool number 1; second operation tool number 2, etc.).

Warn of duplicate tool numbers allows you to get a warning if you enter two tools with the same number.

Override defaults with modal values enables the system to keep the values that you enter.

Feed Calculation set to **From tool** uses feed rate, plunge rate, retract rate, and spindle speed from the tool definition.

- ◆ Select the **Stock Setup** tab to define the stock.
- ◆ Select the **Rectangular** shape option.
- ◆ Select the **All Entities** button to define the stock size as shown.

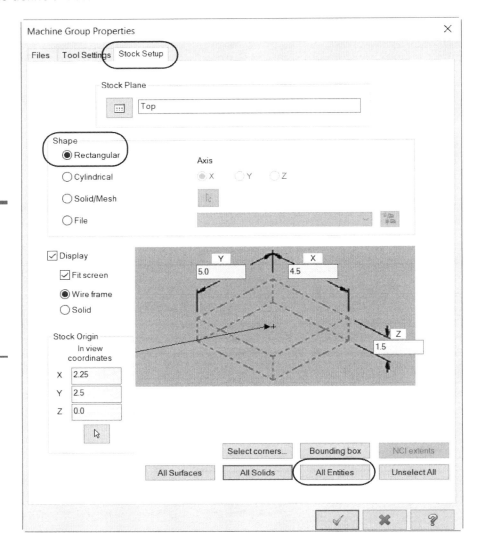

The **Stock Origin** values adjust the positioning of the stock, ensuring that you have an equal amount of extra stock around the finished part.

Display options allow you to set the stock as Wireframe and to fit the stock to the screen. (Fit Screen)

Note: The **stock** model that you create can be displayed with the part geometry when viewing the file or the toolpaths, during backplot, or while verifying toolpaths. In the graphics, the plus sign (+) shows you where the stock origin is. The default position is the middle of the stock.

- ◆ Select the **OK** button to exit **Machine Group Properties**.

◆ The stock model will appear as shown.

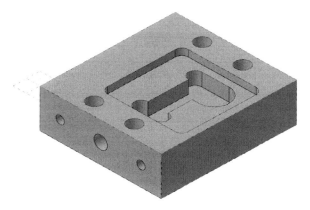

Note: You may not be able to see the stock very clearly due to the fact that the stock is the same size as the part. The stock is not geometry and cannot be selected. There will not be a facing toolpath because the stock is already to size.

STEP 2: 2D HIGH SPEED AREA MILL

2D High Speed Area Mill allows you to machine pockets, material that other toolpaths left behind, and standing bosses or cores. The toolpath depends on the **Machining strategy** that you choose in the **Chain Options**.

If the strategy chosen is **From outside**, the toolpath starts at the outmost chain and works its way in taking on the final shape of the part as it approaches the final pass. You can also machine pockets, in which case the strategy selected is **Start inside**, which keeps the tool inside the machining region's helical entries and tangent stepovers create efficient motion for your machine. **Cut parameters** let you control smoothing to create the best toolpath, avoiding sharp corners or direction changes.

Toolpath Preview:

2.1 Chain selection

♦ From the **2D** group, click on the **Expand gallery** arrow as shown.

♦ Select the **Area Mill** icon as shown.

♦ From the **Chain Options** dialog box, click on the **Select machining chains** button.

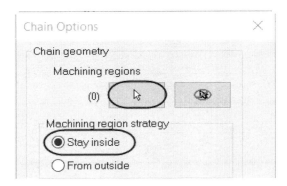

- ◆ When the **Chaining** dialog box appears, select **C-plane** as shown in Figure: 2.1.1.
- ◆ Leave the **Chaining method** set to **Chain** as shown in Figure: 2.1.1.

Figure: 2.1.1

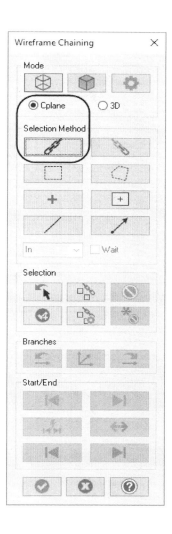

C-plane chains only the entities that are parallel to the current construction plane and at the same Z depth as the first entity you chain.

♦ [Select 2D HST machining chain 1]: Select the bottom of the pocket as shown.

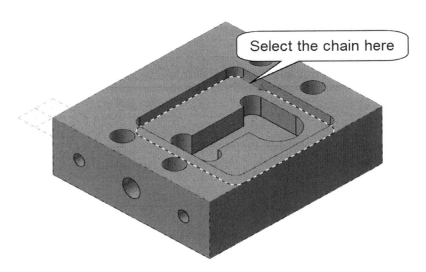

♦ Select the **OK** button to exit the **Chaining** dialog box.

♦ Now the **Chain Options** dialog box should look as shown.

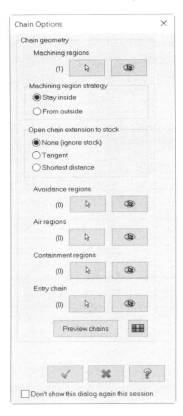

♦ Select the **OK** button to exit the **Chain Options**.

2.2 Preview Chains

The **Preview Chains** function is intended to give the user a quick visual representation of how Mastercam sees the various pieces of geometry that have been selected, how they interact with one another and a general overview of how the toolpath will be calculated with the selections presently made.

♦ Click on the **Color** icon to see the legend for **Preview chains** as shown.

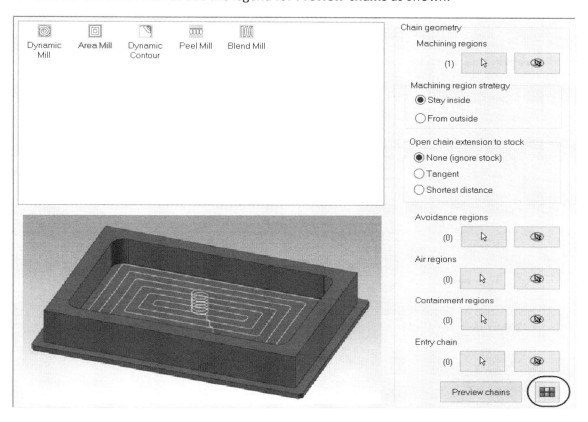

♦ The **Preview Chains Colors** dialog box should look as shown.

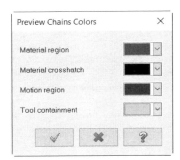

The **Material region** and **Material crosshatch** are the two colors that are used to define the material to be cut. The default colors are red for the background and black for the crosshatch.

The **Motion region** displays the area that Mastercam is making available to the toolpath for motion if it needs it. The color to represent it is dark blue. The primary reason for the display of the entire available (but not necessarily used) **Motion region** is to help the user visualize how the tool may move near or interact with any adjacent geometry.

The **Tool containment** is what you have selected as the containment region in the chain geometry. If you have not selected a containment region, it will default to the outside of the **Motion region** since that is currently the default area the toolpath is being contained to. The color used to represent the **Tool containment** is yellow.

♦ Select the **OK** button to exit **Preview Chains Colors**.

♦ Select the **Preview chains** button as shown.

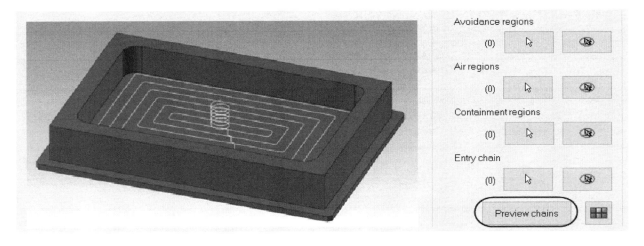

♦ Select the **Hide dialog** button to see the preview in the graphics window.

♦ The **Preview chains** should look as shown.

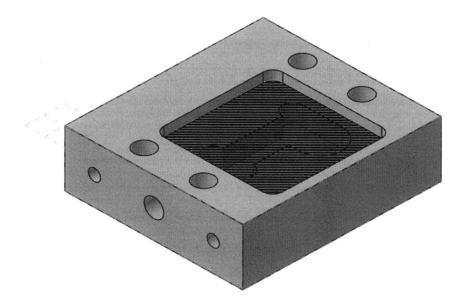

♦ Press **Esc** key to return to the toolpath parameters.
♦ Click on the **Preview chains** button again to clear the **Preview chains** display.

♦ In the **Toolpath Type** page, make sure that **Area Mill** is selected.

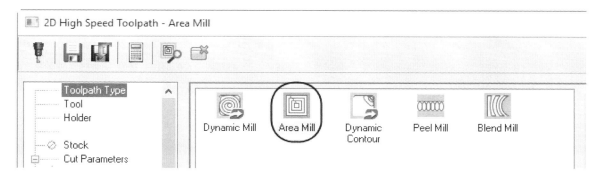

2.3 Select a 3/4" Flat Endmill from the library and set the Tool Parameters

- From the **Tree View list**, select **Tool**.
- Click on the **Select library tool** button.
- Select the **Filter** button.

- Select the **None** button and then under **Tool Types**, choose the **Flat Endmill** icon Figure: 2.3.1.
- Under **Tool Diameter**, pick **Equal** and input a value of **0.75** as shown Figure: 2.3.1.

Figure: 2.3.1

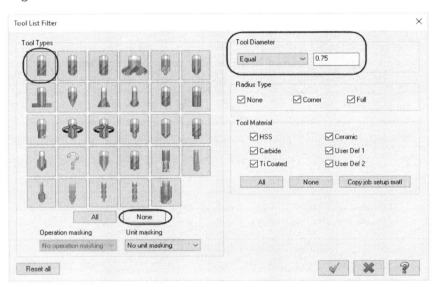

- Select the **OK** button to exit the **Tool List Filter**.
- In the **Tool Selection** panel you should only see a **3/4" Flat Endmill**.

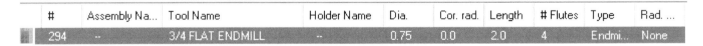

#	Assembly Na...	Tool Name	Holder Name	Dia.	Cor. rad.	Length	# Flutes	Type	Rad. ...
294	--	3/4 FLAT ENDMILL	--	0.75	0.0	2.0	4	Endmi...	None

- Select the **3/4" Flat Endmill** in the **Tool Selection** page and then select the **OK** button to exit.

◆ Make all the necessary changes as shown.

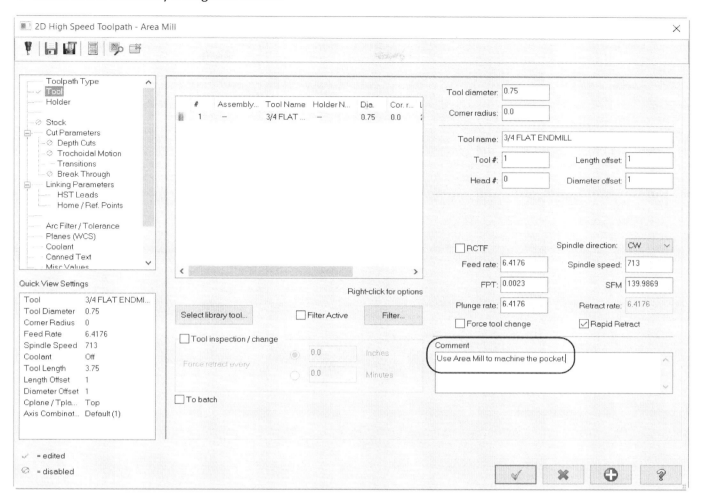

2.4 Set the Cut Parameters

♦ From the **Tree View list**, select **Cut Parameters**.

♦ Change the settings as shown.

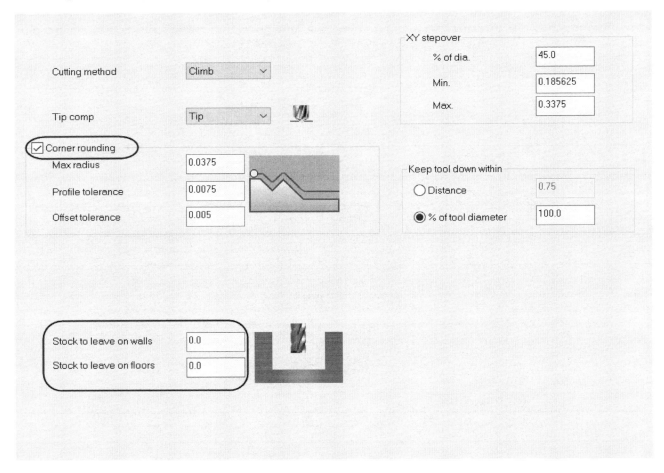

Corner rounding replaces sharp corners with arcs for faster and smoother transitions in tool direction. For more information on the parameters select the **Help** button ![help button]. Once the **Mastercam Help** dialog box appears, click on the **Field definitions** tab to view more details.

Max radius inputs the radius of the largest arc that you will allow Mastercam to insert to replace a corner. Larger arcs will result in a smoother toolpath but with a greater deviation from the part corner.

Profile tolerance represents the maximum distance that the outermost profile of a toolpath with corner rounding can deviate from the original toolpath.

Offset tolerance represents the maximum distance that a profile of a toolpath created with corner rounding can deviate from the original toolpath.

2.5 Set the Depth Cuts Parameters

♦ From the **Tree View list**, select **Depth Cuts** and make sure it is disabled as shown.

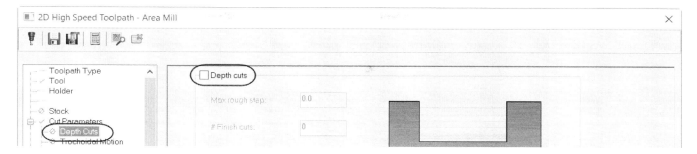

2.6 Set the Transitions

♦ From the **Tree View list**, select **Transitions**. Enable **Entry helix**, set the **Entry helix** to **0.375** and ensure the parameters are the same as shown.

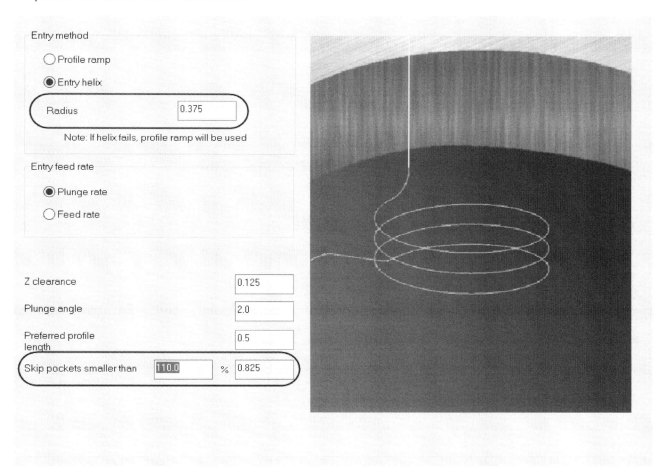

2.7 Set the Linking Parameters

♦ Select **Linking Parameters** and enable **Clearance**, change the **Clearance** value to **1.0**.
♦ You will notice the depth has been input as shown based on the geometry we selected.

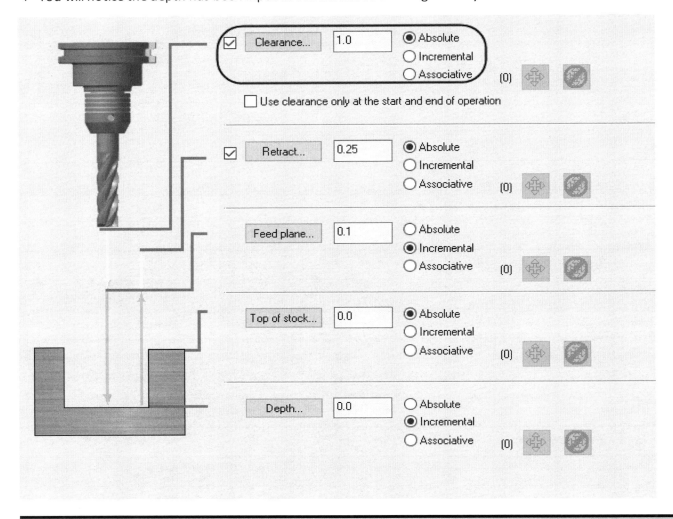

Note: The **Depth** set to **Incremental** and **0.0** is relative to the location of the chained geometry which was selected at the bottom of the pocket.

2.8 Preview the Toolpath

◆ To quickly check how the toolpath will be generated, select the **Preview toolpath** icon as shown.

◆ To hide the dialog box, click on the **Hide dialog** icon as shown.

◆ To see the part from an **Isometric** view, right mouse click in the graphics window and select **Isometric** as shown.

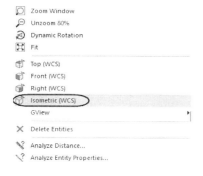

◆ The toolpath should look as shown.

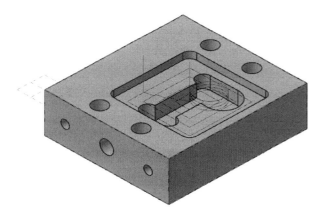

◆ Press **Esc** key to exit the preview.

Note: If the toolpath does not look as shown in the preview, check your parameters again.

◆ Select the **OK** button to generate the toolpath.

STEP 3: BACKPLOT THE TOOLPATHS

Backplotting shows the path the tools take to cut the part. This display lets you spot errors in the program before you machine the part. As you backplot toolpaths, Mastercam displays additional information such as the X, Y, and Z coordinates, the path length, the minimum and maximum coordinates and the cycle time.

♦ Make sure that the toolpaths are selected (signified by the green check mark on the folder icon). If the operation is not selected, choose the **Select all operations** icon.

♦ Select the **Backplot selected operations** button.

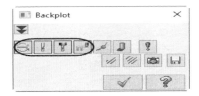

♦ In the **Backplot** dialog box, enable **Display with color codes, Display tool** and **Display rapid moves** icons as shown.

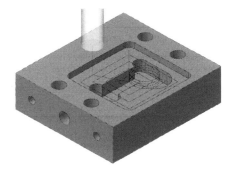

♦ Select the **Play** button to run **Backplot.**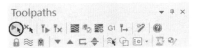

♦ After **Backplot** is completed, the toolpath should look as shown.

♦ Select the **OK** button to exit **Backplot.**

STEP 4: SIMULATE THE TOOLPATH IN VERIFY

♦ From the **Toolpaths Manager**, select **Verify selected operations** icon as shown.

Note: Mastercam launches a new window that allows you to check the part using **Verify**.

♦ Disable **Workpiece** in the **Visibility** group as shown.

♦ Select the **Play** button to run **Verify**.

♦ The part should appear as shown.

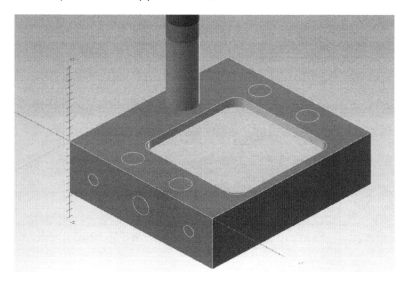

♦ To go back to the Mastercam window, minimize the **Mastercam Simulator** window as shown.

STEP 5: 2D HIGH SPEED AREA MILL

In this step we will learn how to copy a toolpath and reselect geometry. The main advantage of copying a toolpath is the parameters for the 1st toolpath remain intact for the second toolpath.

Toolpath Preview:

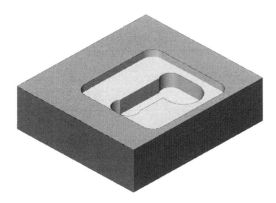

♦ To remove the toolpath display, from the **Toolpaths Manager**, click on the **Toggle display on selected operations** or press **Alt + T**.

5.1 Copy the Previous Toolpath

♦ Select Operation #1.

♦ Right click and hold the right mouse button down and drag the operation to a point below it as shown.

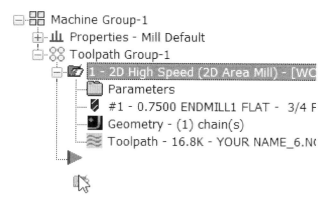

♦ Release the right mouse button and select the option **Copy After**.

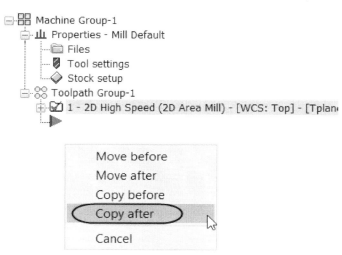

♦ Select the **Move insert arrow down one item** button to move the insert arrow down.

♦ The **Insert Arrow** should appear at the bottom of the list as shown.

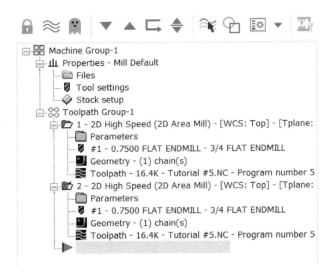

Insert Arrow controls where the new operation will be inserted.

5.2 Re-Chain the Geometry

♦ In Operation #2, select the **Geometry** as shown.

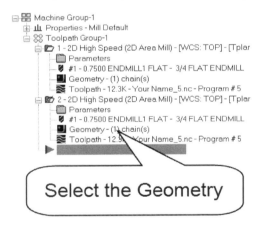

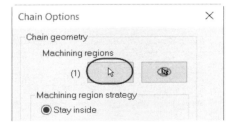

Select the Geometry

♦ Click on the **Select machining chains** button in the **Chain Options** dialog box as shown.

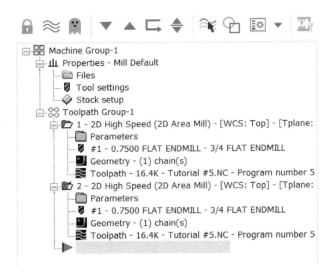

♦ When the **Chain Manager** appears, select **Chain 1**.
♦ Right click and select the option **Rechain all** as shown.

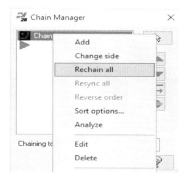

♦ When the Chaining dialog box appears, select **C-plane**.

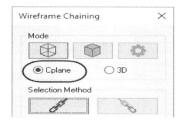

♦ [Add chain 1]: Select the bottom of the pocket as shown.

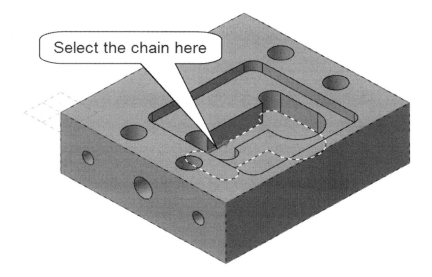

Select the chain here

♦ Once the geometry has been selected, choose the **OK** button to exit the **Chaining** dialog box.
♦ Select the **OK** button to exit the **Chain Manager** dialog box.
♦ Select the **OK** button to exit the **Chain Options** dialog box.

5.3 Preview Chains

♦ Choose **Parameters** under Operation #2.

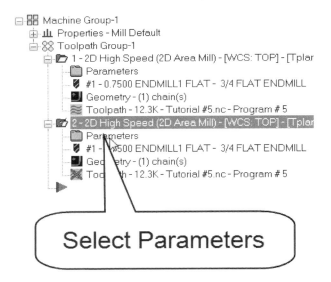

♦ In the **Toolpath Type** page, select the **Preview chains** button as shown.

♦ See **"Preview Chains" on page 541** to review the procedure.
♦ The **Preview chains** should look as shown.

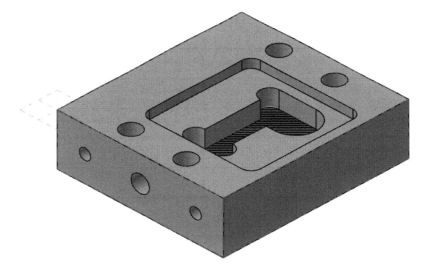

♦ Press **Esc** key to return to the toolpath parameters.

♦ Click on the **Preview chains** button again to clear the **Preview chains** display.

5.4 Select a 5/8" Flat Endmill from the library and set the Tool Parameters

♦ From the **Tree View list**, select **Tool**.

♦ Click on the **Select library tool** button.

♦ Select the **Filter** button.

♦ Select the **None** button and then under **Tool Types**, choose the **Flat Endmill** icon.

♦ Under **Tool Diameter**, pick **Equal** and input a value of **0.625** as shown.

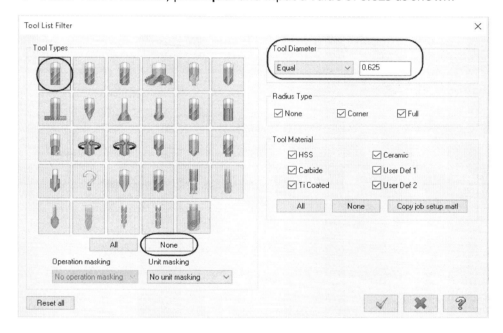

♦ Select the **OK** button to exit the **Tool List Filter**.

♦ In the **Tool Selection** panel you should only see a **5/8" Flat Endmill**.

#	Assembly Name	Tool Name	Holder Name	Dia.	Cor. rad.	Length	# Flutes	Type	Ra...
292	—	5/8 FLAT ...	—	0....	0.0	1.5	4	En...	No...

♦ Select the **5/8" Flat Endmill** in the **Tool Selection** page and then select the **OK** button to exit.

♦ Make all the necessary changes as shown.

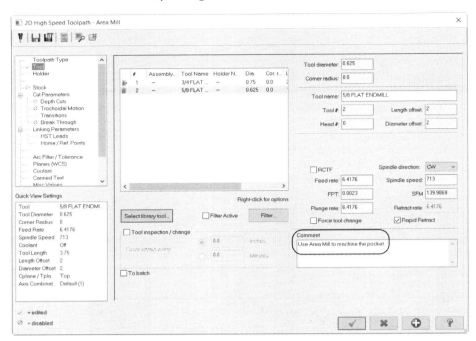

Note: Since this toolpath has been copied, all the parameters remain the same. Therefore the only parameters shown are the ones we will be changing.

5.5 Set the Depth Cuts parameters

♦ From the **Tree View list**, select the **Depth Cuts** and enable **Depth cuts**.
♦ Input a **Max rough step** of **0.25** as shown.

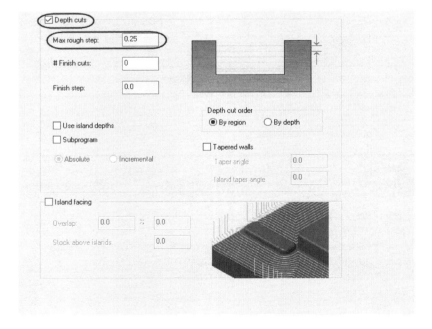

5.6 Set the Transitions

♦ From the **Tree View list**, select **Transitions**. Enable **Entry helix** and enter a Radius of **0.125** as shown.

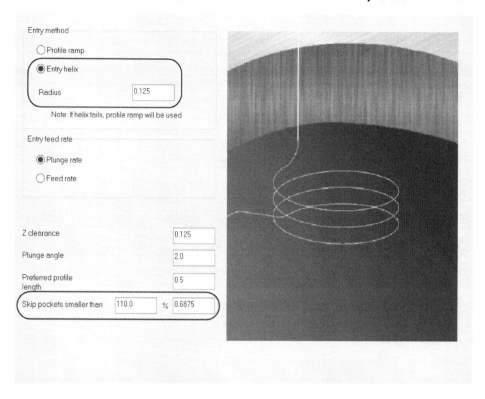

Profile ramp creates a ramp motion to descend the tool.

Preferred profile length enters a minimum size for the profile in order for a ramp to be created.

5.7 Set the Linking Parameters

♦ Select **Linking Parameters** from the Tree View list.
♦ Set the **Top of Stock** and the **Depth** to **Absolute**.
♦ Select the **Top of stock** button (this will return you to the graphics screen).

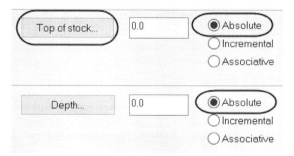

♦ Select the line endpoint as shown.

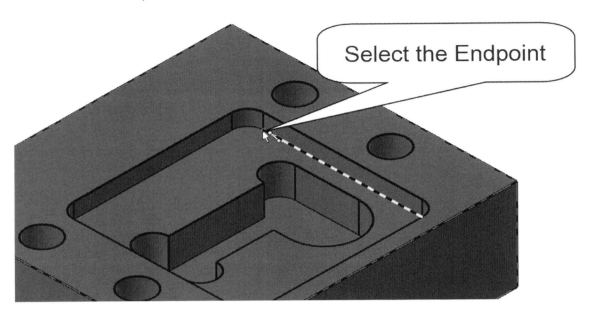

♦ Choose the **Depth** button (this will return you to the graphics screen).
♦ Select the line endpoint as shown.

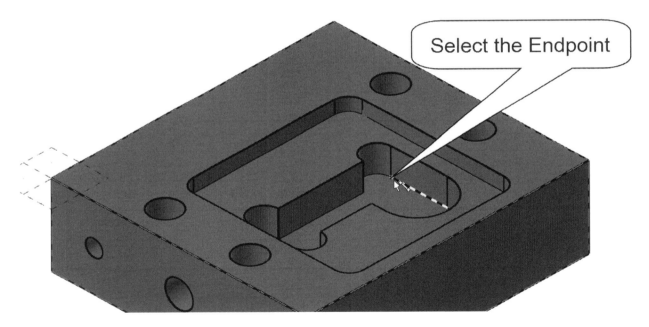

♦ **Top of stock** will be set to **-0.25** and the **Depth** set to **-0.75** as shown.

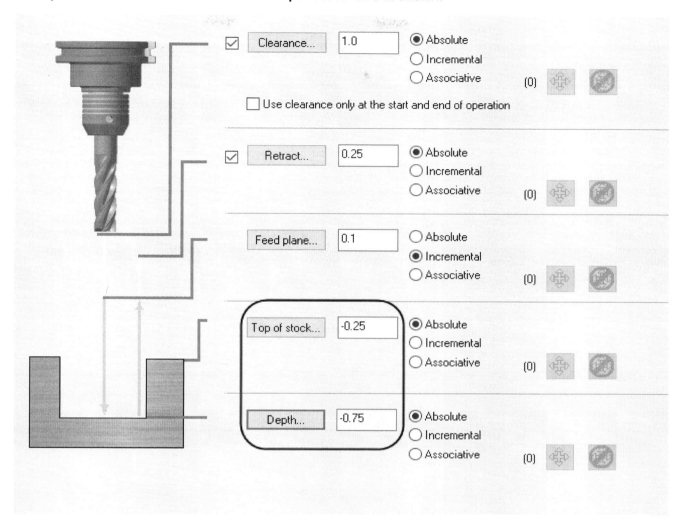

5.8 Preview the Toolpath

♦ To quickly check how the toolpath will be generated, select the **Preview toolpath** icon as shown.

♦ See **"Preview the Toolpath" on page 549** to review the procedure.
♦ The toolpath should look as shown.

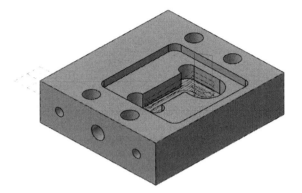

♦ Press **Esc** key to exit the preview.

Note: If the toolpath does not look as shown in the preview, check your parameters again.

♦ Select the **OK** button to generate the **Area Mill** toolpath.
♦ Choose to **Regenerate all dirty operations**.

5.9 Backplot the toolpath

♦ Once the operation has been regenerated, **Backplot** the toolpath. See **"Backplot The Toolpaths" on page 550** to review these procedures.

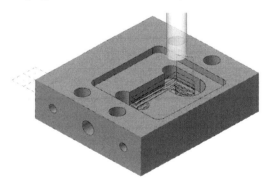

♦ Select the **OK** button to exit **Backplot**.

5.10 Verify the toolpaths

♦ To **Verify** the toolpaths, make sure all the operations are selected. To select all operations, click on the **Select all operations** icon.

♦ See **"Simulate the toolpath in Verify" on page 551** to review these procedures.

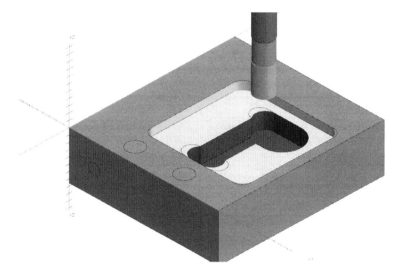

♦ To go back to the Mastercam window, minimize the **Mastercam Simulator** window as shown.

STEP 6: REMACHINE THE REMAINING MATERIAL USING AREA MILL

High Speed Area Mill toolpath with **Rest Material** options enabled targets material left behind by the previous toolpaths.

Toolpath Preview:

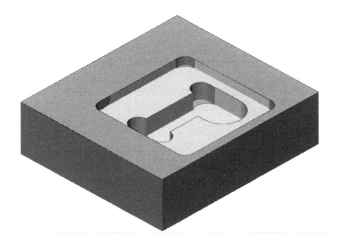

6.1 Copy the previous Toolpaths

♦ Select the **Select all operations** button.

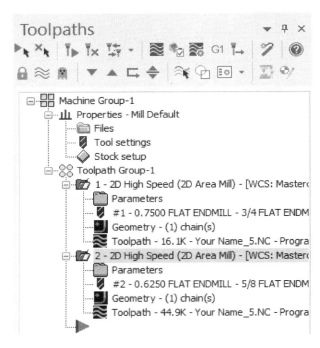

Note: Both toolpaths should be selected as shown.

♦ Right click and hold the right mouse button down and drag the operation to a point below it as shown.

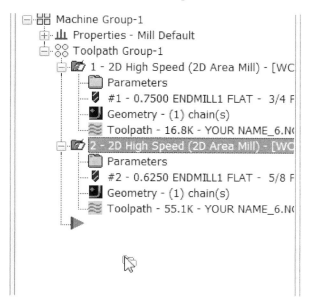

♦ Release the right mouse button and select the option **Copy after** as shown.

♦ Select the **Move insert arrow down one item** button twice to move the insert arrow down as shown.

◆ Choose **Parameters** under Operation #3.

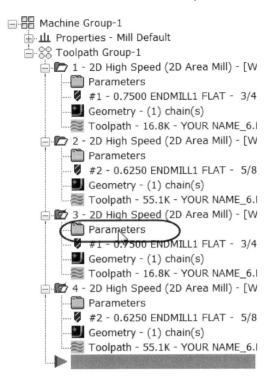

6.2 Preview Chains

◆ In the **Toolpath Type** page, select the **Preview chains** button as shown.

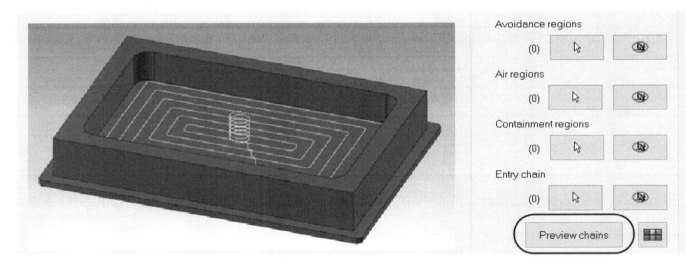

◆ See **"Preview Chains" on page 541** to review the procedure.

◆ The **Preview chains** should look as shown.

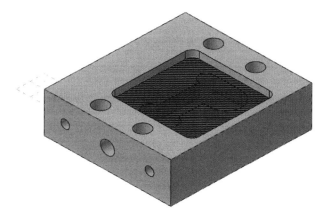

◆ Press **Esc** key to return to the toolpath parameters.

◆ Click on the **Preview chains** button again to clear the **Preview chains** display.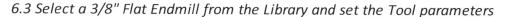

6.3 Select a 3/8" Flat Endmill from the Library and set the Tool parameters

◆ From the **Tree View list**, select **Tool**.

◆ Click on the **Select library tool** button.

◆ Select the **Filter** button.

◆ Select the **None** button and then under **Tool Types**, choose the **Flat Endmill** icon.

◆ Under **Tool Diameter**, pick **Equal** and input a value of **0.375** as shown.

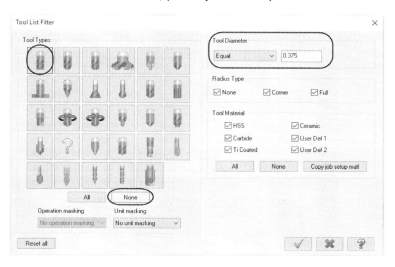

◆ Select the **OK** button to exit the **Tool List Filter**.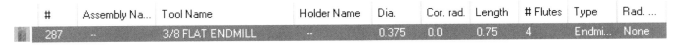
◆ In the **Tool Selection** panel you should only see a **3/8" Flat Endmill**.

#	Assembly Na...	Tool Name	Holder Name	Dia.	Cor. rad.	Length	# Flutes	Type	Rad. ...
287	--	3/8 FLAT ENDMILL	--	0.375	0.0	0.75	4	Endmi...	None

◆ Select the **3/8" Flat Endmill** in the **Tool Selection** page and then select the **OK** button to exit.

◆ Make all the necessary changes as shown.

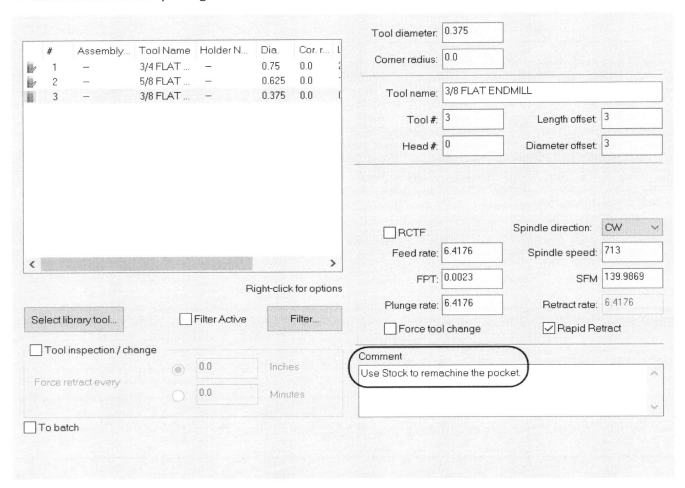

6.4 Set the Rest Material

♦ From the **Tree View list**, select **Stock**. Enable **Rest material** and set the parameters the same as shown.

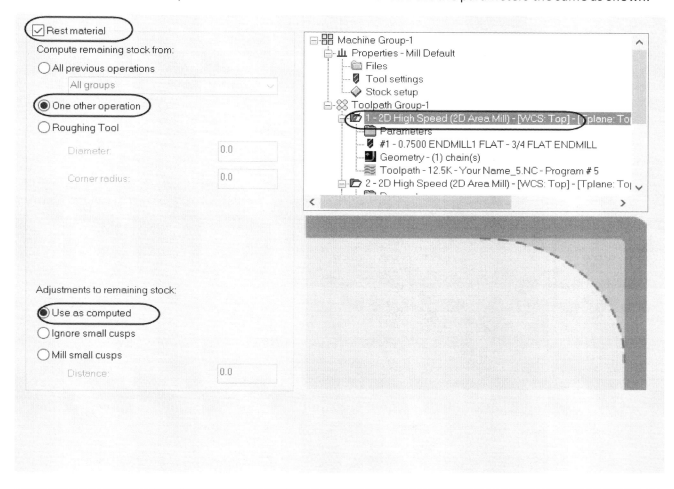

The **Rest material** page allows you to set how Mastercam calculates the remaining stock.

One other operation calculates the remaining stock from one source operation.

6.5 Preview the Toolpath

♦ To quickly check how the toolpath will be generated, select the **Preview toolpath** icon as shown.

♦ See **"Preview the Toolpath" on page 549** to review the procedure.

♦ The toolpath should look as shown.

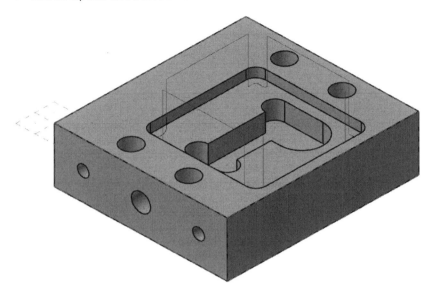

♦ Press **Esc** key to exit the preview.

Note: If the toolpath does not look as shown in the preview, check your parameters again.

♦ Select the **OK** button to generate the toolpath.

Note: Since this toolpath has been copied, all the parameters remain the same. Therefore we do not have to view all the parameters.

6.6 Remachine the second pocket

◆ Select **Parameters** of Operation #4 as shown.

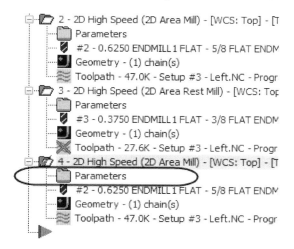

◆ In the **Toolpath Type** page, select the **Preview chains** button as shown.

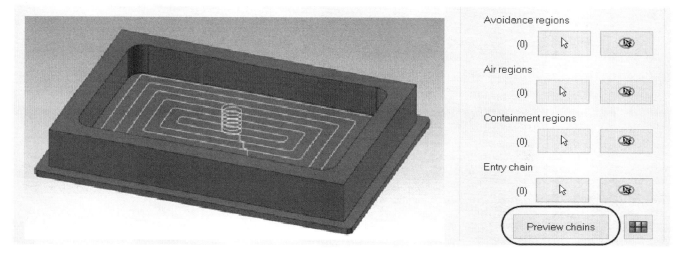

◆ See **"Preview Chains" on page 541** to review the procedure.

♦ The **Preview chains** should look as shown.

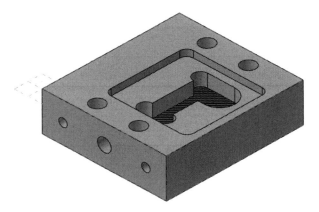

♦ Press **Esc** key to return to the toolpath parameters.

♦ Click on the **Preview** chains button again to clear the **Preview chains** display.

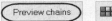

♦ In the **Tool** page, select the same tool used in Operation #3 and input a comment accordingly.

♦ Select **Stock** from the **Tree View list**.

♦ Enable **Rest material**; check **One other operation** for **Compute remaining stock from** and then select Operation #2. Check **Use as computed**.

♦ To quickly check how the toolpath will be generated, select the **Preview toolpath** icon as shown.

♦ See"Preview the Toolpath" on page 549 to review the procedure.

♦ The toolpath should look as shown.

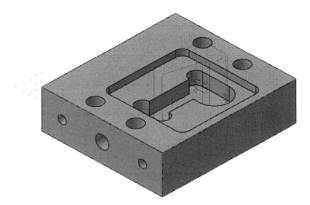

♦ Press **Esc** key to exit the preview.

Note: If the toolpath does not look as shown in the preview, check your parameters again.

♦ Leave the rest of the parameters as they are and click on the **OK** button to generate the toolpath.

♦ Regenerate all dirty operations.

6.7 Backplot and Verify the toolpaths

◆ To **Backplot** both toolpaths see **"Backplot The Toolpaths" on page 550**.

◆ Hold down the **Ctrl** key and select only Operation #3 and #4.

◆ The toolpaths should look as shown.

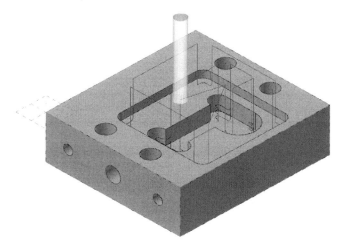

◆ Select the **OK** button to exit **Backplot**.

◆ To **Verify** the toolpaths, make sure all the operations are selected. To select all operations, click on the **Select all operations** icon.

◆ See "Simulate the toolpath in Verify" on page 551 to review these procedures.

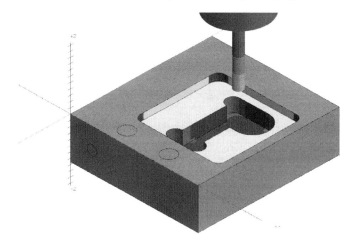

◆ To go back to the Mastercam window, minimize the **Mastercam Simulator** window as shown.

STEP 7: SPOT DRILL THE HOLES

Spot Drilling the holes allows you to start the hole. In this operation, we will use the spot drill to chamfer the hole before drilling it.

Toolpath Preview:

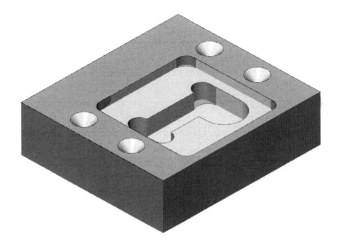

Toolpaths

♦ In the **2D** group, select the **Expand gallery** arrow and click on the **Drill** icon.

♦ Select the circles as shown. The holes will be machined in same order in which you selected the circles.

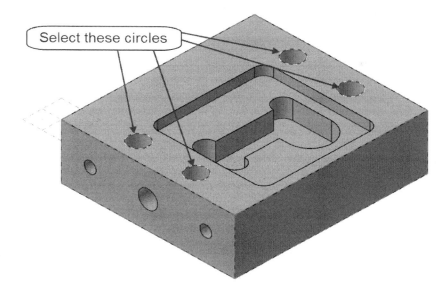

Select these circles

♦ Select the **OK** button to exit the **Toolpath Hole Definition** dialog box.
♦ In the **Toolpath Type** page, the **Drill** toolpath will be selected.

Drill   Circle Mill   Point   Helix Bore   Thread Mill

7.1 Select a 3/4" Spot Drill from the Library and set the Tool Parameters

♦ Select **Tool** from the **Tree view list**.

♦ Click on the **Select library tool** button. Select library tool...

♦ To be able to see just the **spot drill**, select the **Filter** button.

♦ Under **Tool Types**, select the **None** button and then choose the **Spot drill** icon as shown.

♦ Ensure the **Tool Diameter** is set to **Equal** and **0.75** as shown.

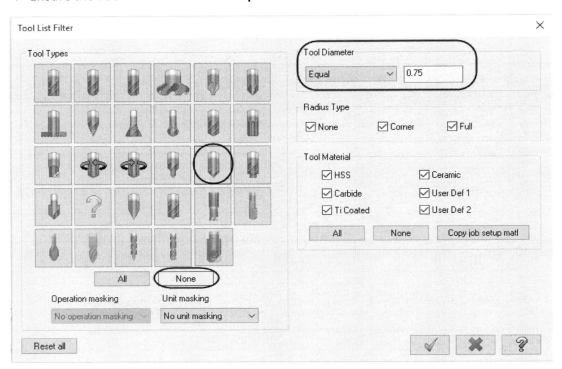

♦ Select the **OK** button to exit the **Tool List Filter** dialog box.

♦ Select the **3/4" Spot Drill**.

#	Assembly Na...	Tool Name	Holder Name	Dia.	Cor. rad.	Length	# Flutes	Type	Rad. ...
25	--	3/4 SPOTDRILL	--	0.75	0.0	2.0	4	Spot ...	None

♦ Select the **OK** button to exit.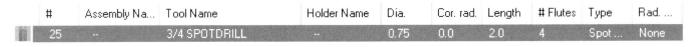

♦ Make the necessary changes to the **Tool** page as shown.

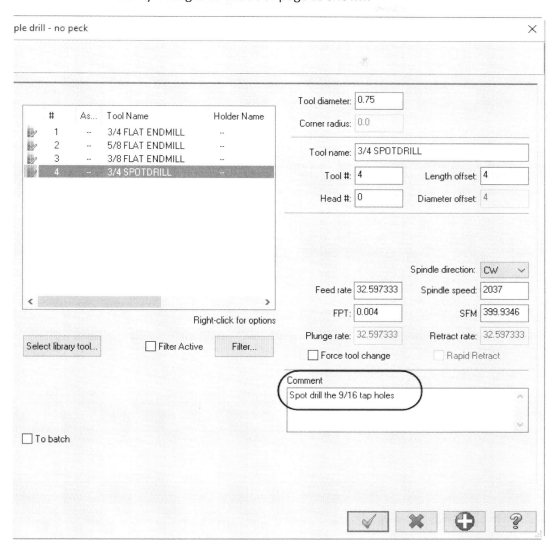

7.2 Set the Cut Parameters

♦ Select Cut Parameters and make the necessary changes as shown.

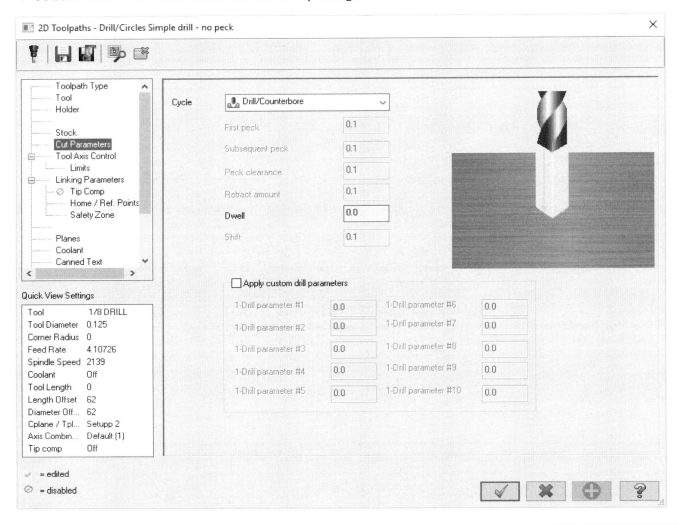

Drill/Counterbore is recommended for drilling holes with depths of less than three times the tool's diameter.

Dwell sets the amount of time in seconds that the tool remains at the bottom of a drilled hole.

7.3 Set the Linking Parameters

- Choose **Linking Parameters**, ensure **Clearance** is enabled, **Top of stock** and **Depth** are set to **Absolute 0.0**.

- To input the depth, select the **Calculator** icon.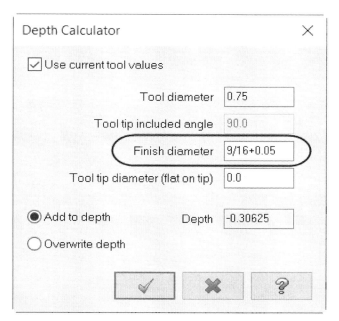
- Input the following equation in the **Finish diameter** area: **9/16 + 0.05** (diameter of the finished hole + 2 X the chamfer size) as shown and hit **Enter** to calculate the **Depth**.

- Select the **OK** button to exit the **Depth Calculator**.

- ♦ You will now see the depth we calculated for the spot drilling operation set in the **Depth** field as shown.
- ♦ This will chamfer the hole for the tapping operation.
- ♦ Change the **Clearance** value to **1.0**.

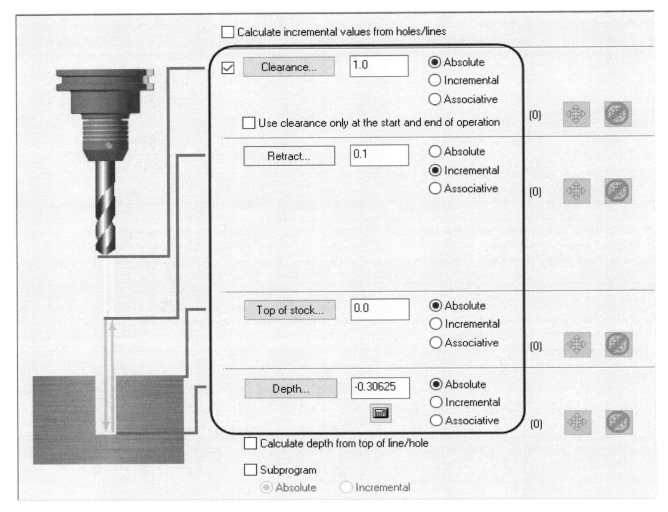

7.4 Preview the Toolpath

♦ To quickly check how the toolpath will be generated, select the **Preview toolpath** icon as shown.

♦ See **"Preview the Toolpath" on page 549** to review the procedure.
♦ The toolpath should look as shown.

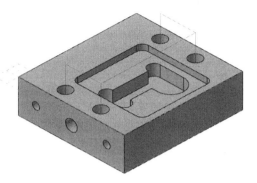

♦ Press **Esc** key to exit the preview.

Note: If the toolpath does not look as shown in the preview, check your parameters again. The holes are machined in the order in which you selected the circles used in the toolpath.

♦ Select the **OK** button to exit the **2D Toolpaths - Drill/Circles Simple drill - no peck** parameters.

7.5 Backplot and Verify the toolpaths

♦ To **Backplot** and **Verify** your toolpaths, see **"Backplot The Toolpaths" on page 550** and **"Simulate the toolpath in Verify" on page 551**.

♦ To **Verify** all toolpaths, from the **Toolpaths Manager**, choose the **Select all operations** icon.
♦ The part should look as shown.

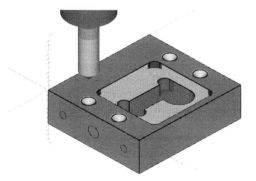

♦ To go back to the Mastercam window, minimize the **Mastercam Simulator** window as shown.

STEP 8: DRILL ALL HOLES

In this example, we will drill the holes through the part.

Toolpath Preview:

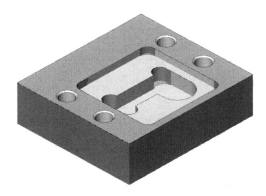

♦ In the **Toolpaths Manager**, select only the drilling operation as shown.

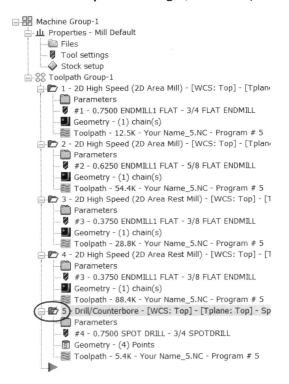

♦ As shown in previous steps, copy the drilling operation and move the insert arrow as shown.

♦ Select the **Parameters** in the second drilling operation as shown.

8.1 Select a 33/64" Drill from the Library and set the Tool Parameters

♦ Select **Tool** from the **Tree View list**.

♦ Click on the **Select library tool** button. [Select library tool...]

♦ To be able to see just the drill, select the **Filter** button.

♦ Under **Tool Types**, select the **None** button and then choose the **Drill** icon.

♦ Under **Tool Diameter**, select **Equal** and enter **33/64** as shown.

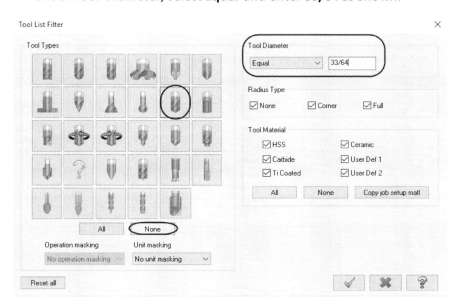

◆ Select the **OK** button to exit the **Tool List Filter** panel.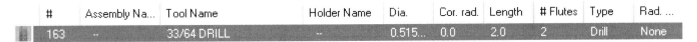

◆ At this point you should see only a **33/64" Drill**.

◆ From that list, select the **33/64" Drill**.

#	Assembly Na...	Tool Name	Holder Name	Dia.	Cor. rad.	Length	# Flutes	Type	Rad. ...
163	--	33/64 DRILL	--	0.515...	0.0	2.0	2	Drill	None

◆ Select the tool in the **Tool Selection** page and then choose the **OK** button to exit.

◆ Make the necessary changes to the **Tool** page as shown.

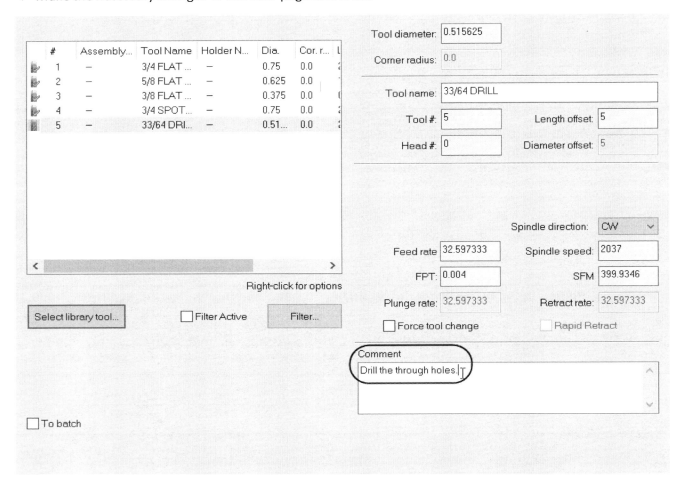

8.2 Set the Cut Parameters

♦ Select **Cut Parameters**, change the drill **Cycle** to **Peck Drill** and input a **Peck** value of **0.25** as shown.

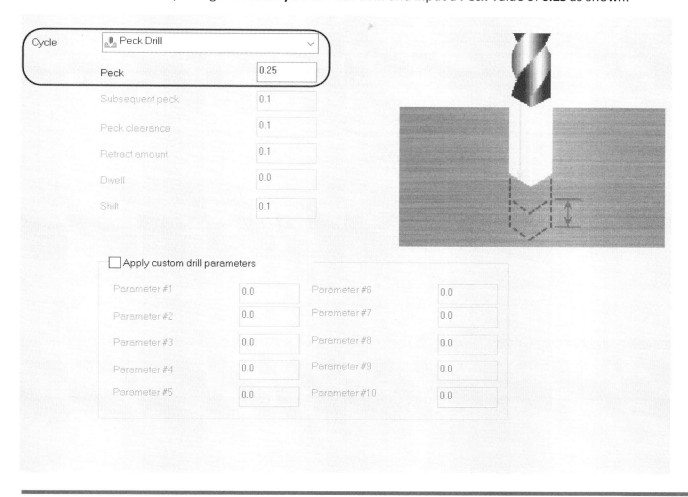

Peck Drill is recommended for drilling holes with depths of more than three times the tool's diameter. The drill retracts fully out of the drilled hole to remove material.

Peck sets the depth for the peck move.

8.3 Set the Linking Parameters

♦ Choose **Linking Parameters** and input a **Depth** value of **-1.5** as shown.

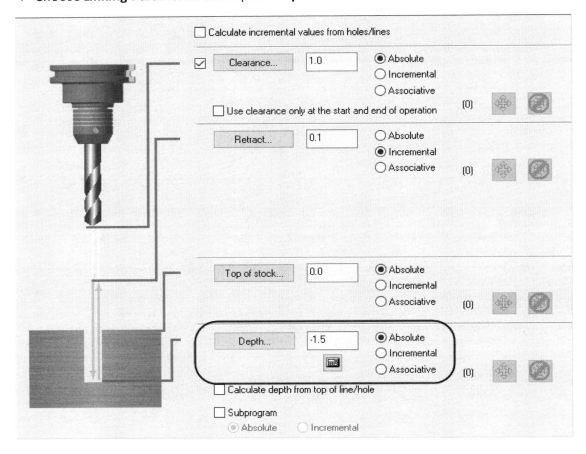

8.4 Set the Tip Compensation page

♦ Choose **Tip Comp** and enable this option. Input a **Breakthrough amount** of **0.1** and make the necessary changes as shown.

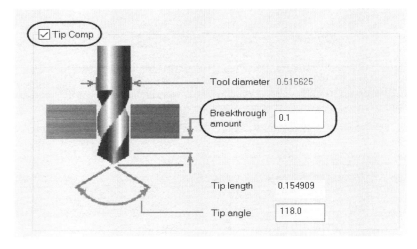

8.5 Preview the Toolpath

♦ To quickly check how the toolpath will be generated, select the **Preview toolpath** icon as shown.

♦ See **"Preview the Toolpath" on page 549** to review the procedure.
♦ The toolpath should look as shown.

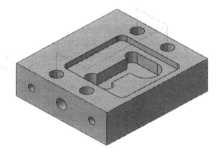

♦ Press **Esc** key to exit the preview.

Note: If the toolpath does not look as shown in the preview, check your parameters again. The toolpath will be the same as the one in Operation #5 since Operation #6 is a copy.

♦ Select the **OK** button to exit the toolpath parameters.
♦ From the **Toolpaths Manager**, select the **Regenerate all dirty operations** icon.

8.6 Backplot and Verify

♦ To **Backplot** and **Verify** your toolpaths, see **"Backplot The Toolpaths" on page 550** and"Simulate the toolpath in Verify" on page 551

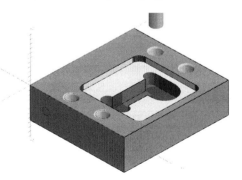

♦ To go back to the Mastercam window, minimize the **Mastercam Simulator** window as shown.

STEP 9: TAP THE HOLES

Tap cycle taps right or left internal threaded holes.

Toolpath Preview:

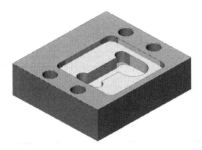

♦ In the **Toolpaths Manager**, select only the last drilling operation as shown.

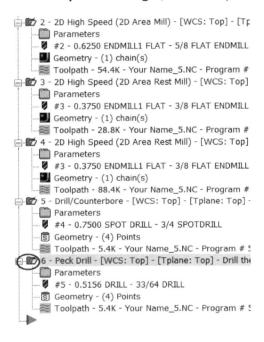

♦ As shown in previous steps, copy the drilling operation and move the insert arrow as shown.
♦ Select the **Parameters** in the third drilling operation as shown.

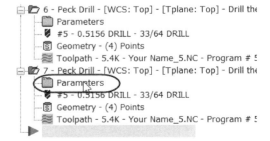

9.1 Select a 9/16 - 18 RH Tap from the Library and set the Tool Parameters

◆ Select **Tool** from the **Tree Viewlist**.

◆ Click on the **Select library tool** button.  Select library tool...

◆ To be able to see just the **Tap RH drill**, select the **Filter** button.

Filter...

☑ Filter Active

3 of 427 tools

◆ Under **Tool Types**, select the **None** button and then choose the **Tap RH** icon. Under **Tool Diameter**, select **Equal** and enter the value **9/16** as shown.

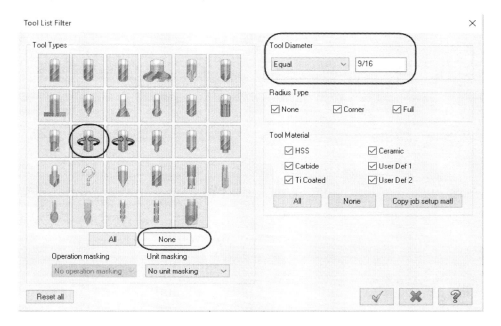

◆ Select the **OK** button to exit the **Tool List Filter** dialog box. ✓

◆ At this point you should see a list full of taps.

◆ From that list, select the **9/16 - 18 Tap RH** as shown.

#	Assembly...	Tool Name	Holder N...	Dia.	Cor. r...	Length	# Flut...	Type	Rad....
229	—	9/16-12 T...	—	0.56...	0.0	2.0	1	Tap ...	None
230	—	9/16-18 T...	—	0.56...	0.0	2.0	1	Tap ...	None

◆ Select the tool in the **Tool Selection** dialog box and then choose the **OK** button to exit. ✓

♦ Make the necessary changes to the **Tool** page as shown.

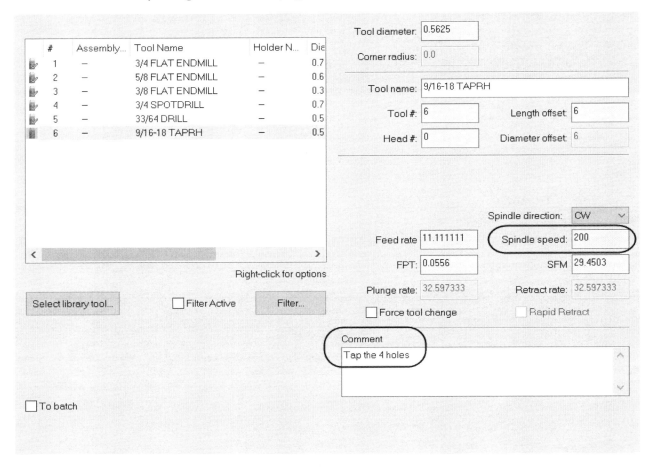

9.2 Set the Cut Parameters

♦ Select **Cut Parameters**, change the drill **Cycle** to **Tap**.

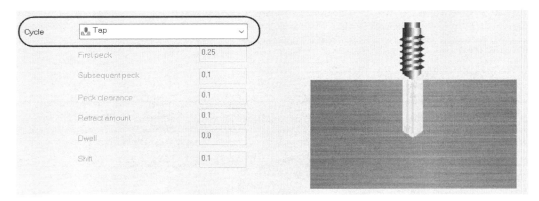

9.3 Set the Linking Parameters

♦ Choose **Linking Parameters** and make sure the **Depth** value is set to **-1.5** as shown.

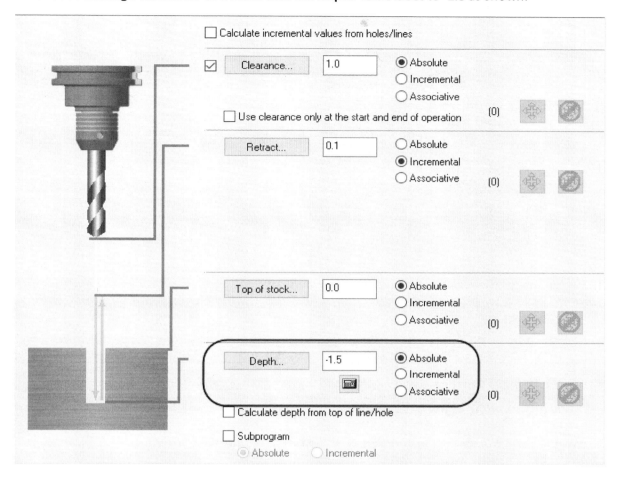

♦ Enable **Tip Comp**.

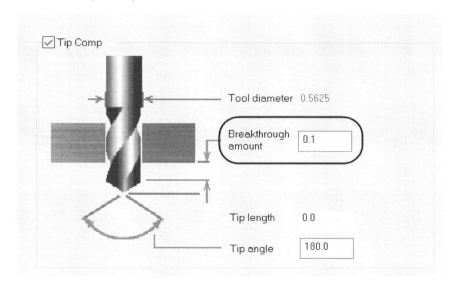

9.4 Preview the Toolpath

♦ To quickly check how the toolpath will be generated, select the **Preview toolpath** icon as shown.

♦ See **"Preview the Toolpath" on page 549** to review the procedure.

♦ The toolpath should look as shown.

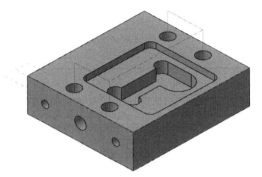

♦ Press **Esc** key to exit the preview.

Note: If the toolpath does not look as shown in the preview, check your parameters again.

♦ Leave the rest of the parameters as they are and select the **OK** button to exit the **2D Toolpaths-Drill/Circles Tapping - feed in, reverse spindle - feed out** parameters.

♦ From the **Toolpaths Manager**, select the **Regenerate all dirty operations** icon.

♦ To **Backplot** and **Verify** your toolpaths, see **"Backplot The Toolpaths" on page 550** and **"Simulate the toolpath in Verify" on page 551**.

♦ To make sure that all toolpaths are selected, choose the **Select all operations** icon.
♦ The part will appear as shown.

♦ To go back to the Mastercam window, minimize the **Mastercam Simulator** window as shown.

Toolpath Creation - Setup 2

SUGGESTED FIXTURE 2:

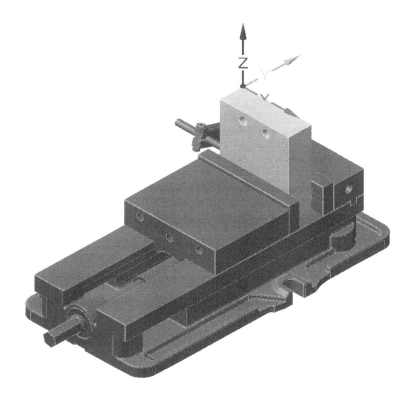

*Note: The part is now flipped over and we will machine the part from the **Front**.*

SETUP SHEET 2:

TOOL LIST

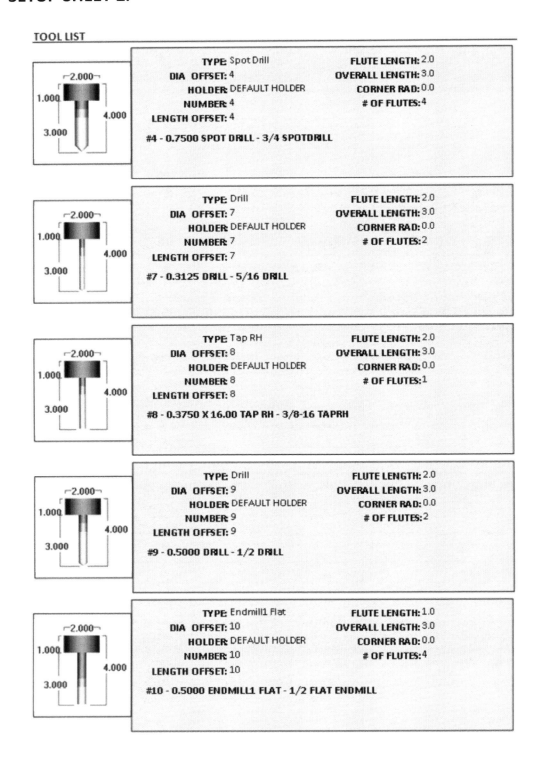

TYPE: Spot Drill	**FLUTE LENGTH:** 2.0
DIA OFFSET: 4	**OVERALL LENGTH:** 3.0
HOLDER: DEFAULT HOLDER	**CORNER RAD:** 0.0
NUMBER: 4	**# OF FLUTES:** 4
LENGTH OFFSET: 4	

#4 - 0.7500 SPOT DRILL - 3/4 SPOTDRILL

TYPE: Drill	**FLUTE LENGTH:** 2.0
DIA OFFSET: 7	**OVERALL LENGTH:** 3.0
HOLDER: DEFAULT HOLDER	**CORNER RAD:** 0.0
NUMBER: 7	**# OF FLUTES:** 2
LENGTH OFFSET: 7	

#7 - 0.3125 DRILL - 5/16 DRILL

TYPE: Tap RH	**FLUTE LENGTH:** 2.0
DIA OFFSET: 8	**OVERALL LENGTH:** 3.0
HOLDER: DEFAULT HOLDER	**CORNER RAD:** 0.0
NUMBER: 8	**# OF FLUTES:** 1
LENGTH OFFSET: 8	

#8 - 0.3750 X 16.00 TAP RH - 3/8-16 TAPRH

TYPE: Drill	**FLUTE LENGTH:** 2.0
DIA OFFSET: 9	**OVERALL LENGTH:** 3.0
HOLDER: DEFAULT HOLDER	**CORNER RAD:** 0.0
NUMBER: 9	**# OF FLUTES:** 2
LENGTH OFFSET: 9	

#9 - 0.5000 DRILL - 1/2 DRILL

TYPE: Endmill1 Flat	**FLUTE LENGTH:** 1.0
DIA OFFSET: 10	**OVERALL LENGTH:** 3.0
HOLDER: DEFAULT HOLDER	**CORNER RAD:** 0.0
NUMBER: 10	**# OF FLUTES:** 4
LENGTH OFFSET: 10	

#10 - 0.5000 ENDMILL1 FLAT - 1/2 FLAT ENDMILL

STEP 10: CREATING AND RENAMING TOOLPATH GROUPS

To machine the part in different setups, we will need to have separate programs. To be able to post the operations separate of each setup, we will create them under different toolpath groups with different NC names.

10.1 Rename the current Toolpath Group - 1 and NC file

◆ Click on the **Toolpath Group - 1** to highlight and then click again on it and rename it "**Setup #1**."

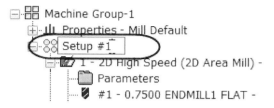

◆ Right mouse click on the toolpath group and select **Edit selected operations** and then select **Change NC file name** as shown.

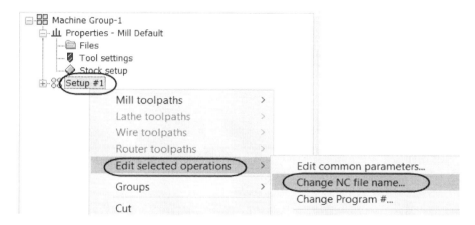

◆ Enter the new NC name: **Setup #1**.

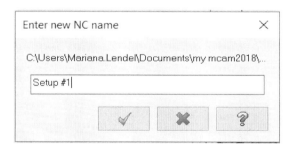

◆ Select the **OK** button to accept the new **NC name**.

10.2 Create a New Toolpath Group

♦ Right mouse click on the **Machine Group-1**.

♦ From the list, select Groups and then the **New Toolpath group.**

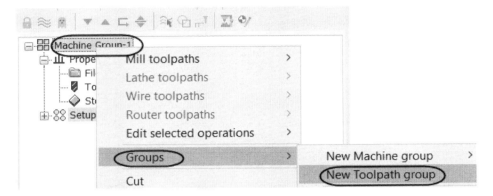

♦ Click on the new **Toolpath Group-1** and rename it "**Setup #2 - Front.**"

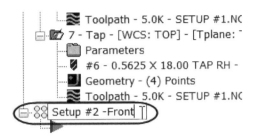

STEP 11: SET WCS TO FRONT

Work coordinate system (WCS) is the active coordinate system in use by Mastercam at any given time. The **WCS** contains the orientation of the **X, Y, Z** axes plus the location of the zero point (the origin). This tells Mastercam how your part is positioned or oriented in the machine.

Construction plane (Cplane) is the plane in which the geometry is created.

Tool plane (Tplane) is the plane normal to Z or to the vertical tool axis in which the tool moves. When creating a toolpath, both Cplane and Tplane should be set to the same plane. If the **Tplane** is different then the **WCS**, the post will produce a rotary motion code. By setting the **Cplane**, **Tplane** and **WCS** to one plane, no rotary move will be generated in the code, which is what you want when machining parts with multiple setups.
In this step you will set the **WCS**, the **Construction plane (Cplane)** and the **Tool plane (Tplane)** to **Front**.

♦ Select **Planes** tab located at the bottom left corner.

♦ Select the **Front side** plane and click on the **equal sign** to set the **WCS, Construction Plane** and **Tool Plane** to the **Front side** as shown.

♦ Press **F9** on your keyboard to display the coordinate axes.

Note: The color of the coordinate axes remains the same because it is the same origin.

♦ Right mouse click in the graphics window and select the **Isometric** view to see the part in the new orientation.
♦ Your part will appear as shown up to this point.

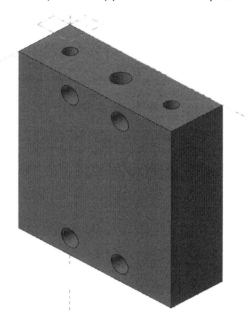

♦ Press **F9** to remove the axes display.
♦ To open the **Toolpaths Manager**, select the **Toolpaths** tab from the lower left corner of the screen.

Toolpaths   Solids   Planes   Levels   Recent Functions

STEP 12: SPOT DRILL ALL 3 HOLES

Toolpath Preview:

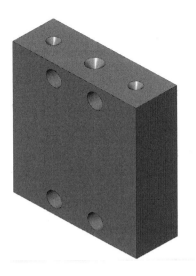

Toolpaths

♦ From the **2D** group, select the **Drill** icon.

♦ Select the 3 circles as shown.

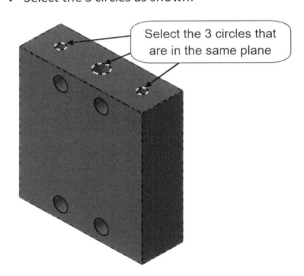

Select the 3 circles that are in the same plane

- Select the **OK** button to exit the **Toolpath Hole Definition** dialog box.

- In the **Toolpath Type** page, the **Drill** toolpath will be selected.

Drill   Circle Mill   Point   Helix Bore   Thread Mill

- Select **Tool** from the **Tree view list**.
- Select the **3/4" Spot Drill** from the list.

- Make the necessary changes to the **Tool** page as shown.

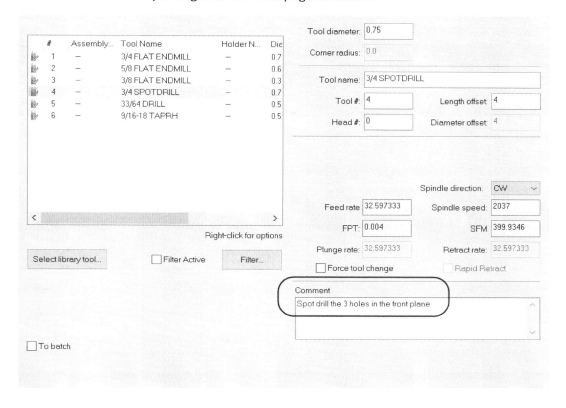

12.1 Set the Cut Parameters

◆ Select **Cut Parameters** and change the **Cycle to Drill/Counterbore** as shown.

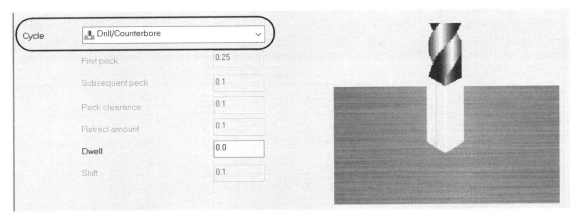

12.2 Set the Linking Parameters

◆ Choose **Linking Parameters**, ensure **Clearance** is enabled, **Top of stock** and **Depth** are set to **Absolute 0.0**.

◆ To input the depth, select the **Calculator** icon.

◆ Input the following equation in the **Finish diameter** area: **3/8+0.04** and hit Enter to calculate the **Depth** as shown.

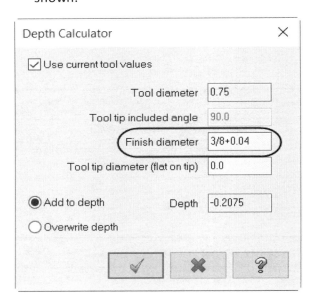

◆ Select the **OK** button to exit the **Depth Calculator**.

♦ You will now see the depth we calculated for the spot drilling operation set in the **Depth** field as shown. This will chamfer the holes for the tapping operation.

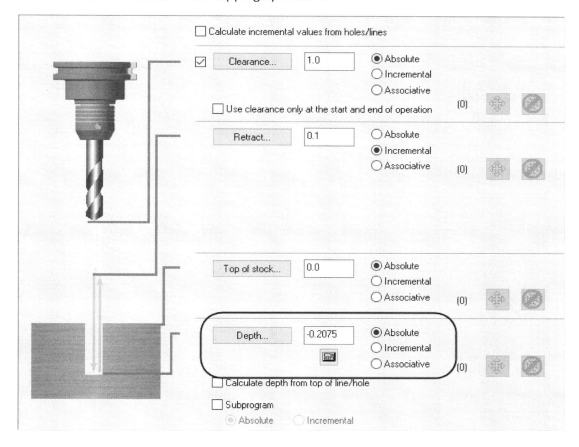

12.3 Set the Tip Compensation page

♦ Select **Tip Comp** and disable this option, as shown. If left enabled, the holes would be drilled much deeper.

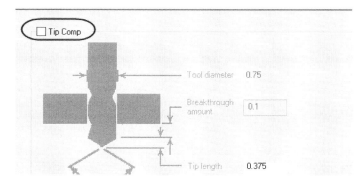

Note: All 3 holes are spot drilled to the same depth. The 0.5" diameter hole has to be drilled to a deeper depth.

12.4 Preview the Toolpath

♦ To quickly check how the toolpath will be generated, select the **Preview toolpath** icon as shown.

♦ See"Preview the Toolpath" on page 549 to review the procedure.
♦ The toolpath should look as shown.

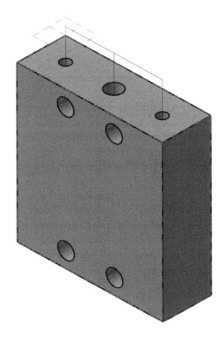

♦ Press **Esc** key to exit the preview.

Note: If the toolpath does not look as shown in the preview, check your parameters again.

♦ Select the **OK** button to exit the **2D Toolpaths - Drill/Circles Simple drill - no peck** parameters.

12.5 Adjust the Depth of the Spot Drill

♦ Left click on **Geometry** in Operation #8.
♦ When the **Toolpath Hole Defintion** appears, select the point which represents the **0.5" diameter hole**.
♦ Then right click on it and select the option to **Change parameters at point** as shown.

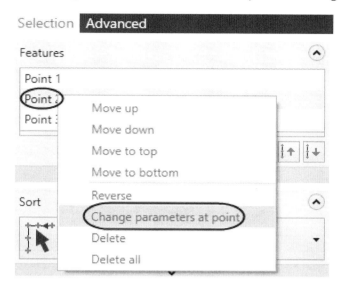

♦ When the **Change Parameters at Point** dialog box appears, enable Depth and change the depth to
  -0.27 as shown.

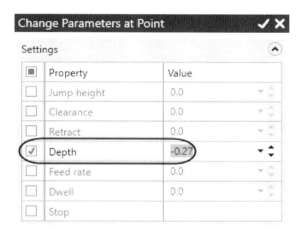

Change Parameters at Point allows you to make point-specific changes to a drill toolpath.

Depth changes the hole depth at the selected point. The coordinate you enter here will be output as either an absolute or incremental value, depending on the original settings for the operation.

♦ Select the **OK** button to apply the changes and exit the **Change Parameters at Point** dialog box.
♦ Choose the **OK** button to exit the **Change Parameters at Point**.
♦ Select the button **Regenerate all dirty operations**. ⌐x

12.6 Backplot and Verify the toolpaths

- ♦ To **Backplot** and **Verify** your toolpaths, see"Backplot The Toolpaths" on page 550and **"Simulate the toolpath in Verify" on page 551.**

- ♦ To **Verify** all toolpaths, from the **Toolpaths Manager**, choose the **Select all operations** icon.

- ♦ To go back to the Mastercam window, minimize the **Mastercam Simulator** window as shown.
- ♦ When backplotting the toolpath, see if you can check the depth of the holes.
- ♦ Select the **Expand or contract this dialog** double arrow to expand the **Backplot** dialog box.

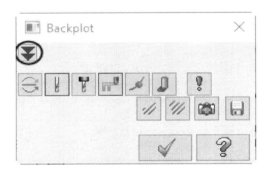

- ♦ Select the **Details** tab as shown below.
- ♦ You can step through the **Backplot** by using the **Step forward** or **Step back** .

♦ The coordinate values of the tip of the tool will be displayed with each step.

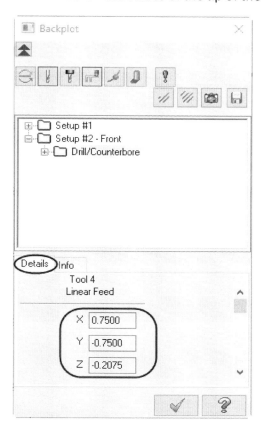

♦ Select the **OK** button to exit.

STEP 13: DRILL THE TWO 3/8" TAPPED HOLES

In this example, we will drill the holes to a specific depth.

Toolpath Preview:

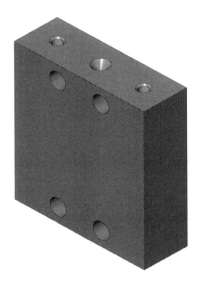

Toolpaths

♦ In the **2D** group, select the **Expand gallery** arrow and click on the **Drill** icon.

♦ Select the circles as shown.

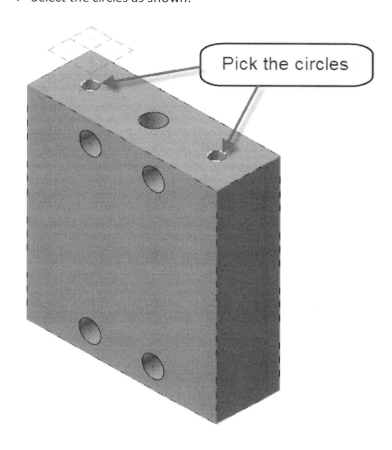

Pick the circles

♦ Select the **OK** button to exit the **Toolpath Hole Definition** dialog box.
♦ In the **Toolpath Type** page, the **Drill** toolpath will be selected.

Drill   Circle Mill   Point   Helix Bore   Thread Mill

13.1 Select a 5/16" Drill from the Library and set the Tool Parameters

♦ Select **Tool** from the **Tree view list**.

♦ Click on the **Select library tool** button.

♦ To be able to see just the **5/16" Drill**, select the **Filter** button.

♦ Under **Tool Types**, select the **None** button and then choose the **Drill** icon.

♦ Under **Tool Diameter**, select **Equal** and enter the value **5/16** as shown.

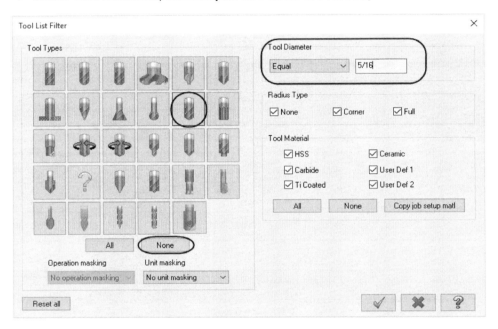

♦ Select **OK** button to exit the **Tool List Filter** dialog box.

♦ At this point, you should see a **5/16" Drill**.

♦ Select the **5/16"Drill**.

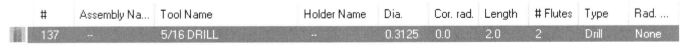

#	Assembly Na...	Tool Name	Holder Name	Dia.	Cor. rad.	Length	# Flutes	Type	Rad. ...
137	--	5/16 DRILL	--	0.3125	0.0	2.0	2	Drill	None

♦ Select the tool in the **Tool Selection** dialog box and then choose the **OK** button to exit.

♦ Make the necessary changes to the **Tool** page as shown.

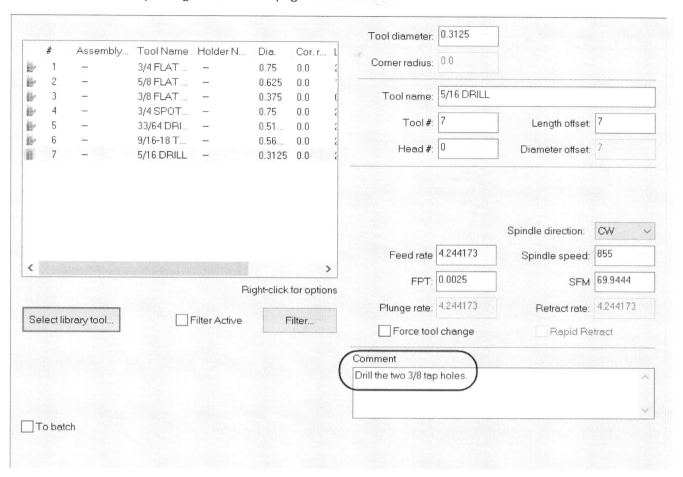

13.2 Set the Cut Parameters

♦ Select **Cut Parameters**, change the drill **Cycle** to **Peck Drill** and input a **Peck** value of **0.25** as shown.

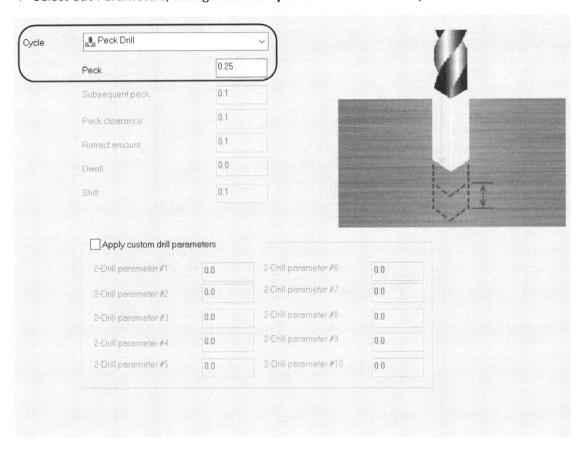

Note: For more information on these settings, see"Set the Cut Parameters" on page 585 .

13.3 Set the Linking Parameters

♦ Choose **Linking Parameters** and input a **Depth** value of **-1.25** as shown.

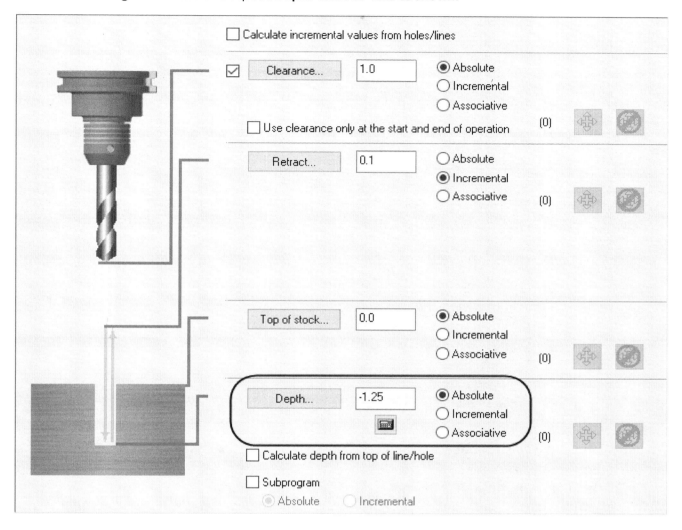

♦ Select **Tip Comp** and ensure this option is disabled.

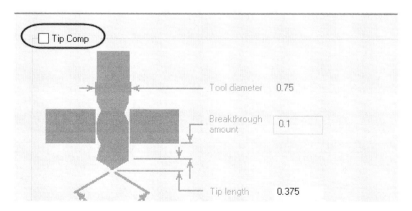

13.4 Preview the Toolpath

♦ To quickly check how the toolpath will be generated, select the **Preview toolpath** icon as shown.

♦ See **"Preview the Toolpath" on page 549** to review the procedure.

♦ The toolpath should look as shown.

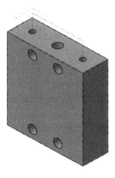

♦ Press **Esc** key to exit the preview.

Note: If the toolpath does not look as shown in the preview, check your parameters again.

♦ Select the **OK** button to exit the **2D Toolpaths - Drill/Circles Simple drill - full retract** parameters.

13.5 Backplot and Verify

♦ To **Backplot** and **Verify** your toolpath. See **"Backplot The Toolpaths" on page 550** and **"Simulate the toolpath in Verify" on page 551** .

♦ Use the mouse wheel to rotate the part as shown.

♦ To go back to the Mastercam window, minimize the **Mastercam Simulator** window as shown.

STEP 14: TAP THE TWO HOLES

Toolpath Preview:

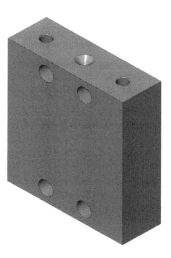

Toolpath

♦ In the **2D** group, select the **Expand gallery** arrow and click on the **Drill** icon.

♦ Right click on the graphics window and choose **Isometric** view if needed.
♦ Select the circles as shown.

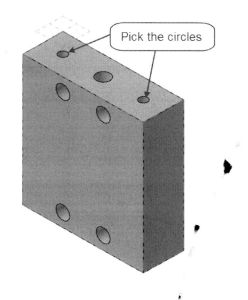

Pick the circles

- Select the **OK** button to exit the **Toolpath Hole Definition** dialog box.
- In the **Toolpath Type** page, the **Drill** toolpath will be selected.

Drill   Circle Mill   Point   Helix Bore   Thread Mill

14.1 Select a 3/8 - 16RH Tap from the Library and set the Tool Parameters

- Select **Tool** from the **Tree View list**.

- Click on the **Select library tool** button. Select library tool...
- To be able to see just the **Tap RH drill**, select the **Filter** button.

Filter...

☑ Filter Active

3 of 427 tools

- Under **Tool Types**, select the **None** button and then choose the **Tap RH** icon. Under **Tool Diameter**, make sure the **Equal** option is selected and enter the diameter **3/8** as shown.

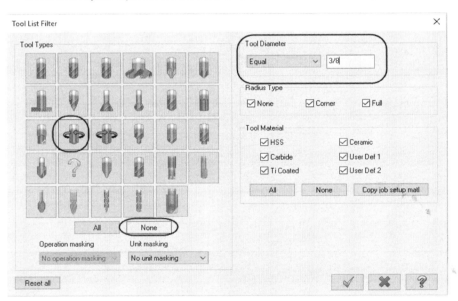

- Select the **OK** button to exit the **Tool List Filter** dialog box.

◆ From that list, select the **3/8 - 16 Tap RH** as shown.

#	Assembly Name	Tool Name	Holder Name	Dia.	Cor. rad.	Length	Type	Ra...
223	--	3/8-24 TAPRH	--	0....	0.0	2.0	Ta...	No...
224	--	3/8-16 TAPRH	--	0....	0.0	2.0	Ta...	No...

◆ Select the tool in the **Tool Selection** dialog box and then choose the **OK** button to exit.

◆ Make the necessary changes to the **Tool** page as shown.

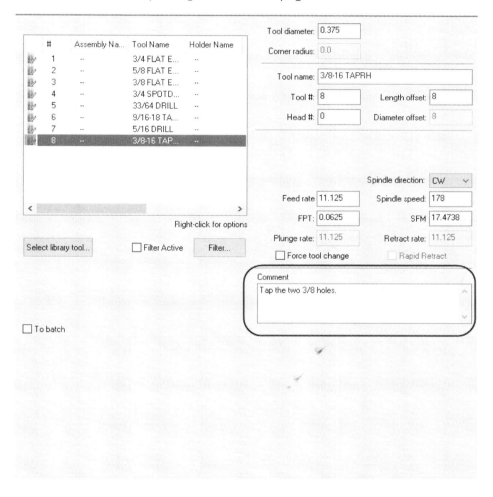

14.2 Set the Cut Parameters

♦ Select **Cut Parameters** from the **Tree View list** and change the drill **Cycle** to **Tap** as shown.

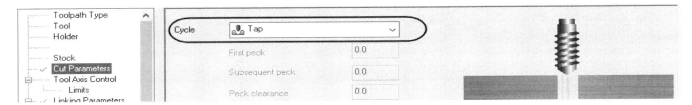

14.3 Set the Linking Parameters

♦ Choose **Linking Parameters** and input a **Depth** of **-1.0** as shown.

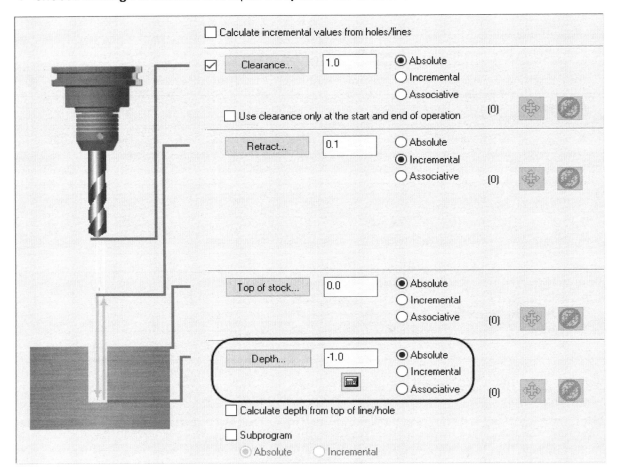

♦ Select **Tip Comp** and ensure this option is disabled. The **Depth** set in the **Linking Parameters** page is as deep as you would like the tap to go.

14.4 Preview the Toolpath

♦ To quickly check how the toolpath will be generated, select the **Preview toolpath** icon as shown.

♦ See **"Preview the Toolpath" on page 549** to review the procedure.

♦ The toolpath should look as shown.

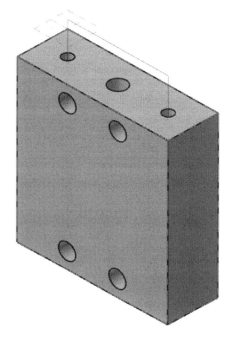

♦ Press **Esc** key to exit the preview.

Note: If the toolpath does not look as shown in the preview, check your parameters again.

♦ Select the **OK** button to exit the **2D Toolpaths - Drill/Circles Peck drill - feed in, reverse spindle - feed out** parameters.

♦ Select the **Regenerate all dirty operations** icon if necessary.

14.5 Backplot and Verify

♦ To **Backplot** and **Verify** the toolpaths, see **"Backplot The Toolpaths" on page 550** and"Simulate the toolpath in Verify" on page 551**.**

♦ To make sure that all toolpaths are selected, choose the **Select all operations** icon.

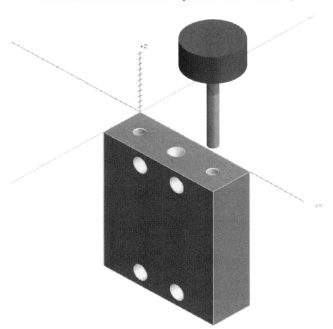

♦ To go back to the Mastercam window, minimize the **Mastercam Simulator** window as shown.

STEP 15: DRILL THE 1/2" HOLE

You will drill the hole to a specific depth.

Toolpath Preview:

Toolpaths

♦ In the **2D** group, select the **Drill** icon.

♦ Pick the circle as shown.

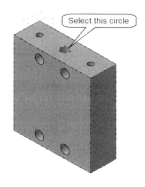

♦ Select the **OK** button to exit the **Toolpath Hole Definition** dialog box.

♦ In the **Toolpath Type** page, the **Drill** toolpath will be selected.

15.1 Select a 1/2" Drill from the Library and set the Tool Parameters

♦ Select **Tool** from the **Tree view list**.

♦ Click on the **Select library tool** button. Select library tool...

♦ To be able to see just the **1/2" Drill**, select the **Filter** button.

♦ Under **Tool Types**, select the **None** button and then choose the **Drill** icon. Under **Tool Diameter**, select **Equal** and enter the value **0.5** as shown.

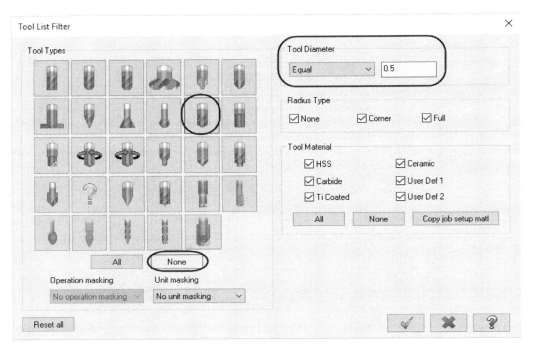

♦ Select **OK** button to exit the **Tool List Filter** dialog box.

♦ Select the **1/2" Drill tool**.

#	Assembly Na...	Tool Name	Holder Name	Dia.	Cor. rad.	Length	# Flutes	Type	Rad. ...
162	--	1/2 DRILL	--	0.5	0.0	2.0	2	Drill	None

♦ Select the tool in the **Tool Selection** dialog box and then choose the **OK** button to exit.

♦ Make the necessary changes to the **Tool** page as shown.

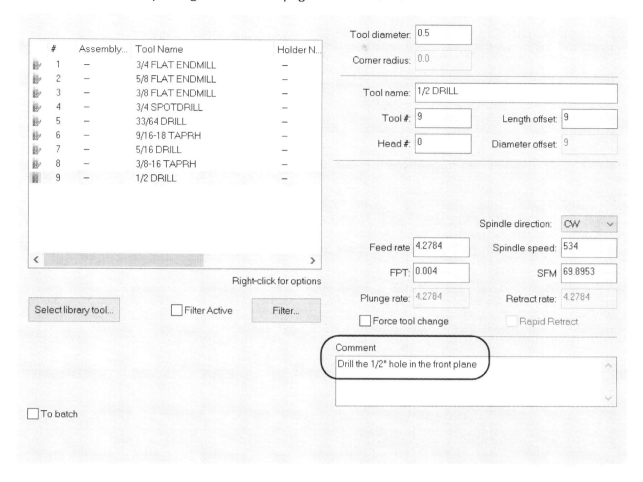

15.2 Set the Cut Parameters

♦ Select **Cut Parameters**, change the drill **Cycle** to **Chip Break** and input a **Peck** of **0.25** as shown.

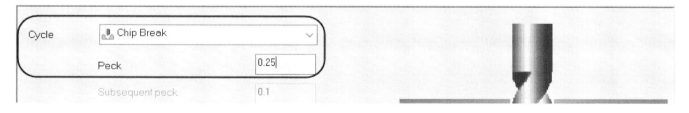

Chip Break retracts partially out of the drilled hole to break the material chips.

15.3 Set the Linking Parameters

♦ Choose **Linking Parameters** and input a **Depth** value of **-0.55** as shown.

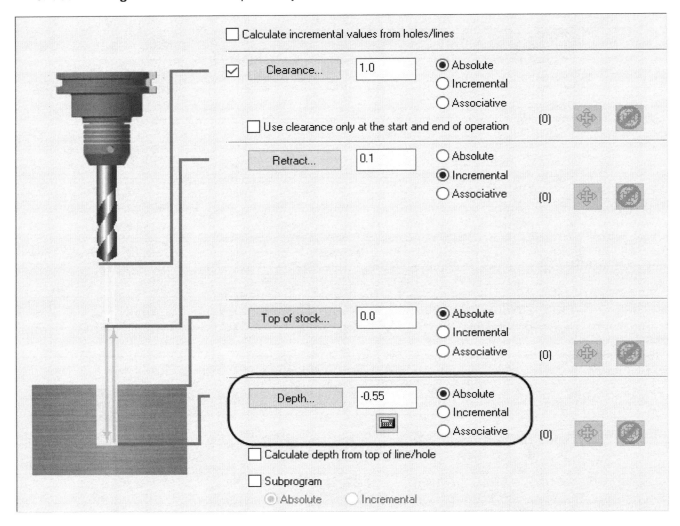

♦ Select **Tip Comp** and ensure this option is disabled.

15.4 Preview the Toolpath

♦ To quickly check how the toolpath will be generated, select the **Preview toolpath** icon as shown.

♦ See **"Preview the Toolpath" on page 549** to review the procedure.

♦ The toolpath should look as shown.

♦ Press **Esc** key to exit the preview.

Note: If the toolpath does not look as shown in the preview, check your parameters again.

♦ Select the **OK** button to exit the **2D Toolpaths - Drill/Circles Chip Break - incremental retract** parameters.

15.5 Backplot and Verify

♦ To **Backplot** and **Verify** your toolpath, see **"Backplot The Toolpaths" on page 550** and"Simulate the toolpath in Verify" on page 551.

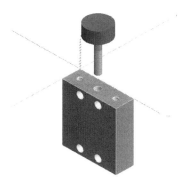

♦ To go back to the Mastercam window, minimize the **Mastercam Simulator** window as shown.

STEP 16: COUNTERBORE THE 1/2" HOLE

In this step you will drill the hole to a specific depth using a **1/2" Flat Endmill** to give you a flat bottom hole.

Toolpath Preview:

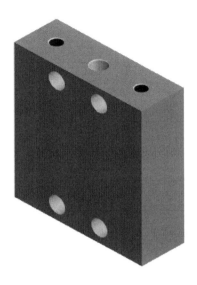

Toolpaths

♦ From the **2D** group, select the **Drill** icon as shown.

◆ Select the circle as shown.

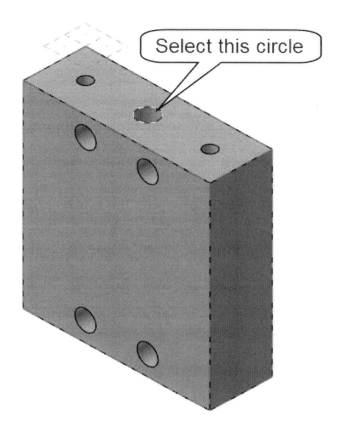

Select this circle

◆ Select the **OK** button to exit the **Toolpath Hole Definition** dialog box.
◆ In the **Toolpath Type** page, the **Drill** toolpath will be selected.

 Drill   Circle Mill   Point   Helix Bore   Thread Mill

16.1 Select a 1/2" Flat Endmill from the Library and set the Tool Parameters

◆ Select **Tool** from the **Tree view list**.

◆ Click on the **Select library tool** button.
◆ To be able to see just the **Flat Endmill**, select the **Filter** button.

♦ Under **Tool Types**, select the **None** button and then choose the **Flat Endmill** icon. Under **Tool Diameter**, select **Equal** and enter the value **0.5** as shown.

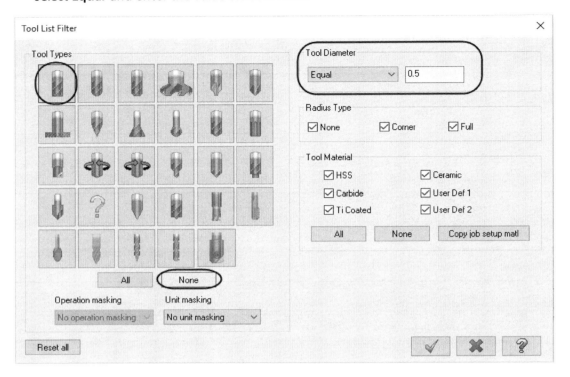

♦ Select **OK** button to exit the **Tool List Filter** dialog box.

♦ Select the **1/2" Flat Endmill** as shown.

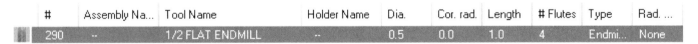

#	Assembly Na...	Tool Name	Holder Name	Dia.	Cor. rad.	Length	# Flutes	Type	Rad. ...
290	--	1/2 FLAT ENDMILL	--	0.5	0.0	1.0	4	Endmi...	None

♦ Select the tool in the **Tool Selection** dialog box and then choose the **OK** button to exit.

♦ Make the necessary changes to the **Tool** page as shown.

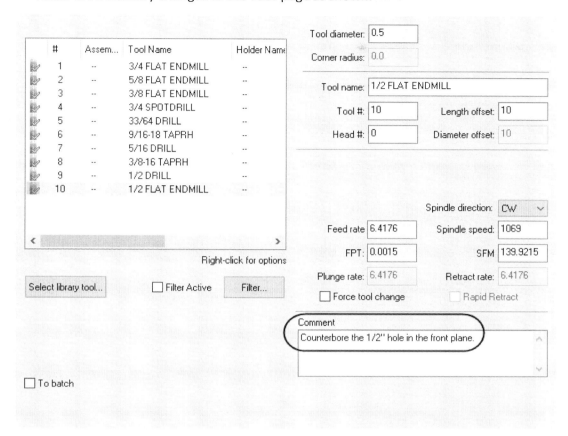

16.2 Set the Cut Parameters

♦ Select **Cut Parameters**, change the drill **Cycle** to **Drill/Counterbore** and input a **Dwell** of **1.0** second as shown.

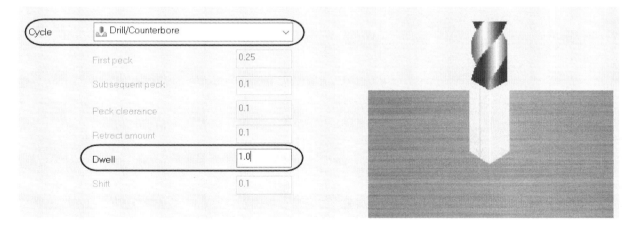

16.3 Set the Linking Parameters

♦ Select **Linking Parameters** and input a **Depth** value of **-0.55** as shown.

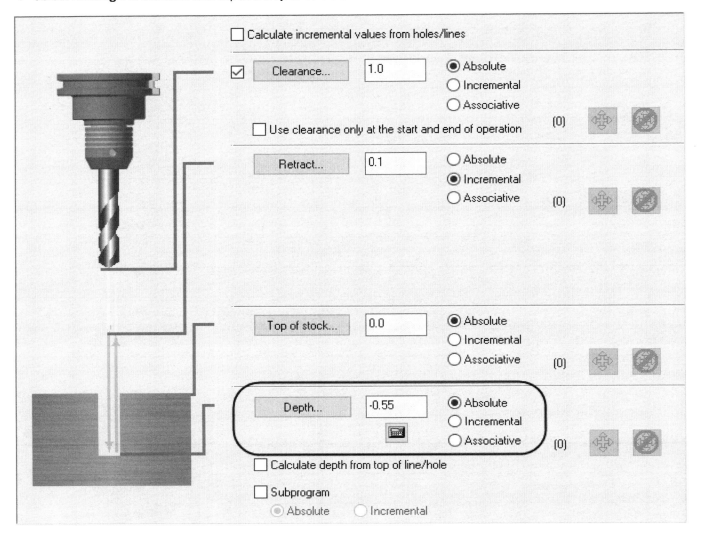

♦ Select **Tip Comp** and ensure this option is disabled.

16.4 Preview the Toolpath

♦ To quickly check how the toolpath will be generated, select the **Preview toolpath** icon as shown.

♦ See **"Preview the Toolpath" on page 549** to review the procedure.
♦ The toolpath should look as shown.

♦ Press **Esc** key to exit the preview.

Note: If the toolpath does not look as shown in the preview, check your parameters again.

♦ Select the **OK** button to exit the **2D Toolpaths - Drill/Circles Simple drill - no peck** parameters and generate the toolpath.

16.5 Backplot and Verify

♦ To **Backplot** and **Verify** your toolpath, see"Backplot The Toolpaths" on page 550 and **"Simulate the toolpath in Verify" on page 551**.

♦ To make sure that all toolpaths are selected, choose the **Select all operations** icon.
♦ The part should look as shown.

♦ To go back to the Mastercam window, minimize the **Mastercam Simulator** window as shown.

STEP 17: RENAME THE NC FILE

The Drilling and Tapping operations in "Setup #2 - Front" kept the NC name from Setup #1. We need to rename this operation so it will create a separate program for this setup.

♦ Select "Setup #2 - Front" (make sure all the operations in Setup #2 are selected).

♦ Right click on the group, choose the option **Edit selected operations** and then select **Change NC file name**.

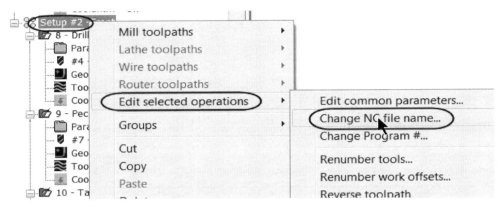

♦ When the **Enter new NC name** dialog box appears enter "**Setup #2 - Front**".

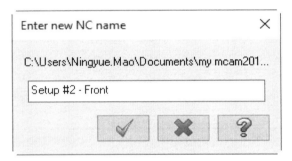

♦ Select the **OK** button to apply the changed NC name to all the operations in the second setup.

♦ The result you should see is **Setup #2 - Front.NC** in all of the operations in the second setup.

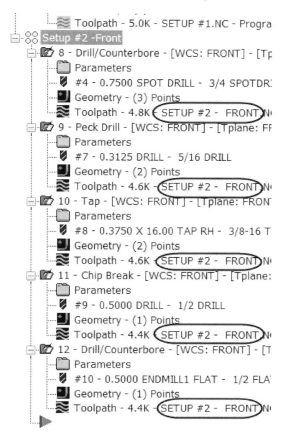

Toolpath Creation - Setup 3

SUGGESTED FIXTURE 3:

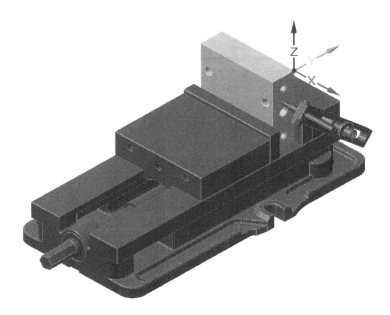

Note: The part is now flipped and you will machine the part from the left side.

SETUP SHEET 3:

TOOL LIST

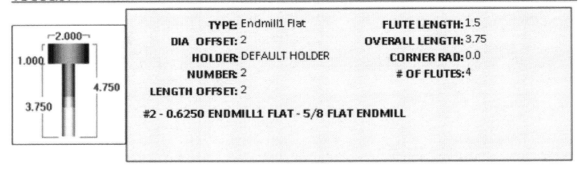

STEP 18: CREATING AND RENAMING TOOLPATH GROUPS

To machine the part in different setups, you will need to have separate programs. To be able to post the operations separate of each setup, you will create them under different toolpath groups with different NC names.

18.1 Create Toolpath Group #3 (Setup #3 - Left)

♦ Right mouse click on the **Machine Group-1**.

♦ Select **Groups** and then **New Toolpath group** as shown.

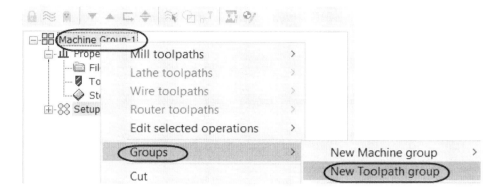

♦ Rename the toolpath group "**Setup #3 - Left**" as shown.

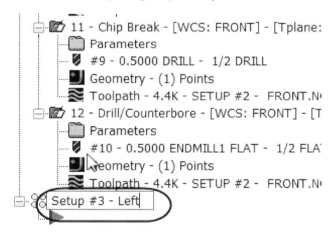

♦ Ensure the arrow is below "**Setup #3 - Left**".

STEP 19: SET THE WCS TO LEFT SIDE

Work coordinate system (WCS) is the active coordinate system in use by Mastercam at any given time. The WCS contains the orientation of the X-Y-Z axes plus the location of the zero point (the origin). This tells Mastercam how your part is positioned or oriented in the machine.

♦ Select **Planes** tab located in the bottom left corner.

♦ Select the **Left side** plane and click on the **equal** sign to set the **WCS**, **C**onstruction **Plane** and **T**ool **Plane** to the **Left side** as shown.

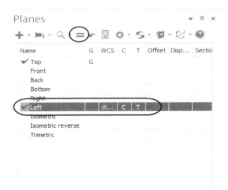

♦ Right mouse click in the graphics window and select the **Isometric** view to see the part in the new orientation.

♦ Press **F9** on your keyboard to view the coordinate axes.
♦ Your part should look as shown.

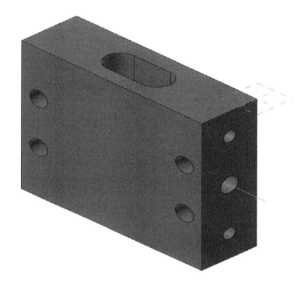

Note: The color of the coordinate axes remains the same because it is the same origin.

♦ Press **F9** to remove the axes display.
♦ To open the **Toolpaths Manager**, select the **Toolpaths** tab in the lower left corner of the screen.

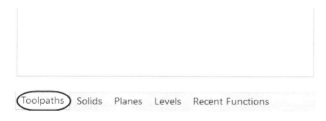

STEP 20: MACHINE THE SLOT

Slot Mill efficiently machines obround slots. This toolpath automatically calculates plunge, entry and exit points appropriate for the slots.

Toolpath Preview:

Toolpaths

♦ From the **2D** group, click on the **Expand gallery** arrow and select **Slot Mill**.

♦ When the **Chaining** dialog box appears, make sure that **C-plane** is enabled as shown.

♦ Select the slot as shown. Ensure the chain is going in a CCW direction.

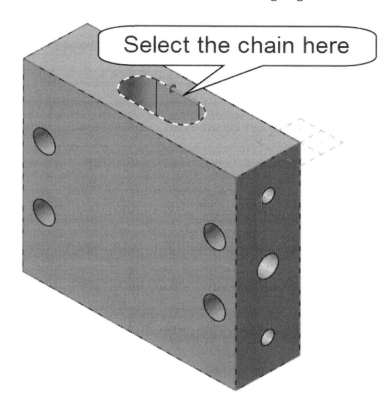

♦ Select the **OK** button in the chaining dialog box to continue.
♦ In the **Toolpath Type** page, the **Slot Mill** toolpath will be selected as shown.

            Facing   Model Chamfer

Contour   Pocket   Facing   Slot mill   Model Chamfer

20.1 Select the 5/8" Flat Endmill from the Tool List

◆ Select **Tool** from the **Tree View list**.
◆ Select the **5/8" Flat Endmill** tool from the list.
◆ Make the necessary changes to the **Tool** page as shown.

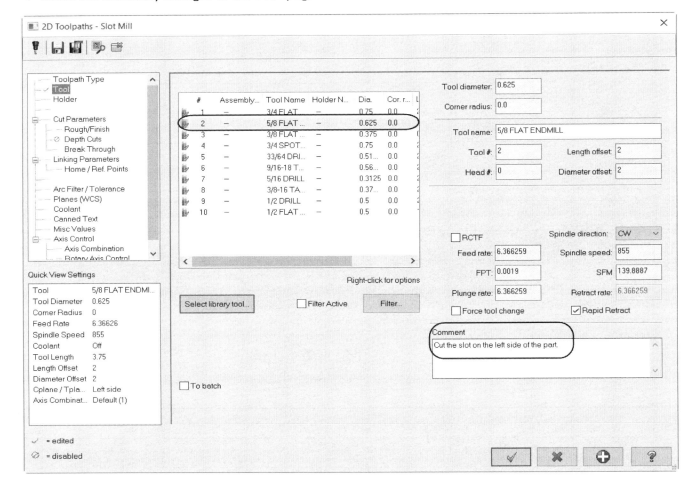

20.2 Set the Cut Parameters

♦ Select **Cut Parameters**, and add an **Overlap** of **0.2** as shown.

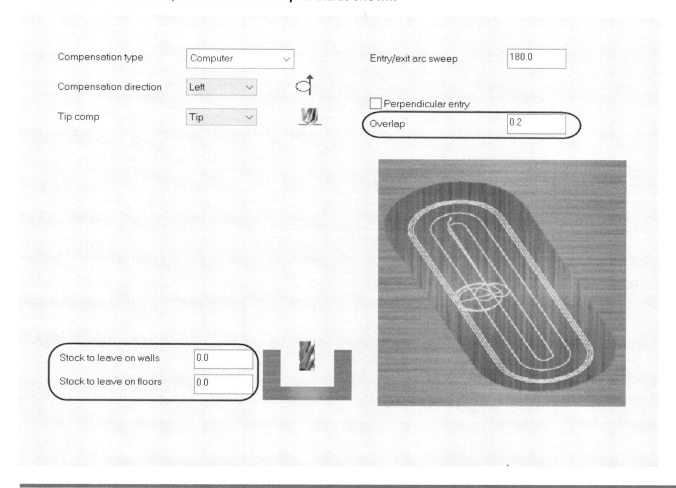

Entry/exit arc sweep sets the included angle of each entry and exit arc. If this value is set to less than 180 degrees, a line will be created.

Overlap sets how far the tool goes past the end of the toolpath before exiting for a cleaner finish.

20.3 Set the Rough/Finish Parameters

♦ Select **Rough/Finish** from the **Tree View list** and ensure your settings appear as shown.

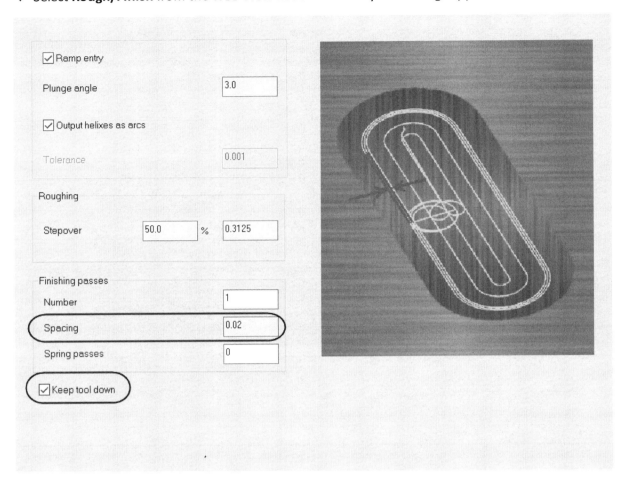

20.4 Set the Depth Cut Parameters

- ◆ Select **Depth Cuts** and input a **Max rough step** of **0.2** as shown.
- ◆ Set the **Finish Cuts** to be **1** and a **Finish step** of **0.02**. Make sure the other parameters appear as shown.

Note: These settings instruct Mastercam to rough the slot leaving 0.05" and then create one lighter cut removing 0.1" of material for a finish pass.

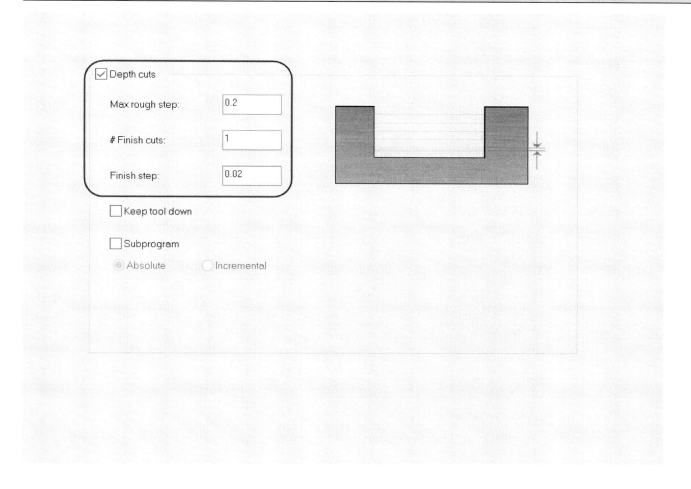

20.5 Set the Linking Parameters

♦ Select **Linking Parameters**, enable **Clearance**, set it to **1.0**, and input a **Depth** of **-1.0** as shown.

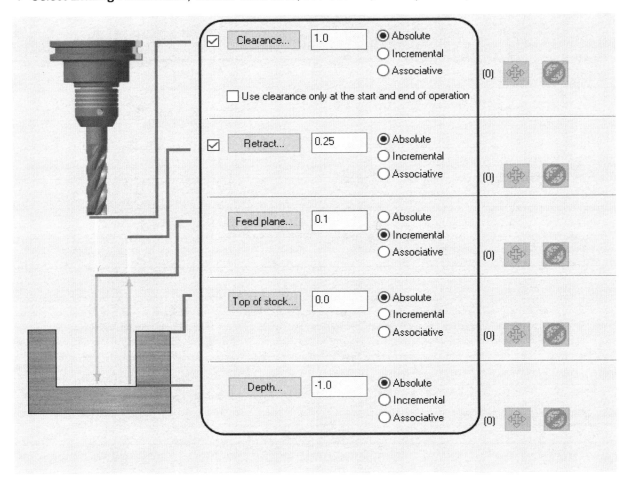

20.6 Preview the Toolpath

♦ To quickly check how the toolpath will be generated, select the **Preview toolpath** icon as shown.

♦ See **"Preview the Toolpath" on page 549** to review the procedure.
♦ The toolpath should look as shown.

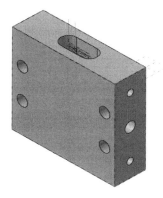

♦ Press **Esc** key to exit the preview.

Note: If the toolpath does not look as shown in the preview, check your parameters again.

♦ Select the **OK** button to exit the **2D Toolpaths - Slot Mill** parameters and generate the toolpath.

20.7 Backplot and Verify

♦ To **Backplot** and **Verify** your toolpath, see **"Backplot The Toolpaths" on page 550** and "Simulate the toolpath in Verify" on page 551 .

♦ To make sure that all toolpaths are selected, choose the **Select all operations** icon.
♦ The part should look as shown.

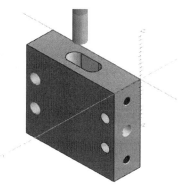

♦ To exit the Mastercam Simulator, click on the **Close** icon.

STEP 21: RENAME THE NC FILE

The Slot milling operation in "Setup #3 - Left" kept the NC name from "Setup #2 - Front". We need to rename this operation so it will create a separate program for this setup.

♦ Select "**Setup #3 - Left**", right click on the group (make sure all the operations in Setup #3 are selected), choose the option **Edit selected operations** and then select **Change NC file name** as shown.

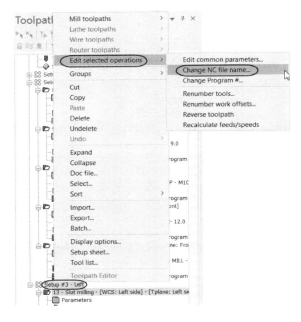

♦ When the **Enter new NC name** dialog box appears enter "**Setup #3 - Left**".

♦ Select the **OK** button to apply the changed **NC name** to all the operations in the second setup.
♦ The result you should see is **Setup #3 - Left.NC** in all of the operations in the second setup as shown.

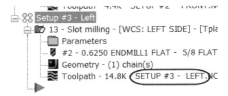

STEP 22: POST THE FILE

♦ Ensure all operations are selected. If not, use the button **Select all operations** in the **Toolpaths Manager**.

♦ Select the **Post selected operations** icon from the **Toolpaths Manager** as shown. G1

♦ In the **Post processing** window, make necessary changes as shown.

NC file enabled allows you to keep the NC file and to assign the same name as the MCAM file.
Edit enabled allows you to automatically launch the default.

♦ Select the **OK** button to continue.

♦ Save your file and name it Setup #1.NC.

♦ Save your file and name it Setup #2 - Front.NC.

♦ Save your file and name it Setup #3 - Left.NC.

♦ A window with **Mastercam Code Expert** will be launched and the NC program will appear as shown.

♦ Select the "**X**" box at the upper right corner to exit the editor.

STEP 23: SAVE THE UPDATED MCAM FILE

CREATE THE TOOLPATHS FOR TUTORIAL #5 EXERCISE

Create the Toolpaths for Tutorial #5 Exercise as per the instructions below.

Select the Mill Default.

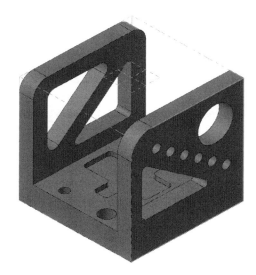

Set the machine properties including the stock setup.

♦ The stock will appear as shown.

Remove the material in the center of the part using 2D HS Dynamic Mill.

♦ In **Machining regions**, select the bottom rectangle (enable C-plane).
♦ Enable **From outside**.

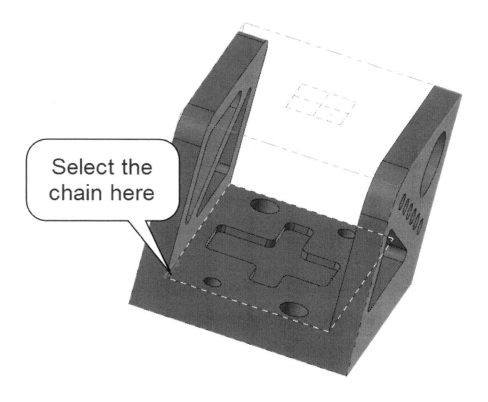

Select the chain here

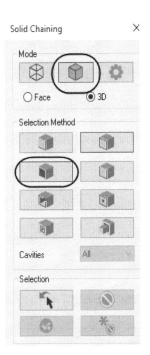

♦ In **Avoidance regions**, switch in the **Chaining**
  dialog box to **Solids** selection and enable only
  the **Face** button as shown.

♦ Select the five faces as shown.

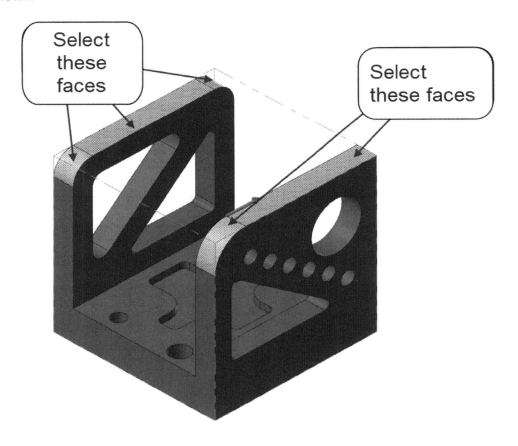

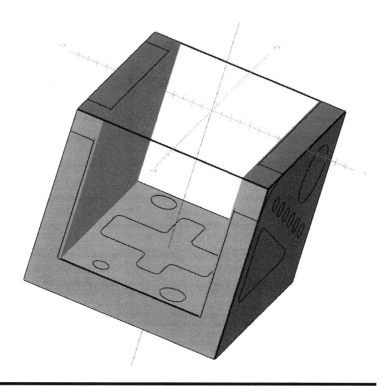

- Use a **1" Flat Endmill**.
- Ensure the **Cutting Method** is set to **Climb**.
- **Approach distance = 1.0.**
- **Stepover** = **25%.**
- **Min toolpath radius** = **10%.**
- **Gap size % of tool diameter** = **100.**
- **Stock to leave on walls** = **0.05.**
- **Stock to leave on floors** = **0.0.**
- **Depth Cuts** set the **Max rough step** = **1.0.**
- Choose an **Entry method** as **Helix**.
- **No Break Through.**
- Set the depth according to the drawing.

*Note: Some of these toolpaths will require you to change the default tool's settings. Refer to **page 868** for more information on how to do this.*

Change Tool Length.

- Select the tool under Operation #1.
- **Overall length** = **6".**
- **Cutting length** = **4".**
- Select **Finish**.

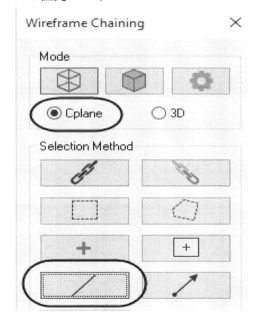

Use Contour toolpath to finish the vertical faces.

- Go back to **Wireframe** mode in the **Chaining** dialog box and use **Single** chain as shown.

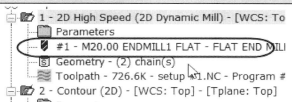

♦ Select the two lines in the clockwise direction.

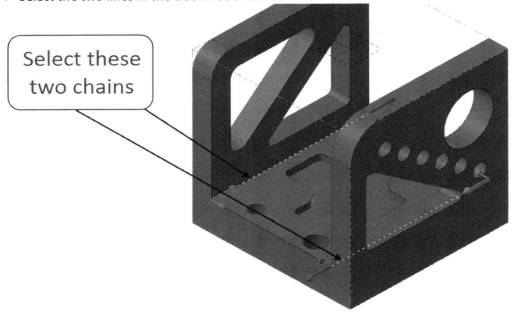

Select these two chains

♦ Use a **3/4" Flat Endmill**.
♦ Increase the tool's **Cutting length** to **3.5"**.
♦ **Overall length = 4"**.
♦ Set the **Compensation direction** to **Right**.
♦ **Depth cuts** set to **Max rough step** of **0.375**.
♦ **Lead In/Out** disable **Entry** and **Exit** and enable **Adjust start/end of contour** setting the **Length** to **Extend 100%**.
♦ Set the **Linking parameters** according to the drawing.

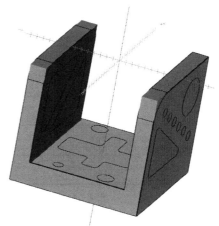

Machine the Pocket.

♦ Use a **1/4" Flat Endmill.**
♦ Edit the tool's **Cutting length** to **4"** and the **Overall length** to **4.5"**.
♦ Ensure the **Machining direction** is set to **Climb**.
♦ **Stock to leave on walls/floors = 0.0**.
♦ Select a desired **Cutting method**.
♦ Choose an **Entry motion**.
♦ Set the **Finishing** parameters.
♦ Enable **Lead In/Out**.
♦ Disable **Depth Cuts**, and **Break Through**.
♦ Set the **Top of stock** and the **Depth** according to the drawing.

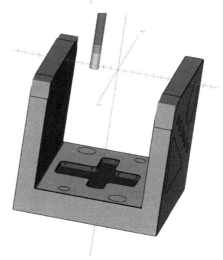

Spot Drill the holes.

- ◆ Use a **3/4" Spot Drill**.
- ◆ Edit the tool **Cutting length** to **3"** and the **Overall length** to **4"**.
- ◆ Set the **Drill Cycle** to **Drill/Counterbore**.
- ◆ Set the **Top of stock** according to the material.
- ◆ Set the **Depth** to leave a **0.05" Chamfer** on all the holes.
- ◆ Ensure to change the **Depth** for the two larger holes.

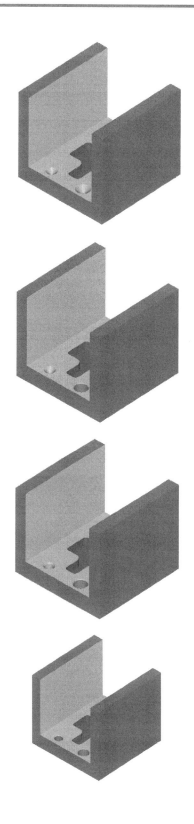

Drill the 1/2" Holes.

- ◆ Use a **1/2" Drill**.
- ◆ Edit the tool **Cutting length** to **3"** and the **Overall length** to **5"**.
- ◆ Set the **Drill cycle** to **Drill/Counterbore**.
- ◆ Set the **Top of stock** according to the material.
- ◆ Set the **Depth** and include **Tip Comp**.

Drill the 3/8"10 Tapped Holes.

- ◆ Use a **5/16" Drill**.
- ◆ Edit the tool **Cutting length** to **3"** and the **Overall length** to **5"**.
- ◆ Set the **Drill Cycle** to **Drill/Counterbore**.
- ◆ Set the **Top of stock** according to the material.
- ◆ Set the **Depth** and include **Tip Comp**.

Tap the 3/8 - 16 Holes.

- ◆ Use a **3/8 - 16NC Tap RH**.
- ◆ Edit the tool **Cutting length** to **3"** and the **Overall length** to **5"**.
- ◆ Set the **Drill Cycle** to **Tap**.
- ◆ Set the **Top of stock** according to the material.
- ◆ Set the **Depth** and include **Tip Comp**.

Set the WCS to a new plane defined by existing geometry.

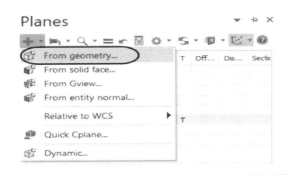

- In the **Planes**, click on the + (plus sign) to create a new plane.
- From the list, select **From Geometry** as shown.
- Press **Alt + S** to see the solid in an wireframe mode.

Note: You will select two lines that can define the plane.

- [Select an entity]: Select the lines in the order as shown.

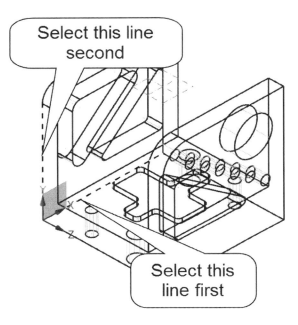

- To change the axes orientation from the **Select plane**, click on the **Next plane** button until the orientation looks as shown.

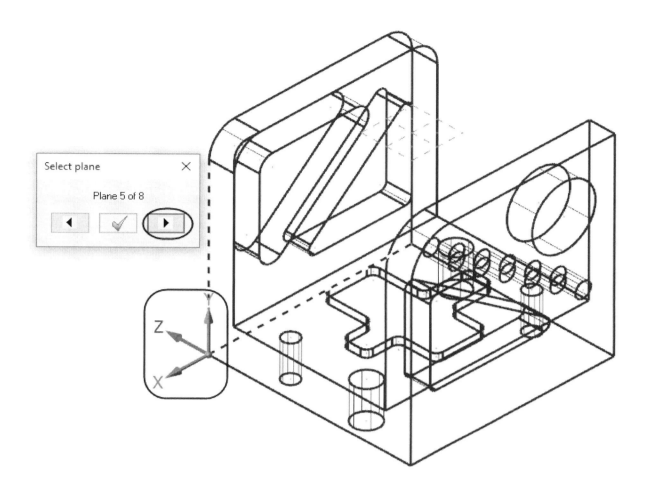

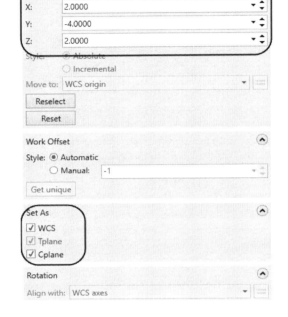

- From **Select plane** click on the **OK** button to continue.
- In the **New Plane** panel, change the plane name to **Setup 2** and enable **Set as WCS**.

- The **Planes Manager** panel should look as shown.

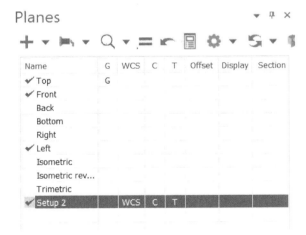

- Right mouse click in the graphics window and select **Isometric**.
- Press **F9** to see where the axes and the Origin is. The origin should be at the top of the part lower right corner.

Create a new Toolpath Group and rename the NC File name for the last toolpath group.

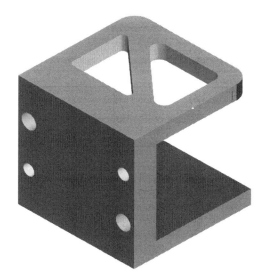

- ◆ **Pocket** the two cut through triangles.
- ◆ Use a **1/4" Flat Endmill**.
- ◆ **Stock to leave on walls** = **0.0**.
- ◆ You may wish to use the original tool lengths from this point on as we no longer need to machine very deep pockets.

Create a Contour toolpath around the two fillets.

- ◆ Use the **1/4" Flat Endmill**.
- ◆ Set the **Depth** according to the drawing.

Set the WCS to new plane based on existing geometry.

- ◆ Select the lines as shown.
- ◆ Select the **Next plane** button until the axes are oriented as shown.

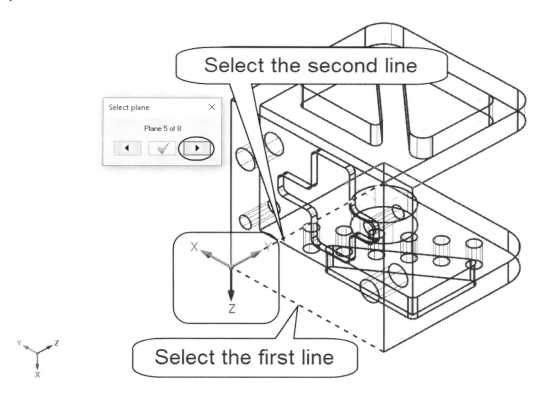

- ◆ In the **New Plane** panel, change the plane name to **Setup 3** and enable **Set As WCS**.
- ◆ Change the graphic view to Isometric and press **F9** to check for the Origin. It should be at the lower right top corner.

Create a new Toolpath Group and rename the NC
File name for the last toolpath group.

◆ **Pocket** the cut through triangle.
◆ Use a **1/4" Flat Endmill**.
◆ **Stock to leave on walls/floors = 0.0**.

◆ **Drill** the 6 holes.
◆ Use the **5/16" HSS/TIN Drill**.
◆ Set the **Drill Cycle** to **Drill/Counterbore**.
◆ **Tap** the 6 holes.
◆ Use the **3/8 - 16Tap**.

◆ Set the **Drill Cycle** to **Tap**.
◆ **Circle Mill** the **1.25"** diameter hole.
◆ Use a **1/2" Flat Endmill**.
◆ **Stock to leave on walls/floors = 0.0**.
◆ Enable **Roughing**.
◆ Enable **Finishing** and set the **Finish Passes** to **2**
  with a spacing of **0.02"**.
◆ Set the depth according to the drawing.

◆ Create a **Contour** operation to remove the material
  around the fillet.
◆ Use a **1/2" Flat Endmill**.

Once complete, your part will appear as shown.

TUTORIAL #5 TOOLPATH CREATION QUIZ

♦ What settings do you need to use to remachine a pocket using High Speed Area Mill Toolpath?

♦ What is the use of WCS in Mastercam?

♦ After creating a new toolpath group, why do you rename the NC file?

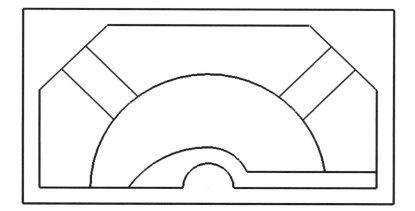

OVERVIEW OF STEPS TAKEN TO CREATE THE PART GEOMETRY:

From Drawing to CAD Model:

♦ The student should examine the drawing on the following page to understand what part is being created in the tutorial.

♦ From the drawing we can decide how to create the geometry in Mastercam.

Create the 2D CAD Model:

♦ The student will create the Top 2D geometry needed to create the toolpaths.

♦ Geometry creation commands such as Rectangle, Circle Center Point, Line Endpoints, and Line Parallel will be used.

♦ The student will also learn how to clean up the geometry using the trimming functions.

TUTORIAL #6 DRAWING

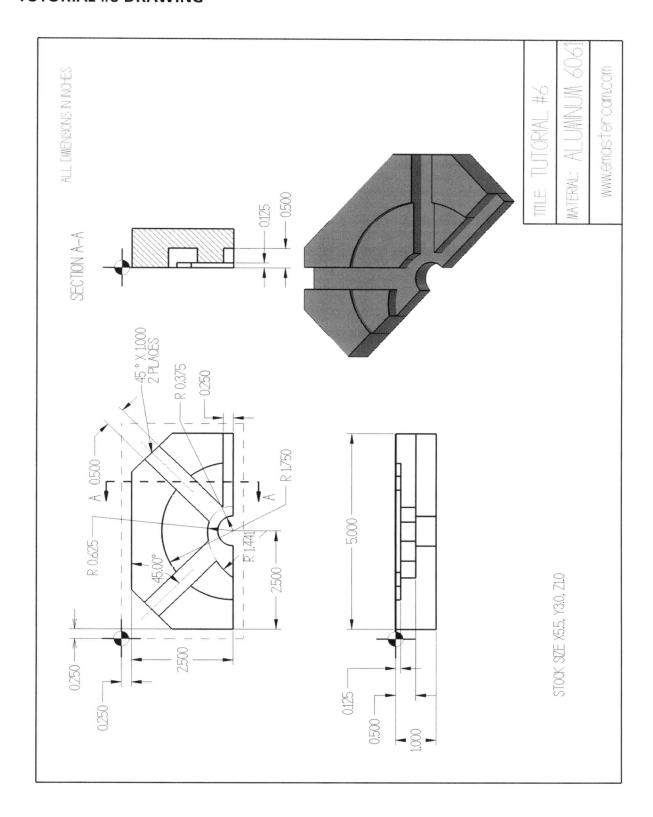

SECTION A-A

ALL DIMENSIONS IN INCHES

0.125
0.500

45° X 1.000
2 PLACES

R 0.375

0.250

A 0.500

R 1.750

R 0.625

45.00°

R 1.441

2.500

A

0.250

0.250

2.500

5.000

0.125

0.500

1.000

STOCK SIZE X5.5, Y3.0, Z1.0

TITLE: TUTORIAL #6

MATERIAL: ALUMINUM 6061

www.emastercam.com

STEP 1: SETTING UP THE GRAPHICAL USER INTERFACE

Please refer to the **Getting Started** section to set up the graphical user interface.

STEP 2: CREATE RECTANGLES

In this step you will create rectangles using the **Rectangle** command. The rectangle you create will be based on the origin.

Step Preview:

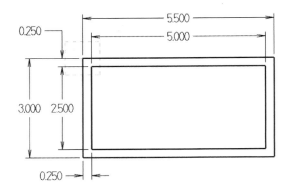

2.1 Create the 5.5" by 3.0" rectangle

Wireframe

♦ From the **Shapes** group, select **Rectangle**.

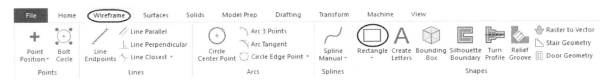

♦ To select the position of the base point, from the **General Selection** toolbar, click on the drop down arrow next to the **AutoCursor** as shown.

♦ From the fly-out menu, select **Origin**.

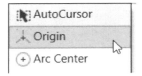

- [Select position of second corner]: Select a point to right of the origin and below it as shown.

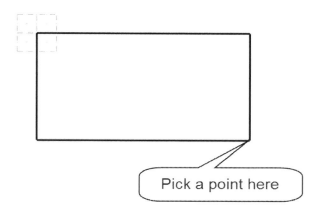

Pick a point here

> Note: You can make this rectangle as small or as large as you want. The entities are still live and therefore you can modify the values to get the size you want.

- Enter a **Width** of **5.5** and a **Height** of **-3.0** as shown.

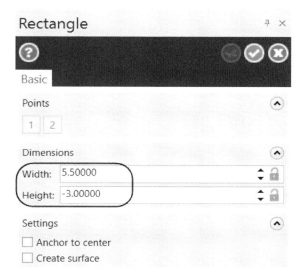

- Press **Enter** to finish the rectangle and continue in the same command.

> Note: While creating geometry for this tutorial, if you make a mistake, you can undo the last step using the **Undo** icon. ↶ You can undo as many steps as needed. If you delete or undo a step by mistake, just use the **Redo** icon. ↷ To delete unwanted geometry, select the geometry first and then press **Delete** from the keyboard.

- Press **Alt + F1** to fit the drawing to the graphics window.

2.2 Create the 5.0" by 2.5" rectangle

♦ [Select position of first corner]: Select the **AutoCursor Fast Point** icon from the **General Selection** toolbar and the field where you can type the coordinates will open at the upper left side of the graphics window as shown.

♦ Enter the coordinate values of **0.25, -0.25** as shown.

0.25,-0.25|

♦ Hit **Enter** on your keyboard to set the first position of the corner.
♦ In the **Rectangle** panel, enter a **Width** of **5.0** and a **Height** of **-2.5** as shown.

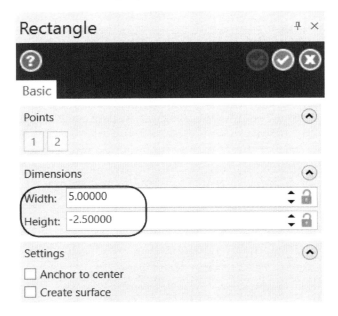

♦ Choose the **OK** button to exit the command.

STEP 3: CREATE CIRCLES AND ARC TANGENT

Circle Center Point lets you create circles given the center point and the radius or the diameter.
Arc Tangent One Entity lets you create an arc given the radius, the entity to which it is tangent and the tangency point.

Step Preview:

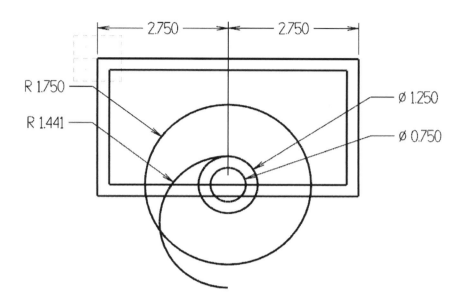

Wireframe

♦ From **Arcs** group, select the **Circle Center Point** as shown.

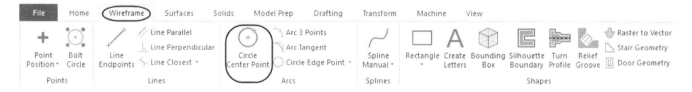

♦ In the **Circle Center Point** panel, enter a **Radius** value of **0.375** as shown. Press **Enter** and the diameter will be updated too.

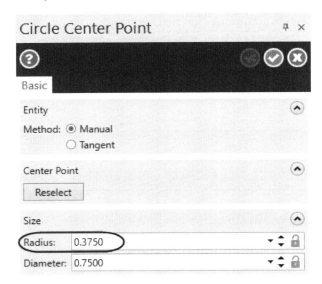

♦ [Enter the center point]: Select the line **Midpoint** as shown.

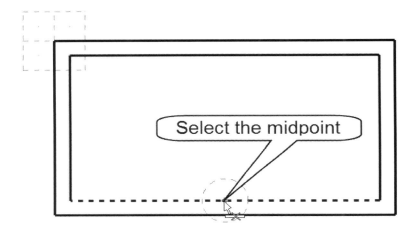

♦ Make sure that when selecting the center, the visual cue of the cursor changes as shown.

♦ Press **Enter** to continue.

♦ Change the **Radius** value to **0.625**, press **Enter** and select the same line midpoint.

♦ Press **Enter** to continue.

♦ Change the **Radius** value to **1.75**, press **Enter** and select the same line midpoint.

♦ Choose the **OK** button to exit the command.

- Press **Alt + F1** to fit the geometry to the graphics window.
- The geometry should look as shown.

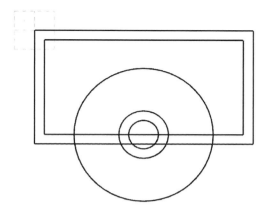

- In the **General Selection** bar, click on the **Selection Setting**s icon, and enable **Quadrant** as shown.

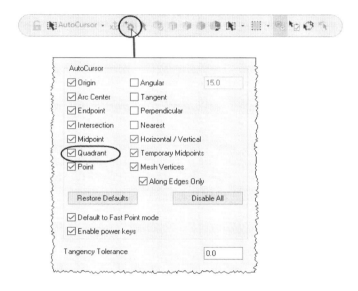

- Select the **OK** button to exit the **Selection** dialog box.
- Select the **Yes** button to save the current settings to the configuration file.

3.1 Create the Arc tangent to an entity

Wireframe

- From the **Arcs** group, select **Arc Tangent**.

- In the **Arc Tangent** panel, in the **Method** field, select **Arc one entity** as shown.
- Enter a **Radius** value of **1.441** and press **Enter**.

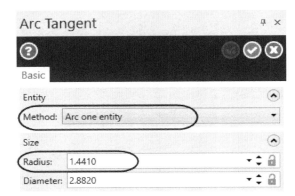

- [Select the entity that the arc is to be tangent to]: Select the arc as shown.

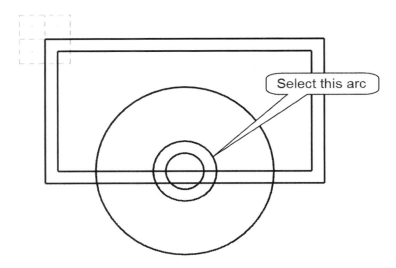

- [Specify the tangent point]: Select the **Quadrant** as shown.

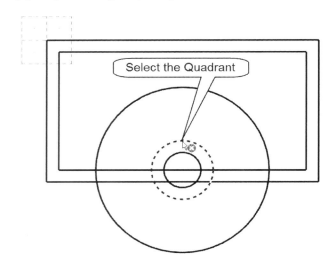

♦ [Select an arc]: Select the arc as shown.

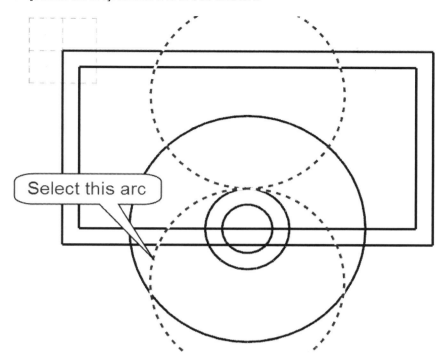

Select this arc

♦ Choose the **OK** button to exit the command.
♦ Press **Alt + F1** to fit the geometry to the graphics window.

♦ The geometry should look as shown.

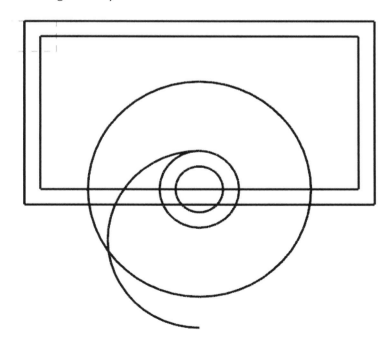

STEP 4: TRIM THE ARCS

Trim to point trims an entity to a point or any defined position in the graphics window. If the point you enter does not lie on the selected entity, Mastercam calculates the closest position on the entity and trims the entity to that point.

Step Preview:

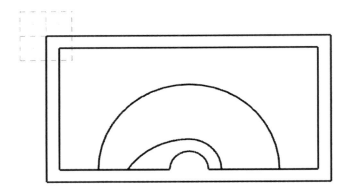

Wireframe

♦ From the **Modify** group, select the **Trim to Entities** drop down menu as shown.

4.1 Trim the entities using Trim to point command

♦ Select **Trim to point** in the drop down menu as shown.

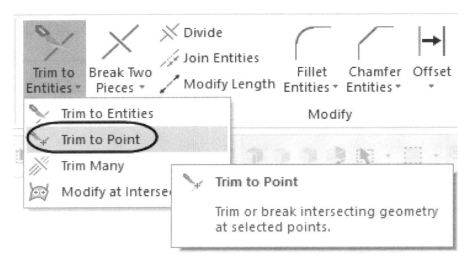

♦ [Select the entity to trim/extend]: Select the arc as shown in Figure: 4.1.1.
♦ [Indicate the trim/extend location]: Select the Endpoint as shown in Figure: 4.1.1.

Figure: 4.1.1

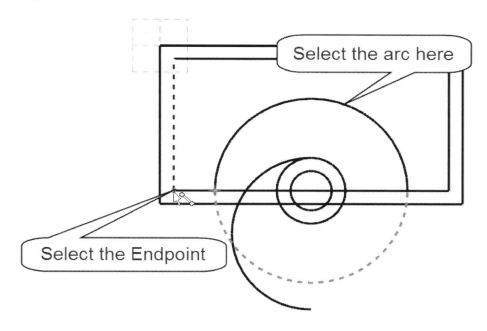

♦ [Select the entity to trim/extend]: Select the arc as shown in Figure: 4.1.2.
♦ [Indicate the trim/extend location]: Select the Intersection as shown in Figure: 4.1.2.

Figure: 4.1.2

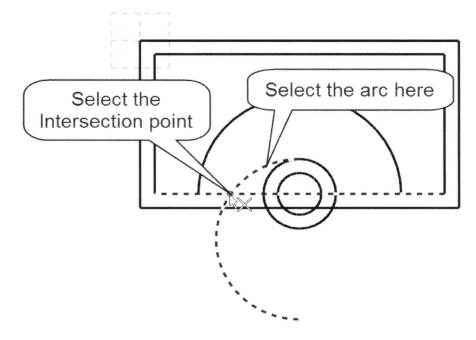

♦ [Select the entity to trim/extend]: Select the 0.375 radius circle as shown in Figure: 4.1.3.
♦ [Indicate the trim/extend location]: Select the Endpoint as shown in Figure: 4.1.3.

Figure: 4.1.3

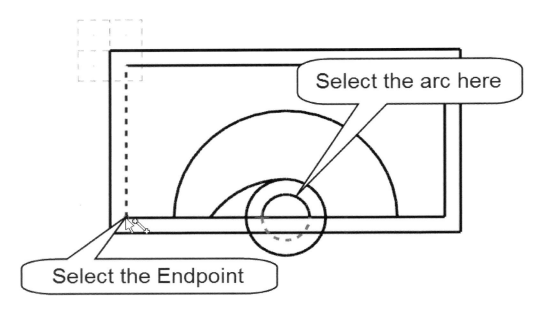

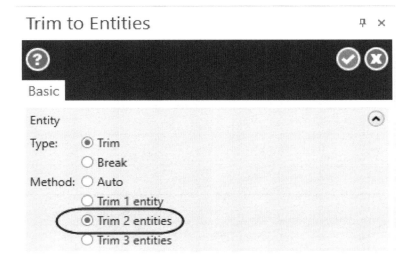

4.2 Trim the entities using Trim 2 entities

♦ In the **Trim to Point** panel, enable **Trim 2 entities** as shown.

♦ [Select the entity to trim/extend]: Select Entity A as shown in Figure: 4.2.1.

♦ [Select the entity to trim/extend to]: Select Entity B as shown in Figure: 4.2.1.

Figure: 4.2.1

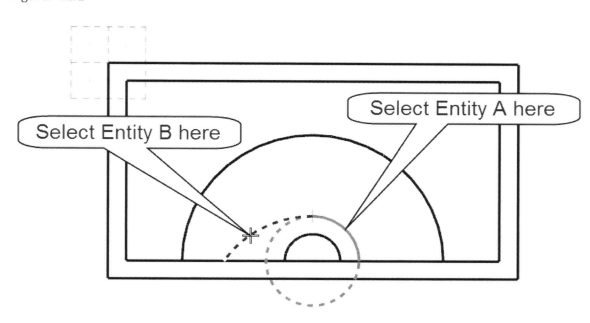

Wireframe

♦ From the **Modify** group, select **Divide** icon as shown.

4.3 Trim Entities using Divide

♦ In the **Divide** panel, enable **Trim** as shown.

♦ Select the line in between the half circle endpoints as shown.

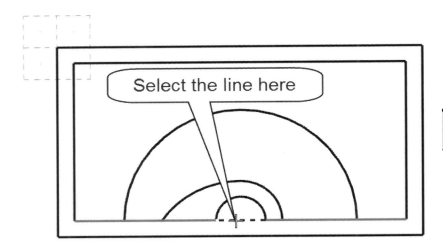

Note: **Divide** *trims a line or arc to the intersection point between it.*

♦ Select the **OK** button to exit the **Divide** command.
♦ The part will appear as shown.

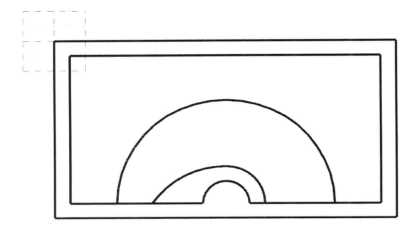

STEP 5: CREATE LINE PARALLEL

In this step you will learn how to create a line parallel given the distance and direction.

Step Preview:

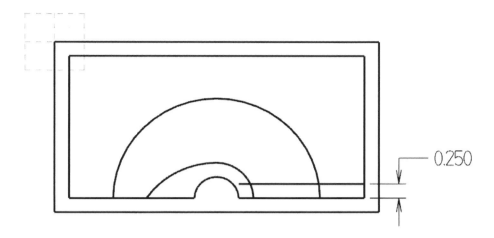

Wireframe

♦ From the **Lines** group, select **Line Parallel** as shown.

♦ [Select a line]: Select the line as shown.

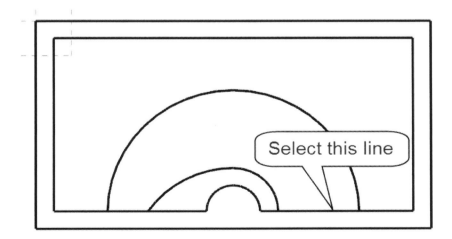

♦ [Select the point to place a parallel line through]: Select a point above that line as shown.

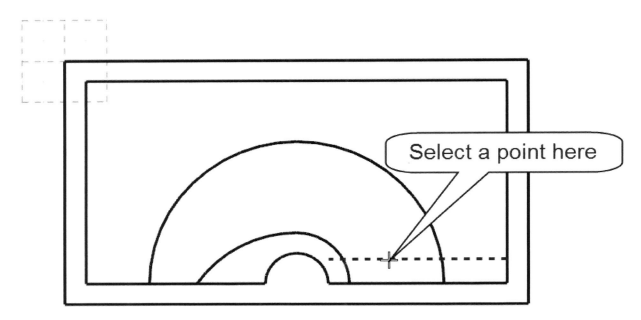

♦ In the Line Parallel panel, change the Distance to **0.25** as shown.

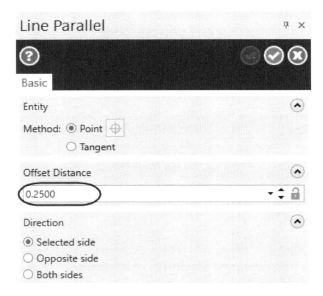

♦ Choose the **OK** button to exit the command.

STEP 6: CREATE CHAMFERS

In this step you will learn how to create a chamfer on two corners of the part. You will create this chamfer given the width and angle.

Step Preview:

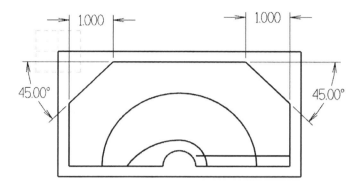

Wireframe

♦ From the **Modify** group, select **Chamfer Entities** as shown.

♦ In the **Chamfer Entities** panel, make sure the **Style** is set to **1 Distance**, **Distance 1** is set to **1.0** and ensure **Trim entities** is enabled.

♦ [Select line or arc]: Select the vertical line and then the horizontal line as shown.

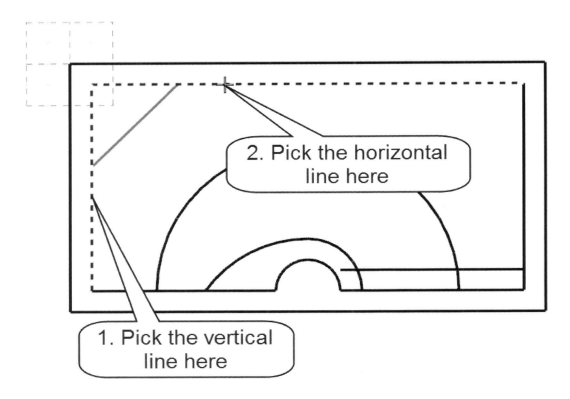

♦ Repeat this process for the opposite corner.

♦ Choose the **OK** button to exit the command.

STEP 7: CREATE POLAR LINES

In this step you will learn how to create a line given one endpoint and angle.

Step Preview:

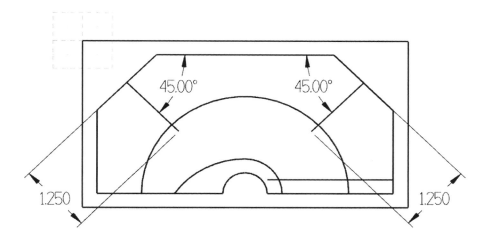

Wireframe

♦ From the **Lines** group, select **Line Endpoints** as shown.

♦ [Specify the first endpoint]: Select the **Midpoint** of the left chamfer.

♦ Ensure the **AutoCursor** icon has changed to represent the line midpoint.

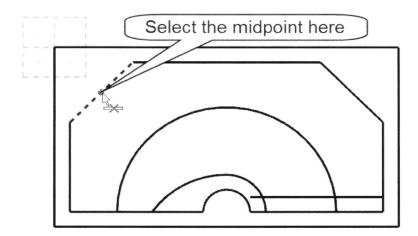

♦ [Specify the second endpoint]: Sketch a line at any angle and any length as shown.

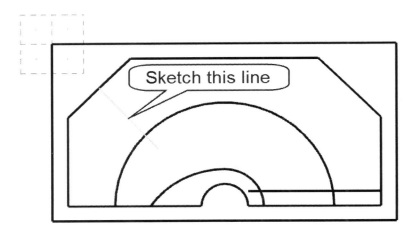

Note: At this point the line is still live and can be modified to any angle or length you desire.

♦ In the **Line Endpoints** panel, enter a **Length** of **1.25** and an **Angle** of **-45** degrees.

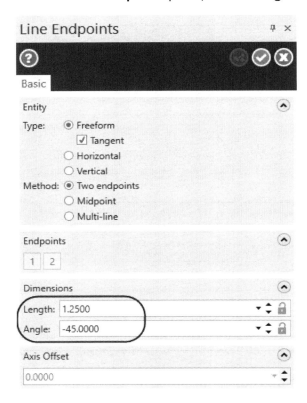

♦ Hit **Enter** on your keyboard to preview the line.
♦ Hit **Enter** again to continue in the same command.
♦ Select the midpoint of the opposite chamfer and sketch a line.

♦ Enter a **Length** of **1.25** and an **Angle** of **270-45** degrees as shown.

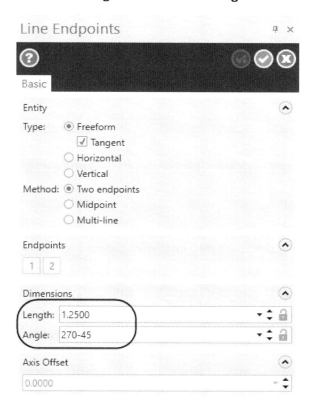

♦ Select the **OK** button to exit the **Line Endpoints** command.

♦ The geometry should look as shown.

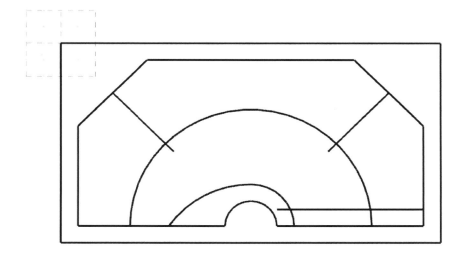

STEP 8: CREATE LINE PARALLEL

In this step you will learn how to create a line parallel given the distance and side on which to create the line.

Step Preview:

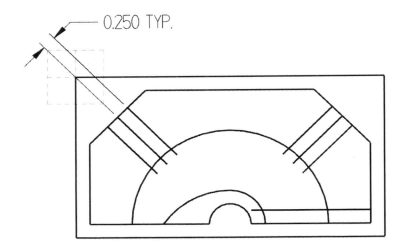

Wireframe

♦ From the **Lines** group, select **Line Parallel** as shown.

♦ [Select a line]: Select the line as shown.

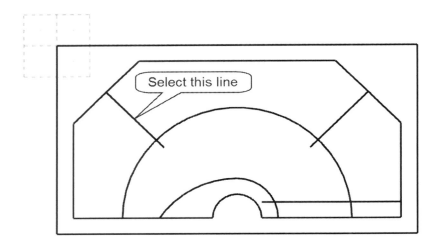

♦ [Select the point to place a parallel line through]: Select a point on either side of this line.
♦ Input an **Offset Distance** of **0.25**, hit **Enter** on your keyboard and enable **Both sides** as shown.

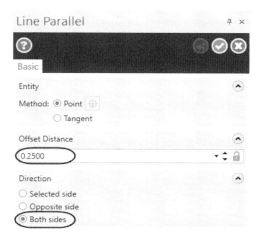

♦ This will position lines on either side of the originally selected entity as shown.

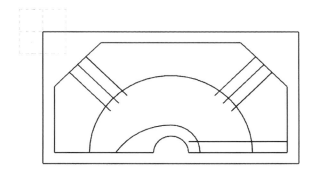

♦ Press **Enter** to continue in the same command and repeat the step for the opposite side of the part.
♦ The geometry should look as shown.

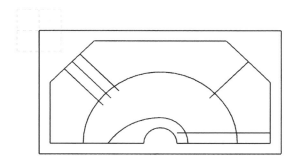

♦ Select the **OK** button to exit the **Line Parallel** command.

STEP 9: DELETE ENTITIES

Step Preview:

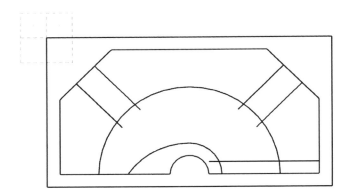

◆ Select the entities as shown. Then press the **Delete** key from the keyboard.

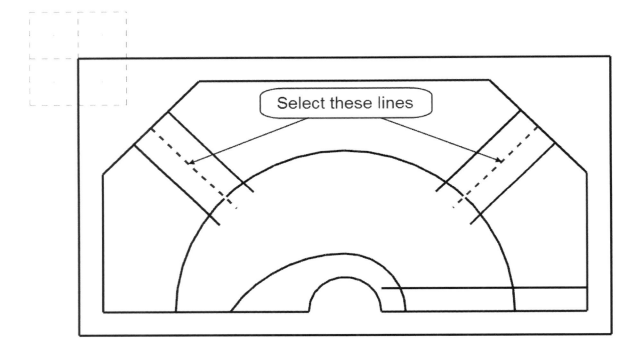

STEP 10: TRIM ENTITIES

To **Trim 1 entity**, select the entity you wish to trim, then select the entity you wish to trim to.

Step Preview:

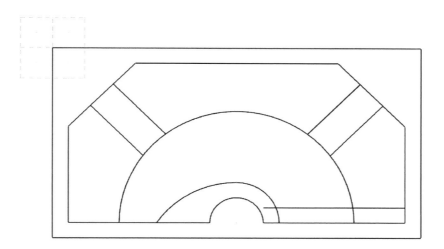

10.1 Trim entities using Trim 1 entity command

Wireframe

♦ From the **Modify** group, select **Trim to Entities** icon as shown.

♦ In the **Trim to Entities** panel, enable the **Trim 1 entity** as shown.

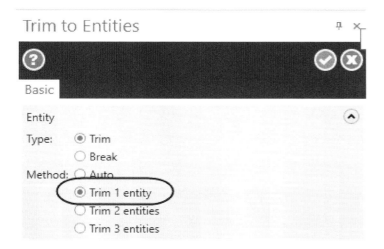

- ◆ [Select the entity to trim/extend]: Select the line as shown in Figure: 10.1.1.
- ◆ [Select the entity to trim/extend to]: Select the arc as shown in Figure: 10.1.1.

Figure: 10.1.1

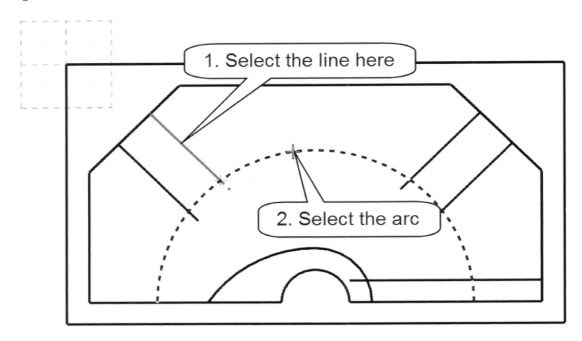

- ◆ Repeat the step for the other 3 lines.
- ◆ Your part should look as shown.

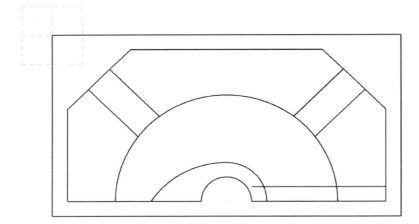

♦ Select the half circle and then select the line as shown.

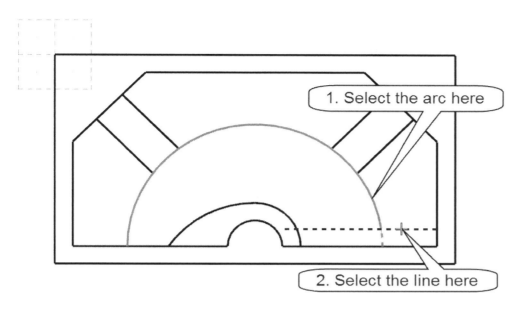

1. Select the arc here

2. Select the line here

10.2 Trim entities using Trim 2 entities

♦ In the **Trim to Entities** panel, enable **Trim 2 entities** as shown.

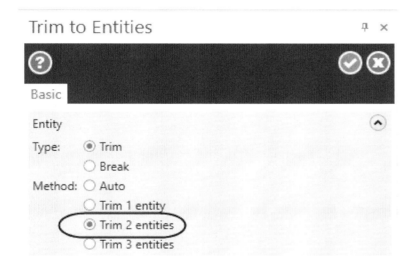

♦ Select the line and arc as shown.

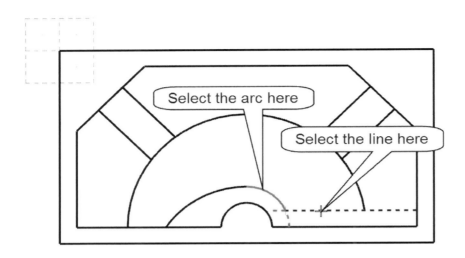

♦ Select the **OK** button to exit the **Trim Break Extend** command.
♦ The part will appear as shown once complete.

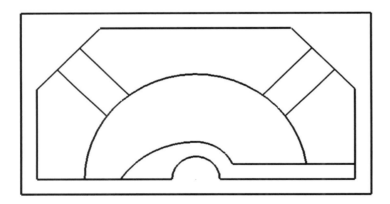

STEP 11: SAVE THE FILE

File

♦ **Save As.**

♦ Click on the **Browse** icon as shown.
♦ Find a location on the computer to save your file.
♦ File name: "Your Name_6".

TUTORIAL #6 REVIEW EXERCISE

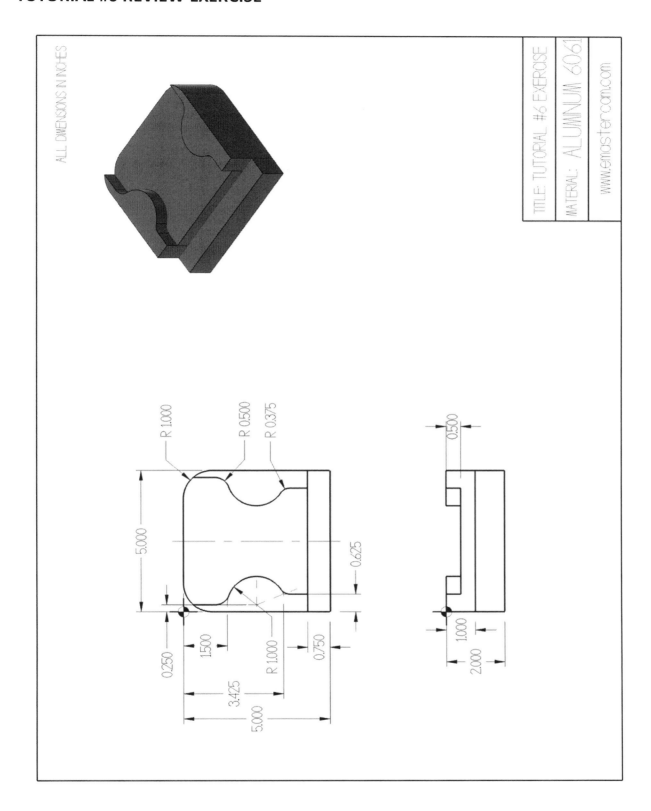

CREATE THE GEOMETRY FOR TUTORIAL #6 EXERCISE

Use these commands to create the geometry.

- ◆ Rectangle.
- ◆ Line Parallel.
- ◆ Arc Endpoints.
- ◆ Fillet Entities.

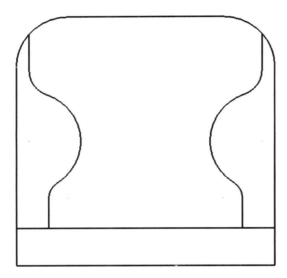

TUTORIAL #6 GEOMETRY CREATION QUIZ

♦ What do you need to know to create an arc by using Arc Tangent One Entity?

♦ What do you need to know to create chamfers and what is 1 Distance chamfer method?

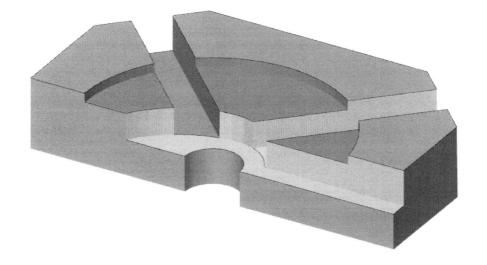

OVERVIEW OF STEPS TAKEN TO CREATE THE FINAL PART:

Create the necessary Toolpaths to machine the part:

♦ The student will set up the stock size to be used and the clamping method to be used.
♦ A 2D High Speed Dynamic Mill toolpath will be created to remove the material outside of the step.
♦ A 2D High Speed Area Mill toolpath will be created to machine the step.
♦ A 2D High Speed Blend Mill toolpath will be created to machine the semi arc shape pocket.
♦ Two 2D High Speed Peel Mill toolpaths will be created to machine the two slots.

Backplot and Verify the file:

♦ Backplot will be used to simulate a step-by-step process of the tool's movements.
♦ Verify will be used to watch a tool machine the part out of a solid model.

Post Process the file to generate the G-code:

♦ The student will then post process the file to obtain an NC file containing the necessary code for the machine.

SUGGESTED FIXTURE

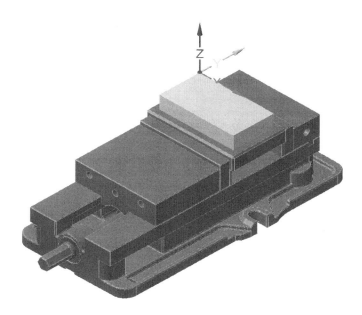

SETUP SHEET

TOOL LIST

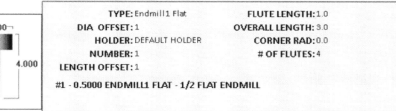

TYPE: Endmill1 Flat	**FLUTE LENGTH:** 1.0
DIA OFFSET: 1	**OVERALL LENGTH:** 3.0
HOLDER: DEFAULT HOLDER	**CORNER RAD:** 0.0
NUMBER: 1	**# OF FLUTES:** 4
LENGTH OFFSET: 1	

#1 - 0.5000 ENDMILL1 FLAT - 1/2 FLAT ENDMILL

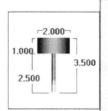

TYPE: Endmill1 Flat	**FLUTE LENGTH:** 0.5
DIA OFFSET: 2	**OVERALL LENGTH:** 2.5
HOLDER: DEFAULT HOLDER	**CORNER RAD:** 0.0
NUMBER: 2	**# OF FLUTES:** 4
LENGTH OFFSET: 2	

#2 - 0.2500 ENDMILL1 FLAT - 1/4 FLAT ENDMILL

STEP 1: SELECT THE MACHINE AND SET UP THE STOCK

In Mastercam, you select a **Machine Definition** before creating any toolpath. The **Machine Definition** is a model of your machine's capabilities and features. It acts like a template for setting up your machine. The machine definition ties together three main components: the schematic model of your machine's components, the control definition that models your control capabilities, and the post processor that will generate the required machine code (G-code). For a Mill Essentials exercise (2D toolpaths), we need just a basic machine definition.

*Note: For the purpose of this tutorial, we will be using the **Default Mill** machine.*

1.1 Unhide the Toolpaths Manager panel

♦ From the left side of the graphics window, click on the **Toolpaths** tab as shown.

♦ Pin the **Toolpaths Manager** by clicking on the **Auto Hide** icon as shown.

1.2 Select the machine

*Note: Select the **Mill Default** only if there is no **Machine Group** in the **Toolpaths Manager**.*

Machine

♦ From the **Machine Type** group, select the drop down arrow below **Mill**. Select the **Default**.

*Note: Once you select the **Mill Default**, the **Ribbon bar** changes to reflect the toolpaths that could be used with **Mill Default**.*

♦ Select the plus sign (**+**) in front of **Properties** in the **Toolpaths Manager** to expand the **Toolpaths Group Properties**.

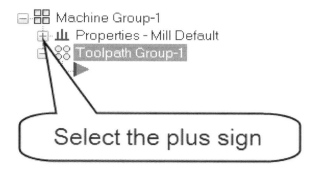

♦ Select **Tool settings** to set the tool parameters.

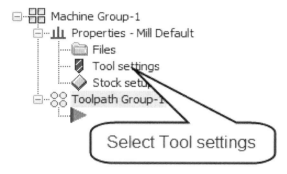

♦ Change the parameters to match the screen shot as shown.

Default program number is used to enter a number if your machine requires a number for a program name.

Assign tool numbers sequentially allows you to overwrite the tool number from the library with the next available tool number. (First operation tool number 1; second operation tool number 2, etc.).

Warn of duplicate tool numbers allows you to get a warning if you enter two tools with the same number.

Override defaults with modal values enables the system to keep the values that you enter.

Feed Calculation set to **From tool** uses feed rate, plunge rate, retract rate, and spindle speed from the tool definition.

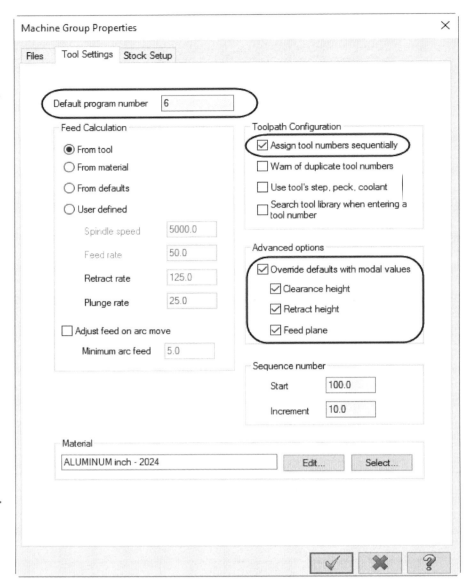

- ◆ Select the **Stock Setup** tab to define the stock.
- ◆ Select the **Rectangular** shape option.
- ◆ Select the **All Entities** button and input a **Z** value of **1.0** as shown.

The **Stock Origin** values adjust the positioning of the stock, ensuring that you have an equal amount of extra stock around the finished part.

Display options allow you to set the stock as Wireframe and to fit the stock to the screen. (Fit Screen)

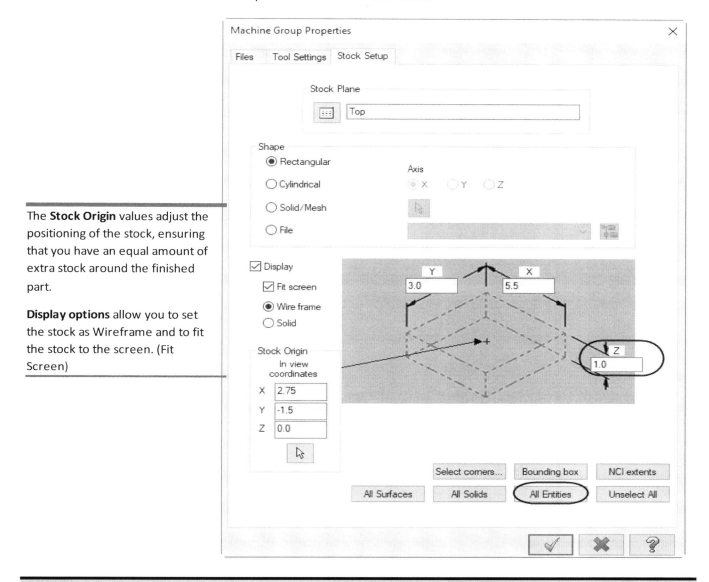

Note: The **stock** model that you create can be displayed with the part geometry when viewing the file or the toolpaths, during backplot, or while verifying toolpaths.

- ◆ Select the **OK** button to exit **Machine Group Properties**.

♦ Right mouse click in the graphics window and select the **Isometric** view to see the stock.

♦ Press **Alt + F1** to fit the drawing to the screen.

♦ The stock model will appear as shown.

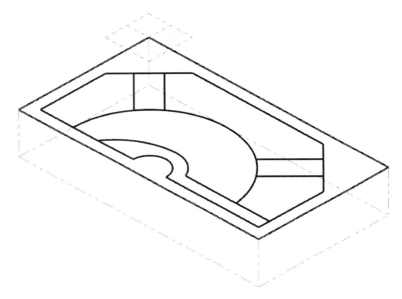

Note: The stock is not geometry and cannot be selected. There will not be a facing toolpath because the stock is already to size.

STEP 2: 2D HIGH SPEED DYNAMIC MILL

2D High Speed Dynamic Mill utilizes the entire flute length of the cutting tools to produce the smoothest, most efficient tool motion for high speed pocketing and core milling. The **Dynamic Mill** toolpath machines pockets, material that other toolpaths left behind, and standing bosses or cores.

The toolpath depends on the **Machining strategy** that you choose in the **Chain Options**. If the strategy chosen is **From outside**, the toolpath starts at the outmost chain and moves freely outside of this area; the inner chain defines the limit of the toolpath. You can also machine pockets, in which case the strategy selected is **Start inside**, which keeps the tool inside the machining regions.

Toolpath Preview:

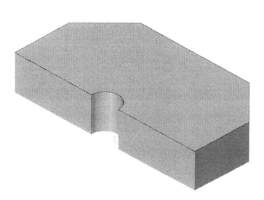

2.1 Break Lines prior to Chaining

Note: We are breaking these pieces to be able to select the geometry chains required by the toolpath. This will ensure we cut the correct geometry.

Wireframe

♦ From the **Modify** group, select **Break Two Pieces** as shown.

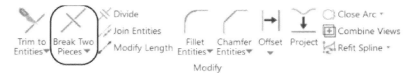

- ◆ [Select an entity to break]: Select the line as shown below.
- ◆ [Indicate the break position]: Select the line Endpoint which is where we want to break the line as shown below.

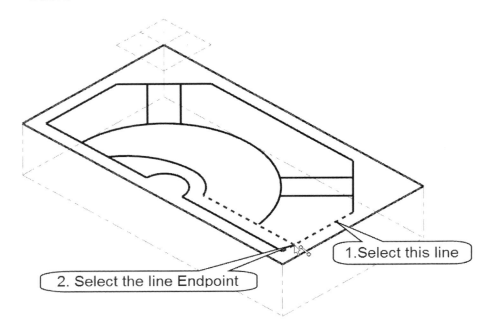

- ◆ [Select an entity to break]: Select the line as shown below.
- ◆ [Indicate the break position]: Select the endpoint of the arc as shown below.

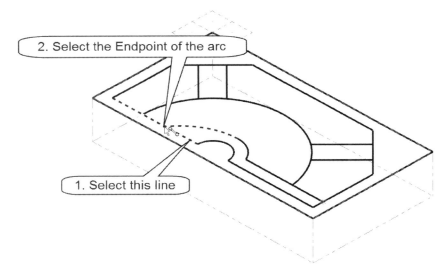

- ◆ Press **Esc** key to exit the command.

2.2 Chain Selection

Toolpaths

♦ From the **2D** group, select the **Dynamic Mill** icon.

♦ In the **Chain Options** dialog box, **Machining region strategy**, enable **From outside** and click on the **Select machining chains** button as shown.

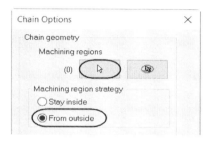

♦ In the **Chaining** dialog box appears, leave the default settings.
♦ [Select 2D HST machining chain 1]: Select the rectangle as shown.

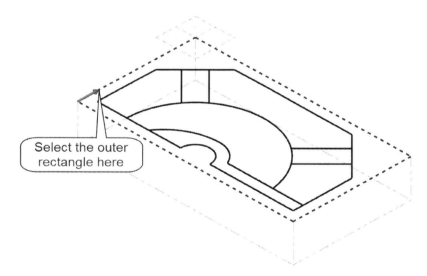

Select the outer rectangle here

♦ Select the **OK** button to exit the **Chaining** dialog box.

♦ In the **Chain Options** dialog box, **Avoidance regions**, click on the **Select avoidance chains** button as shown.

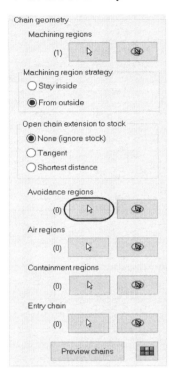

♦ [Select 2D HST avoidance chain 1]: Select the chain of the part as shown.

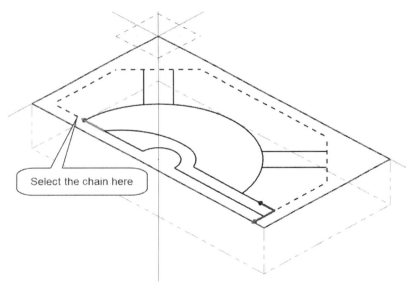

Select the chain here

Note: The chain will stop at the branch point. A branch point in a chain is the point where the endpoints of three or more entities meet. Branch points indicate where there are different paths that the chain can take. When Mastercam encounters a branch point during chaining, it prompts you to choose the path for the chain to follow.

- ◆ [Branch point reached]: Select the line past that point to continue the chain as shown.

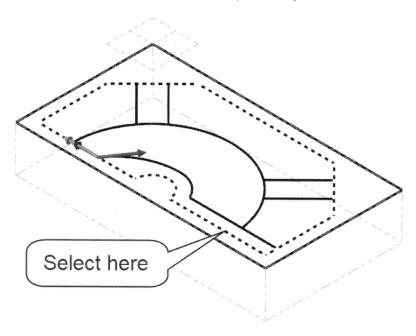

Select here

- ◆ Select the **OK** button to exit the **Chaining** dialog box.

- ◆ Select the **OK** button to exit the **Chain Options** dialog box.

♦ In the **Toolpath Type** page, **Dynamic Mill** with **From outside** option should be already selected.

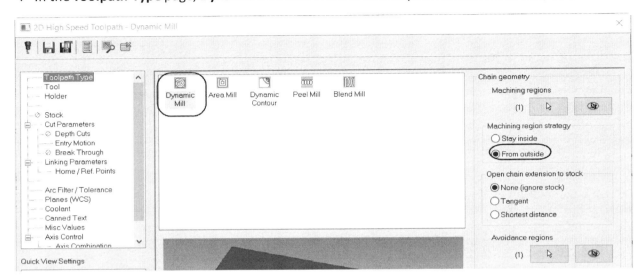

2.3 Preview Chains

The **Preview Chains** function is intended to give the user a quick visual representation of how Mastercam sees the various pieces of geometry that have been selected, how they interact with one another and a general overview of how the toolpath will be calculated with the selections presently made.

♦ Click on the **Color** icon to see the legend for **Preview chains** as shown.

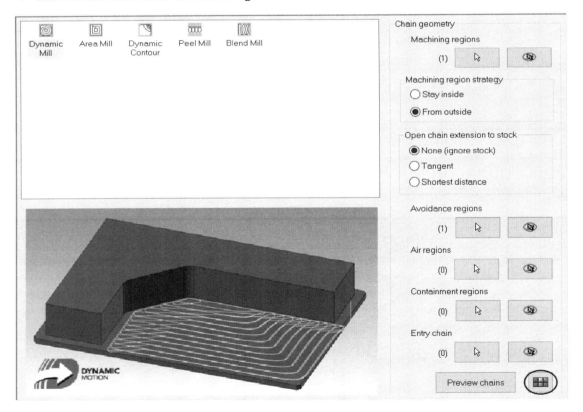

♦ The **Preview Chains Colors** dialog box should look as shown.

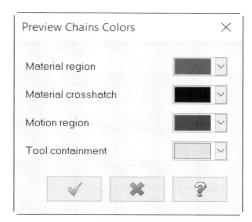

The **Material region** and **Material crosshatch** are the two colors that are used to define the material to be cut. The default colors are red for the background and black for the crosshatch.

The **Motion region** displays the area that Mastercam is making available to the toolpath for motion if it needs it. The color to represent it is dark blue. The primary reason for the display of the entire available (but not necessarily used) **Motion region** is to help the user visualize how the tool may move near or interact with any adjacent geometry.

The **Tool containment** is what you have selected as the containment region in the chain geometry. If you have not selected a containment region, it will default to the outside of the **Motion region** since that is currently the default area the toolpath is being contained to. The color used to represent the **Tool containment** is yellow.

♦ Select the **OK** button to exit **Preview Chains Colors.**

♦ Select the **Preview chains** button as shown.

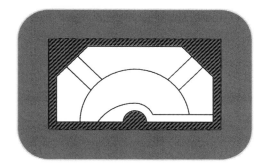

♦ Press **Esc** key to return to the toolpath parameters.

♦ Click on the **Preview chains** button again to clear the **Preview chains** display.

2.4 Select a 1/2" Flat Endmill from the library and set the Tool Parameters

♦ From the **Tree View list**, select **Tool**.

♦ Click on the **Select library tool** button.

♦ Select the **Filter** button.

♦ Select the **None** button and then under **Tool Types**, choose the **Flat Endmill** icon.
♦ Under **Tool Diameter**, pick **Equal** and input a value of **0.5** as shown.

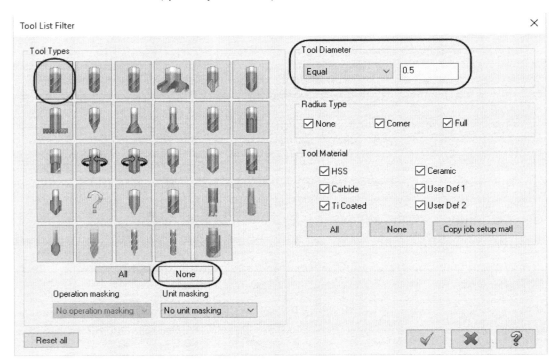

♦ Select the **OK** button to exit the **Tool List Filter**.
♦ In the **Tool Selection** panel you should only see a **1/2" Flat Endmill**.

#	Assembly...	Tool Name	Holder N...	Dia.	Cor. r...	Length	# Flut...	Type	Rad....
290	—	1/2 FLAT ...	—	0.5	0.0	1.0	4	End...	None

♦ Select the **1/2" Flat Endmill** in the **Tool Selection** page and then select the **OK** button to exit.

◆ Make all the necessary changes as shown.

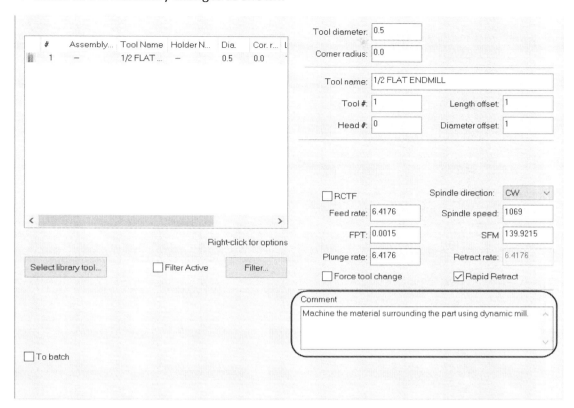

2.5 Set the Cut Parameters

♦ From the **Tree View list**, select **Cut Parameters** and ensure the parameters appear the same as shown.

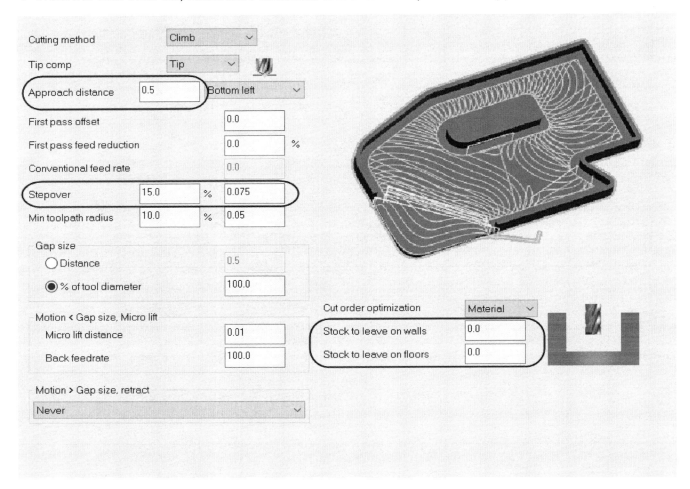

2.6 Set the Depth Cuts Parameters

◆ From the **Tree View list**, select **Depth Cuts** and disable **Depth cuts** if needed as shown.

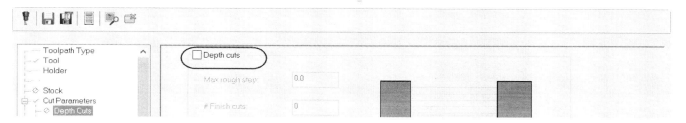

2.7 Set the Entry Motion

*Note: The **Machining strategy** is set **From outside** for this toolpath. The **Entry motion** parameters will be disregarded.*

2.8 Set the Linking Parameters

◆ Select **Linking Parameters** and enable **Clearance**, input a value of **Absolute 1.0** and input a **Depth** value of **Absolute -1.0** as shown.

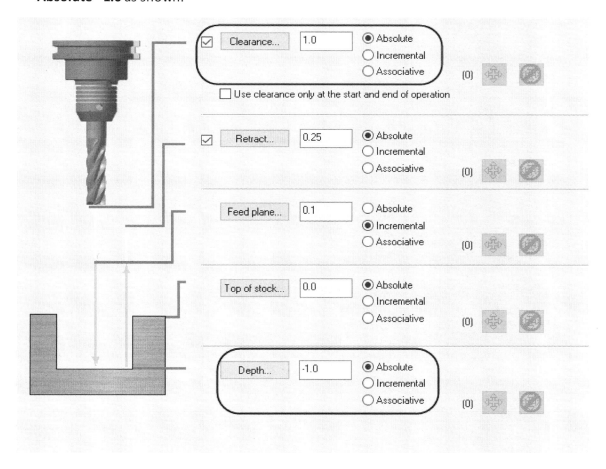

2.9 Preview the Toolpath

♦ To quickly check how the toolpath will be generated, select the **Preview toolpath** icon as shown.

♦ To hide the dialog box, click on the **Hide dialog** icon as shown.

♦ To see the part from an **Isometric** view, right mouse click in the graphics window and select **Isometric** as shown.

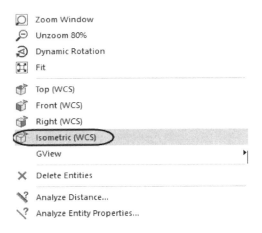

♦ The toolpath should look as shown.

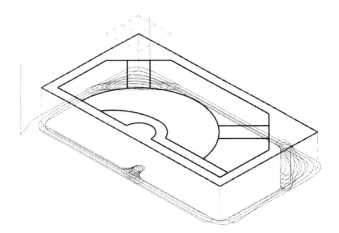

♦ Press **Esc** key to exit the preview.

Note: If the toolpath does not look as shown in the preview, check your parameters again.

♦ Select the **OK** button to generate the toolpath.

STEP 3: BACKPLOT THE TOOLPATHS

Backplotting shows the path the tools take to cut the part. This display lets you spot errors in the program before you machine the part. As you backplot toolpaths, Mastercam displays additional information such as the X, Y, and Z coordinates, the path length, the minimum and maximum coordinates, and the cycle time.

♦ Make sure that the toolpath is selected (signified by the green check mark on the folder icon). If the operation is not selected, choose the **Select all operations** icon.

♦ Select the **Backplot selected operations** button.

♦ Select the **Play** button to run **Backplot**.

♦ After **Backplot** is completed, the toolpath should look as shown.

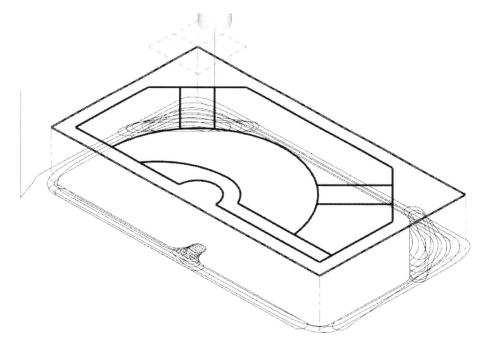

♦ Select the **OK** button to exit **Backplot** dialog box.

STEP 4: SIMULATE THE TOOLPATH IN VERIFY

Verify Mode shows the path the tools take to cut the part with material removal. This display lets you spot errors in the program before you machine the part. As you verify toolpaths, Mastercam displays additional information such as the X, Y, and Z coordinates, the path length, the minimum and maximum coordinates and the cycle time. It also shows any collisions between the workpiece and the tool.

♦ From the **Toolpaths Manager**, select **Verify selected operations** icon as shown.

Note: Mastercam launches a new window that allows you to check the part using **Backplot** or **Verify**.

♦ Select the **Play** button to run **Verify**.

♦ The part should appear as shown.

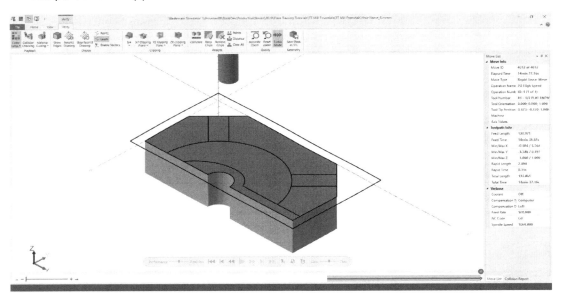

♦ To go back to the Mastercam window, minimize the **Mastercam Simulator** window as shown.

STEP 5: 2D HIGH SPEED AREA MILL

2D High Speed Area Mill toolpath machines pockets, material that other toolpaths left behind, and standing bosses or cores. Similarly **Dynamic Mill**, based on the **Machining strategy** selected, can generate the free flowing motion needed to machine features such as standing bosses and cores in a single operation. We need to chain the outer boundary of the part to define the machining region, and then chain the inner boundary which will be defined as the avoidance region and will not be machined.

Toolpath Preview:

5.1 Chain the Entities

♦ Move the cursor in the **Toolpaths Manager** panel and press **T** or **Alt + T** to remove the toolpath display.

Toolpaths

♦ From the **2D** group, click on the **Expand gallery** icon.

♦ From the Toolpath Gallery, select the **Area Mill** icon as shown.

♦ In the **Chain Options** dialog box, **Machining regions**, enable **From outside** and click on the **Select machining chains** button as shown.

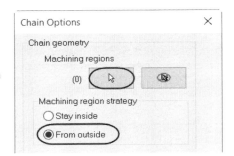

Note: The **Machining regions** chain determines where the tool starts to machine from.

♦ When the **Chaining** dialog box appears, leave the default settings.

♦ [Select 2D HST machining chain 1]: Select the rectangle as shown.

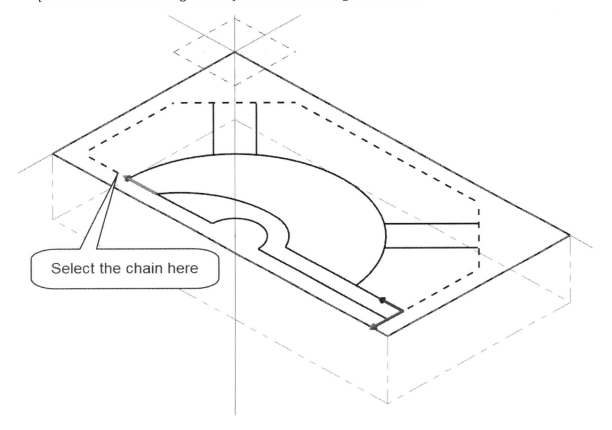

Select the chain here

♦ [Branch point reached]: Select the line past that point to continue the chain as shown.

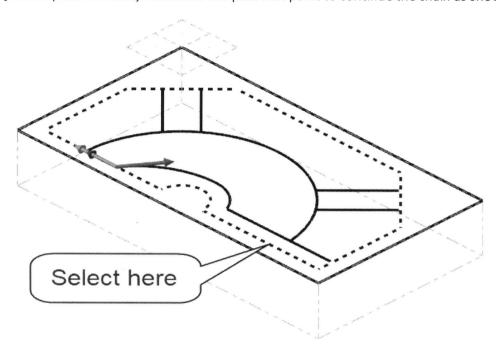

Select here

♦ Select the **OK** button to exit the **Chaining** dialog box.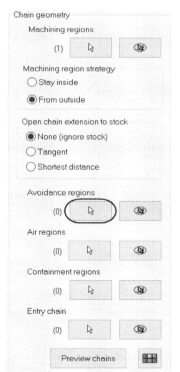
♦ In the **Chain Options** dialog box, **Avoidance regions**, click on the **Select avoidance chains** button as shown.

*Note: The **Avoidance regions** are areas that will be avoided during machining. In our case the chain selected in the **Avoidance regions** is the chain up to where the tool needs to machine the part.*

♦ [Select 2D HST avoidance chain 1]: Select the chain of the part as shown.

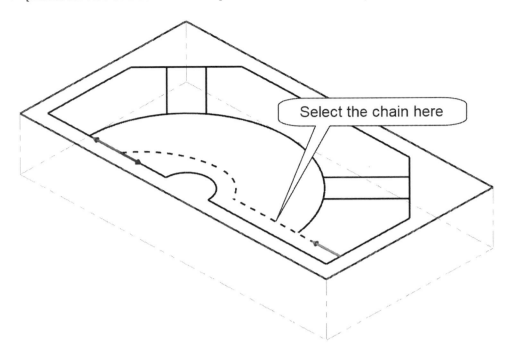

♦ [Branch point reached. Select next branch.]: Select the branch to complete the chain as shown.

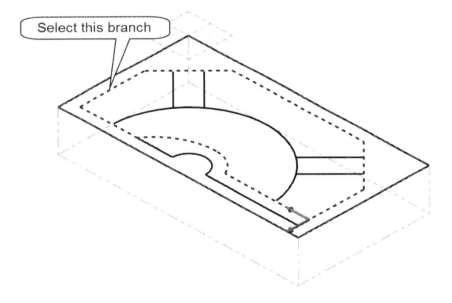

♦ Select the **OK** button to exit the **Chaining** dialog box.

♦ Select the **OK** button to exit the **Chain Options** dialog box.

♦ On the **Toolpath Type** page, **Area Mill** will be selected and **From outside** enabled as shown.

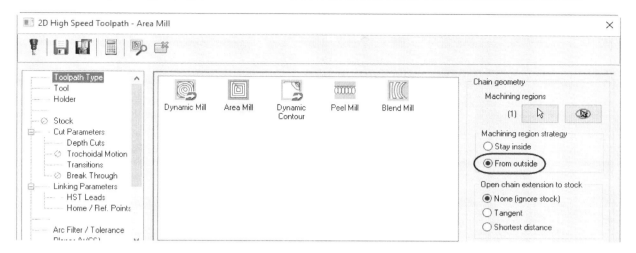

♦ Select the **Preview chains** button as shown.

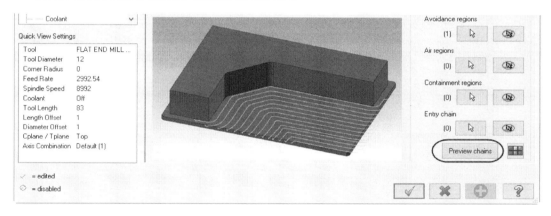

♦ See **"Preview Chains" on page 708** to review the procedure.
♦ The **Preview chains** should look as shown.

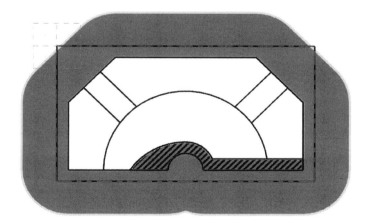

◆ Press **Esc** key to return to the toolpath parameters.

◆ Click on the **Preview chains** button again to clear the Preview chains display.

◆ Select the **Tool** page.

◆ Select the **1/2" Flat Endmill** from the list and make all the necessary changes as shown.

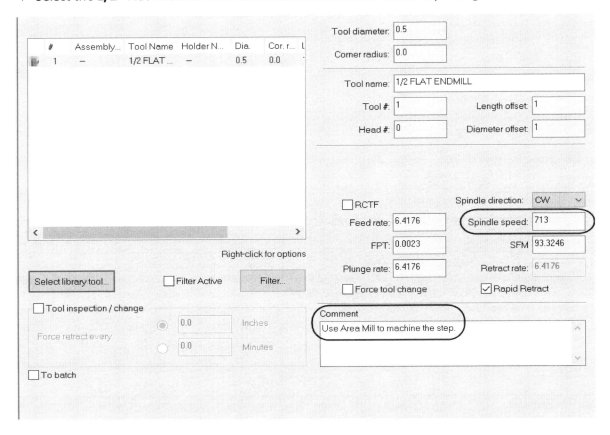

5.2 Set the Cut Parameters

♦ Choose **Cut Parameters** and enable **Corner rounding** as shown.

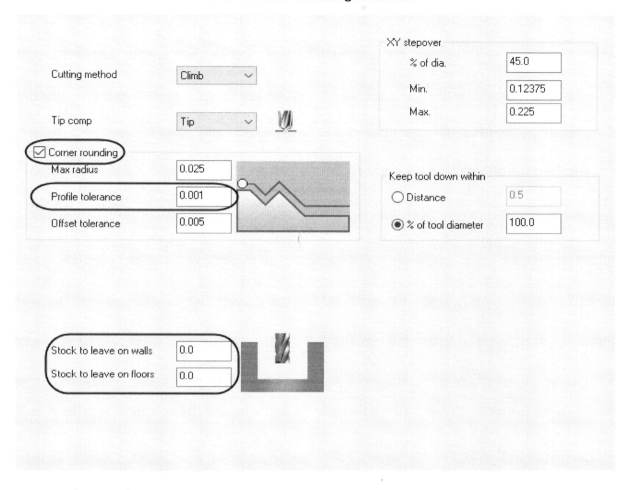

5.3 Set the Depth Cuts parameters

♦ From the **Tree View list**, select the **Depth Cuts**, enable **Depth cuts** and make the changes as shown.

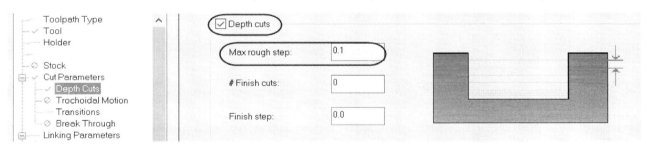

5.4 Set the Transitions

Note: The **Machining strategy** is set **From outside** for this toolpath. The **Entry motion** parameters will be disregarded.

5.5 Set the Linking Parameters

◆ Select **Linking Parameters** and input a **Depth** of **Absolute -0.5** as shown.

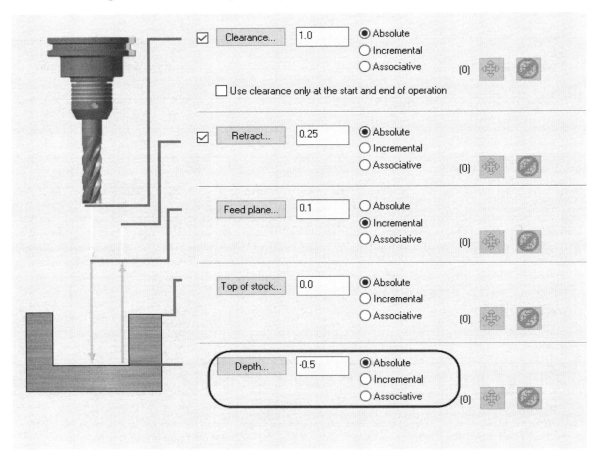

5.6 Preview the Toolpath

♦ To quickly check how the toolpath will be generated, select the **Preview toolpath** icon as shown.

♦ See **"Preview the Toolpath" on page 714** to review the procedure.
♦ The toolpath should look as shown.

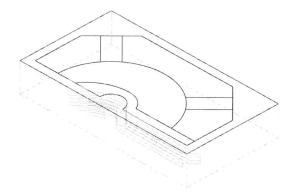

♦ Press **Esc** key to exit the preview.

Note: If the toolpath does not look as shown in the preview, check your parameters again.

♦ Select the **OK** button to exit the **2D Area Mill** parameters. ✔

5.7 Backplot the toolpath

♦ See **"Backplot The Toolpaths" on page 715** to review **Backplot** procedures.

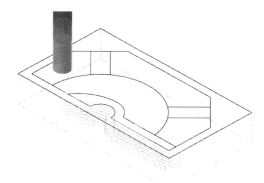

♦ Select the **OK** button to exit **Backplot**. ✔

5.8 Verify the toolpaths

◆ See "Simulate the toolpath in Verify" on page 716 for more info.

◆ To verify all toolpaths, from the **Toolpaths Manager**, choose the **Select all operations** icon.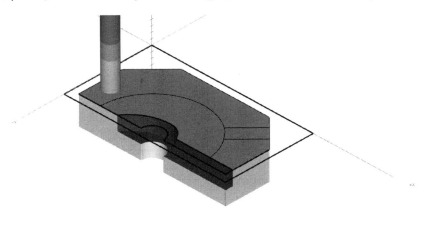

◆ To go back to the Mastercam window, minimize the **Mastercam Simulator** window as shown. ⊖ ▢ ✕
◆ Press **Alt + T** to remove the toolpath display.

STEP 6: 2D HIGH SPEED BLEND MILL

2D High Speed Blend Mill toolpath morphs smoothly between two open chains. You can create the toolpath along or across the selected chains. This machining strategy supports the full depth of cutting, utilizing more of cutter flute lengths and resulting in less cycle time and tool wear.

Toolpath Preview:

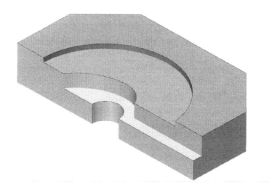

6.1 Chain the Entities

♦ From the **2D** group, click on the **Expand gallery** arrow as shown.

♦ Select the **Blend Mill** icon as shown.

♦ When the **Chaining** dialog box appears, select the **Single** button.

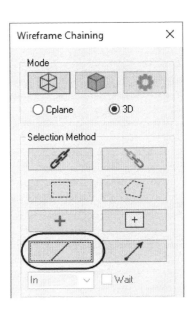

The **Single** button allows you to select one entity (a single line, arc, or spline) in a chain.

♦ [Blend: define chain 1]: Select the arc as shown.

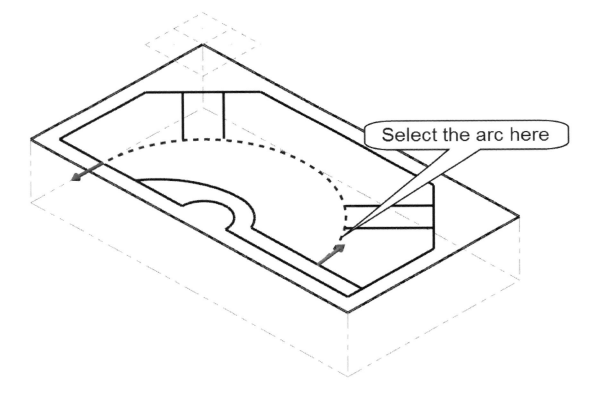

Select the arc here

♦ To chain the second arc, choose the **Partial** chaining method as shown.

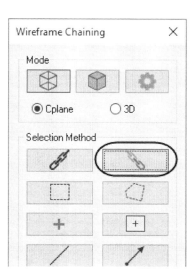

Partial creates an open chain with two mouse clicks. In the graphics window, click on the entity where you want to start the chain, then click where you want to end the chain.

♦ [Blend: define chain 2]: Select Entity A as shown.

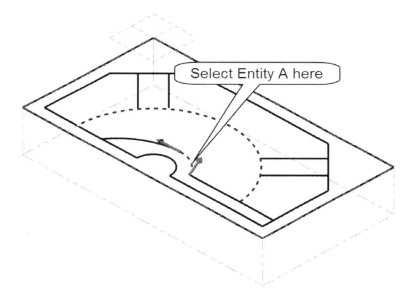

Select Entity A here

Note: Make sure the chain direction is as shown. Otherwise, in the Chaining dialog box, click on the **Reverse** button.

♦ [Select the last entity]: Select Entity B as shown.

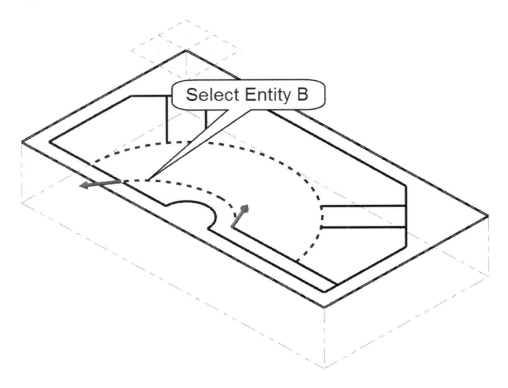

♦ Select the **OK** button to exit the **Chaining** dialog box.
♦ Select **Toolpath Type** from the **Tree View list** and ensure that **Blend Mill** is enabled.

Dynamic Mill   Area Mill   Dynamic   Peel Mill   Blend Mill
                             Contour

6.2 Select a 1/4" Flat Endmill from the Library and set the Tool Parameters

♦ Select **Tool** from the **Tree view list**.

♦ Click on the **Select library tool** button. | Select library tool... |

♦ Select the **Filter** button as shown.

♦ Select the **None** button and then under **Tool Types** choose the **Flat Endmill** icon.

♦ Ensure the **Tool Diameter** is set to **Equal** and input a value **0.25** as shown.

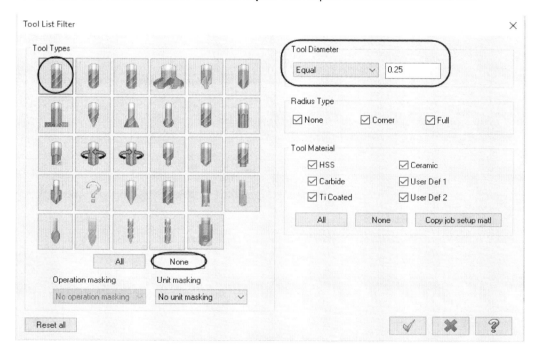

♦ Select the **OK** button to exit the **Tool List Filter**.

♦ In the **Tool Selection** panel you should only see a **1/4" Flat Endmill**.

#	Assembly Name	Tool Name	Holder Name	Dia.	Cor. rad.	Length	# Flutes	Ra..
285	--	1/4 FLAT ENDMILL	--	0...	0.0	0.5	4	No.

♦ Select the **1/4" Flat Endmill** in the **Tool Selection** dialog box and then choose the **OK** button to exit.

♦ Make the necessary changes as shown.

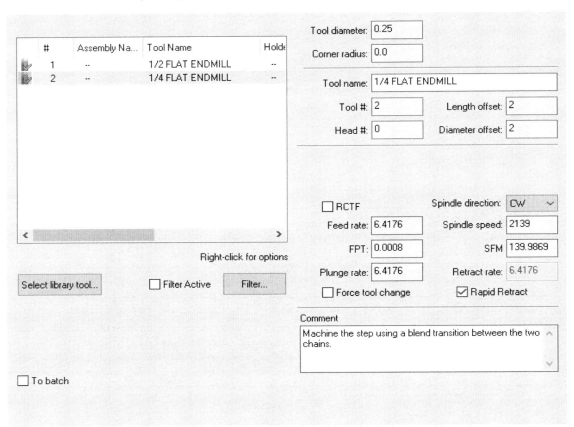

6.3 Set the Cut Parameters

♦ Select **Cut Parameters** from the **Tree View list**.

♦ Set the **Cutting method** to **Zigzag** and **Along** as shown. This will start the cut along the first chain and then morph it towards the second chain.

♦ Make any other necessary changes as shown.

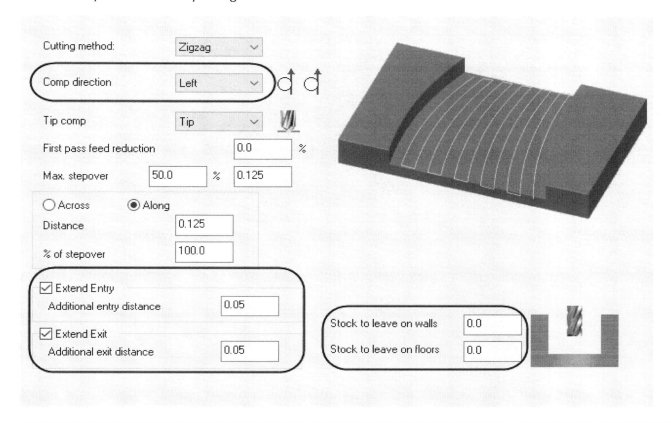

Compensation direction set to **Left** will allow the tool to travel to the left of the selected chains.

Along cuts in the along direction, stepping over in the across direction.

Max Stepover sets the distance between adjacent passes.

Distance/% of stepover sets the spacing between the temporary across moves. These moves are used to generate the final toolpath but are not included in the final toolpath.

6.4 Set the Depth Cuts

♦ From the **Tree View list**, select **Depth Cuts** and ensure **Depth cuts** is disabled.

6.5 Finish passes

♦ From the **Tree View list** select **Finish Passes**. Enable **Finish pass** and change the parameters as shown.

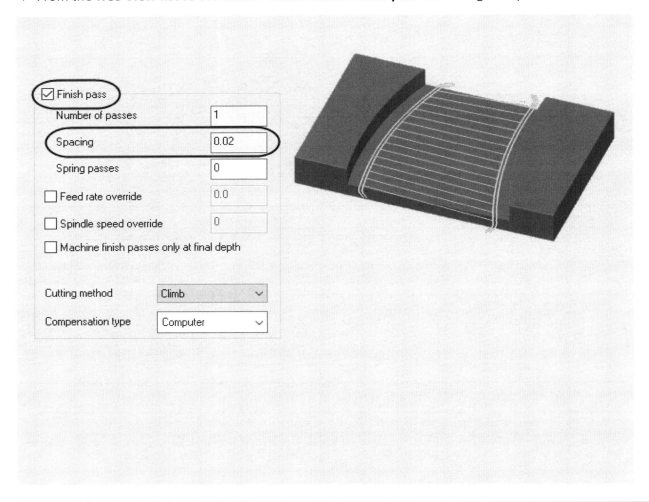

Finish pass page allows you to add finish passes along the selected chains of the toolpath.

Number of passes sets the number of finish passes.

Spacing sets the distance between the finish passes.

Machine finish passes only at final depth performs the finish passes only at the final cutting depth.

6.6 Set the Linking Parameters

♦ Select **Linking Parameters** and enter a **Depth** of **-0.125** as shown.

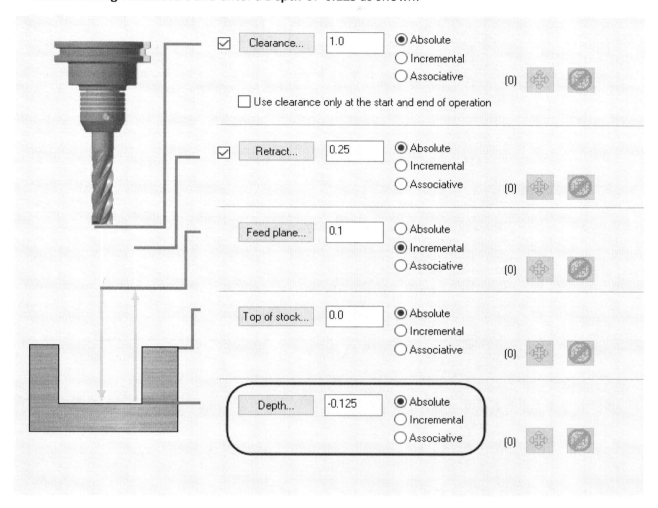

6.7 Preview the Toolpath

♦ To quickly check how the toolpath will be generated, select the **Preview toolpath** icon as shown.

♦ See **"Preview the Toolpath" on page 714** to review the procedure.
♦ The toolpath should look as shown.

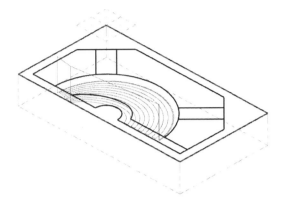

♦ Press **Esc** key to exit the preview.

Note: If the toolpath does not look as shown in the preview, check your parameters again.

♦ Select the **OK** button to exit the toolpath parameters.

6.8 Backplot the toolpath

♦ **Backplot** the toolpath. See **"Backplot The Toolpaths" on page 715** for more information.

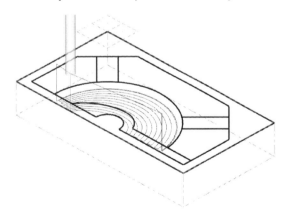

♦ Select the **OK** button to exit **Backplot**.

6.9 Verify the toolpaths

♦ **Verify** the toolpaths. See **"Simulate the toolpath in Verify" on page 716** for more information.

♦ To verify all toolpaths, from the **Toolpaths Manager**, choose the **Select all operations** icon.

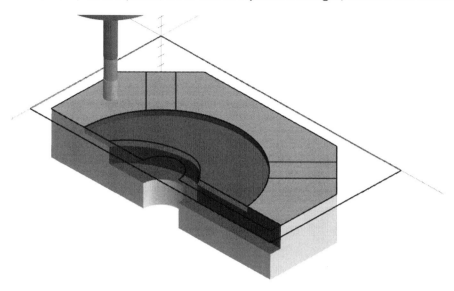

♦ To go back to the Mastercam window, minimize the **Mastercam Simulator** window as shown.

♦ Press **Alt + T** to remove the toolpath display.

STEP 7: 2D HIGH SPEED PEEL MILL

2D High Speed Peel Mill toolpath allows for efficient constant climb milling between two selected contours or along a single contour. It uses a trochoidal style of motion to cut the slot. For single chains, you need to define the width of the cut. Otherwise, the width is defined by the area between the two contours.

Toolpath Preview:

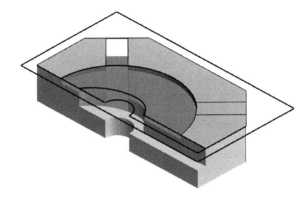

Toolpaths

♦ From the **2D** group, click on the **Expand gallery** arrow as shown.

♦ Select the **Peel Mill** icon as shown.

♦ Leave the default chaining method and select the lines as shown. Ensure both chains go in the same direction as shown.

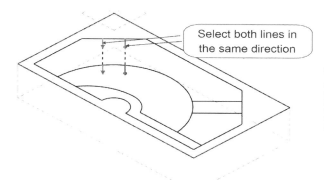

Select both lines in the same direction

*Note: To change the direction of chaining if needed, click on the **Reverse** button from the **Chaining** dialog box.*

♦ Select the **OK** button to exit the **Chaining** dialog box.

Dynamic Mill　Area Mill　Dynamic Contour　Peel Mill　Blend Mill

♦ Select **Toolpath Type**, **Peel Mill** should already be selected.

♦ Select the **Tool** page from the **Tree View list** and select the **1/4" Flat Endmill** from the list of tools.
♦ Make any necessary changes as shown.

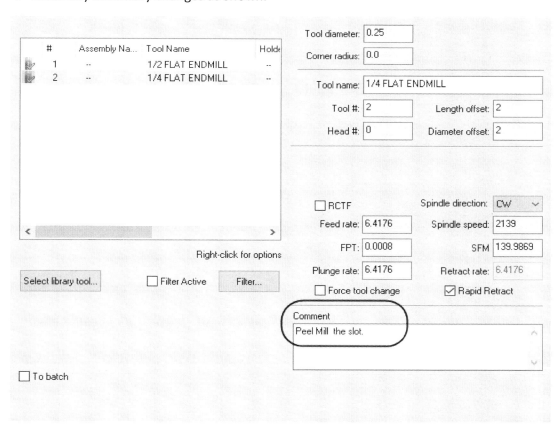

7.1 Set the Cut Parameters

♦ From the **Tree View list** select **Cut Parameters** and change the **Stepover** amount to **15%** as shown.

♦ Enable the **Extend Entry** option and **Extend Exit** option. Input a value to extend the entry by **0.25** and to extend the exit by **1.25** as shown. If necessary, set **Stock to leave on walls/floors** as **0.0**.

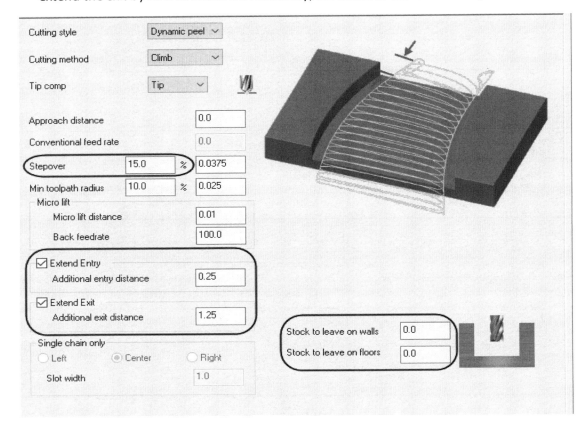

Stepover sets the distance between adjacent cuts of the toolpath.

Min toolpath radius defines the radius of the arc that the tool follows along its semi-circular path. This value must be greater than the stepover amount.

Micro lift distance is the distance the tool lifts off of the part on back moves. Micro lifts are slight lifts that help clear chips and minimize excessive tool heating.

Back feedrate controls the speed (inches per minute or millimeters per minute) of the backfeed movement of the tool. This allows 3D arcs between cuts to have a different feed rate than the rest of the toolpath, which can help reduce cycle time.

Extend Entry/Exit allows you to adjust the initial and final tool engagement with the material.

7.2 Set the Depth Cuts

♦ Select **Depth Cuts** from the **Tree View list** and ensure **Depth cuts** is disabled.

7.3 Set the Finish Passes Parameters

◆ Select **Finish Passes** from the **Tree View list** and enable **Finish pass**. Ensure **Machine finish passes only at final depth** is checked and **Spacing** is set as shown.

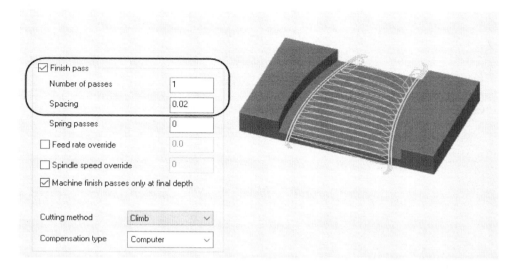

Finish pass performs a high speed finish pass along the walls of the slot.

Machine finish passes only at final depth performs the finish passes at the final cutting depth only.

7.4 Set the Linking Parameters

◆ Select **Linking Parameters** from the **Tree View list** and set the **Depth** to **-0.5** as shown.

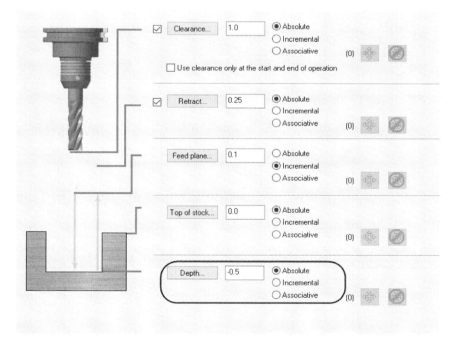

7.5 Preview the Toolpath

♦ To quickly check how the toolpath will be generated, select the **Preview toolpath** icon as shown.

♦ See **"Preview the Toolpath" on page 714** to review the procedure.
♦ The toolpath should look as shown.

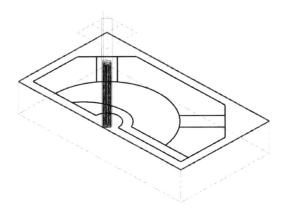

♦ Press **Esc** key to exit the preview.

Note: If the toolpath does not look as shown in the preview, check your parameters again.

♦ Select the **OK** button to exit the toolpath parameters.

7.6 Backplot the toolpath

♦ See **"Backplot The Toolpaths" on page 715** for more information.

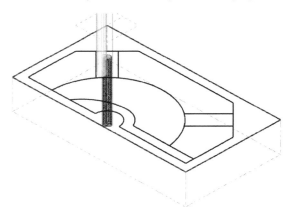

♦ Select the **OK** button to exit **Backplot**.

7.7 Verify the toolpaths

◆ See **"Simulate the toolpath in Verify" on page 716** for more information.

◆ To verify all toolpaths, from the **Toolpaths Manager**, choose the **Select all operations** icon.

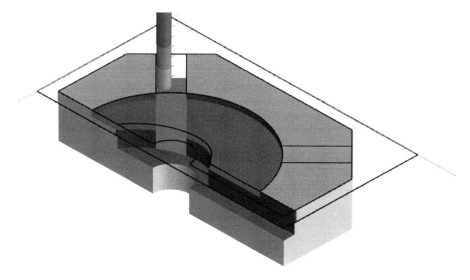

◆ To go back to the Mastercam window, minimize the **Mastercam Simulator** window as shown. ⊖ ⬜ ✕
◆ Press **Alt + T** to remove the toolpath display.

STEP 8: 2D HIGH SPEED PEEL MILL

In this step you will review how to copy an existing toolpath in the Toolpaths Manager. You will also learn how to rechain the geometry used in the toolpath.

Toolpath Preview:

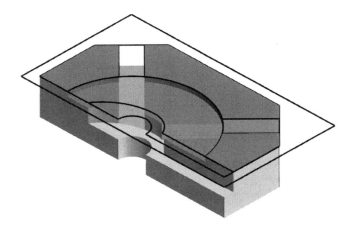

8.1 Copy the Previous Toolpath

♦ From the **Toolpaths Manager**, select only operation #4 (the peel mill toolpath).

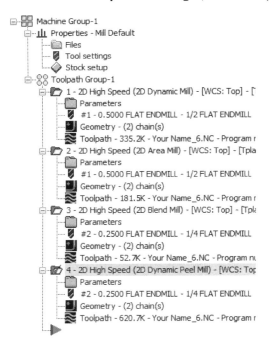

◆ Right click and hold the right mouse button down and drag the operation to a point below it as shown.

◆ Release the right mouse button and select the option **Copy after** as shown.

◆ Make sure that the red insert arrow is below the last toolpath as shown. If not, select the icon to move the insert arrow down.

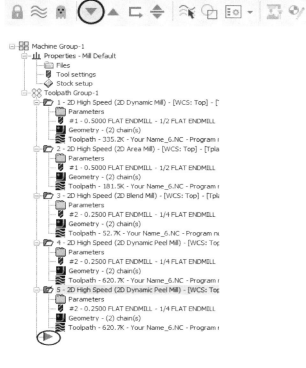

8.2 Re-Chain the Geometry

♦ Under operation #5, select **Geometry**.

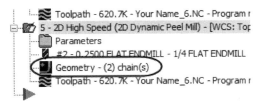

♦ Right mouse click in the **Chain Manager** and select **Rechain all** as shown.

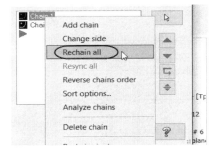

♦ When the **Chaining** dialog box appears, leave the default settings and choose the line as shown (this time we will chain one entity only to create the toolpath).

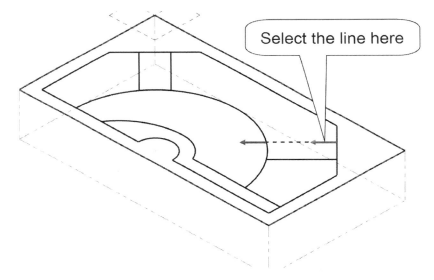

Select the line here

♦ Once the geometry has been selected, choose the **OK** button to exit the **Chaining** dialog box.
♦ Choose the **OK** button again to exit the **Chain Manager**.

◆ Select **Parameters** in **Operation #5**.

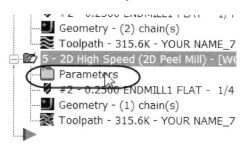

8.3 Set the Cut Parameters

◆ Select **Cut Parameters** and change **Single chain only** to **Left** and enter a **Slot width** of **0.5** as shown.

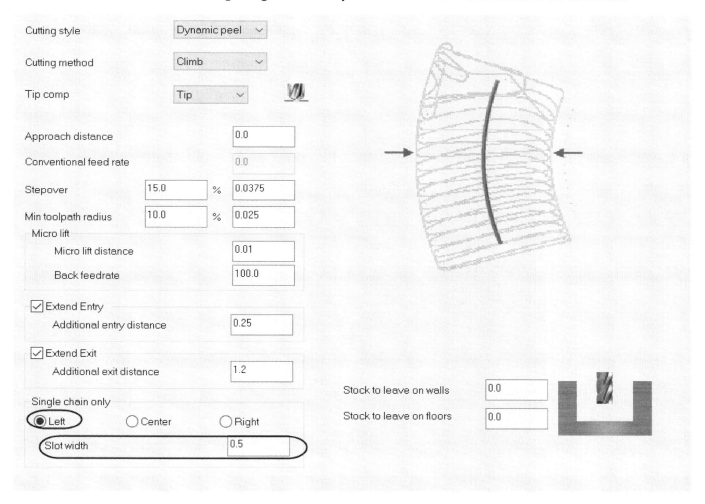

8.4 Set the Linking Parameters

♦ Select **Linking Parameters** and make sure that the **Depth** is set to **-0.5** as shown.

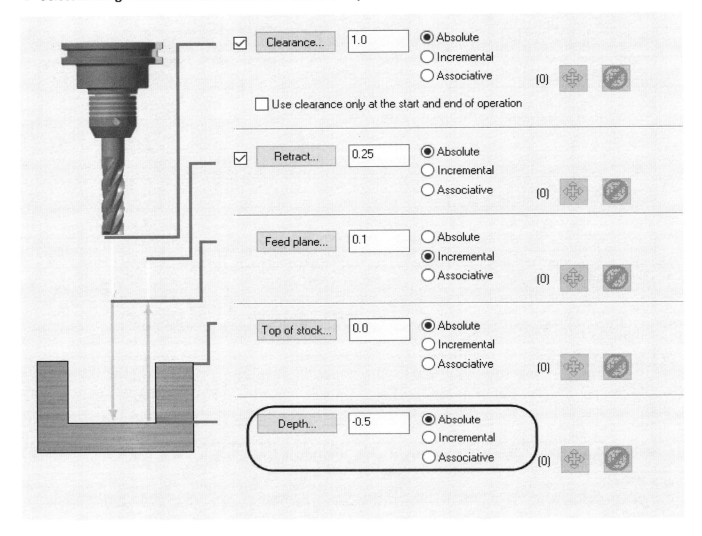

8.5 Preview the Toolpath

♦ To quickly check how the toolpath will be generated, select the **Preview toolpath** icon as shown.

♦ See **"Preview the Toolpath" on page 714** to review the procedure.
♦ The toolpath should look as shown.

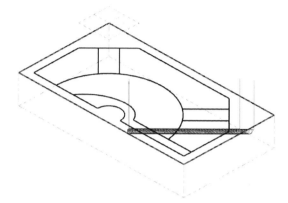

♦ Press **Esc** key to exit the preview.

Note: If the toolpath does not look as shown in the preview, check your parameters again.

♦ Select the **OK** button to exit the toolpath parameters.
♦ Select the button to **Regenerate all dirty operations**.

8.6 Backplot the toolpath

♦ **Backplot** the toolpath. See **"Backplot The Toolpaths" on page 715** for more information.

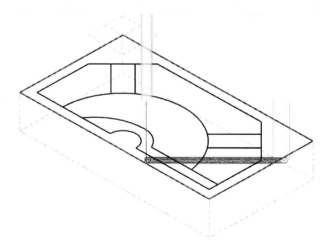

♦ Select the **OK** button to exit **Backplot**.

8.7 Verify the toolpaths

- Verify the toolpaths. See **"Simulate the toolpath in Verify" on page 716** for more information.

- To verify all toolpaths, from the **Toolpaths Manager**, choose the **Select all operations** icon.

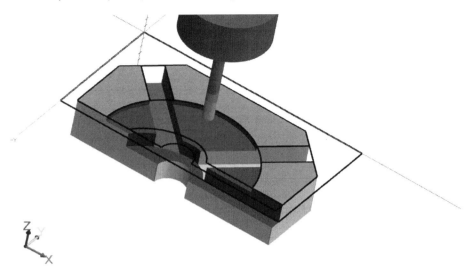

- To go back to the Mastercam window, close **Mastercam Simulator** window as shown.

STEP 9: POST THE FILE

♦ Ensure all operations are selected. If not, use the button **Select all operations** in the **Toolpaths Manager**.

♦ Select the **Post selected operations** icon from the **Toolpaths Manager** as shown. G1

♦ In the **Post processing** window, make necessary changes as shown.

NC file enabled allows you to keep the NC file and to assign the same name as the MCAM file.
Edit enabled allows you to automatically launch the default.

♦ Select the **OK** button to continue.

♦ Save your file and name it **YOUR NAME_6.NC**.

♦ A window with **Mastercam Code Expert** will be launched and the **NC** program will appear as shown.

♦ Select the "**X**" box at the upper right corner to exit the editor.

STEP 10: SAVE THE UPDATED MCAM FILE

CREATE THE TOOLPATHS FOR TUTORIAL #6 EXERCISE

Create the Toolpaths for Tutorial #6 Exercise as per the instructions below.

Set the machine properties including the stock setup.
Remove the material on the step using Contour (2D).

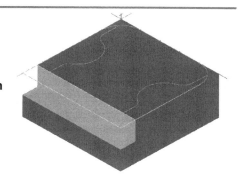

- Use a **7/8" Flat Endmill**.
- Based on your chaining direction, ensure the **Compensation direction** is set correctly.
- Enable **Depth Cuts**.
- **Lead In/Out**, ensure the **Arc Radius** is set to zero.
- No **Break Through, Multi Passes**.
- Set the depth according to the drawing.

Remove the material around the fillets using Contour (2D).

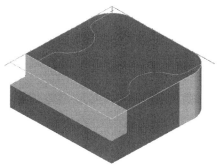

- Use the **7/8" Flat Endmill**.
- Based on your chaining direction ensure the **Compensation direction** is set correctly.
- Enable **Depth Cuts**.
- Set a **Lead In/Out** and **Break Through**.
- No **Multi Passes**.
- Set the depth according to the drawing.

Create a 2D High Speed Blend Mill toolpath to remove the material in the center of the part.

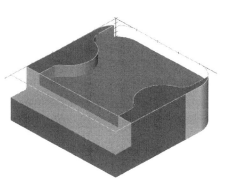

- Select the two chains.
- Use a **1/2" Flat Endmill**.
- Set the **Compensation** direction to **Inside**.
- Select **Along** for the tool cutting direction.
- Set the **Max. stepover** and **% of stepover** to **25**.
- **Extend Exit/Entry** by **0.5"**.
- Disable **Depth Cuts** and **Break Through**.
- Set the depth according to the drawing.
- Your part will appear as shown.

TUTORIAL #6 TOOLPATH CREATION QUIZ

◆ What does the Translate 3D do?

◆ How does a Blend Mill toolpath work?

◆ What does Peel Mill toolpath do?

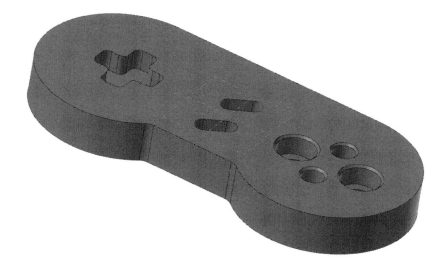

OVERVIEW OF STEPS TAKEN TO CREATE THE PART GEOMETRY:

From Drawing to CAD Model:

♦ The student should examine the drawing on the following page to understand what part is being created in the tutorial.

♦ From the drawing we can decide how to create the geometry in Mastercam.

Create the 2D CAD Model:

♦ The student will create the Top 2D geometry needed to create the toolpaths.

♦ Geometry creation commands such as Circle Center Point, Line Tangent, Line Parallel, Rectangular Shapes, Trim, and Fillet Chains will be used.

♦ Create a solid using Solid extrude, Chamfer and Fillet commands.

TUTORIAL #7 DRAWING

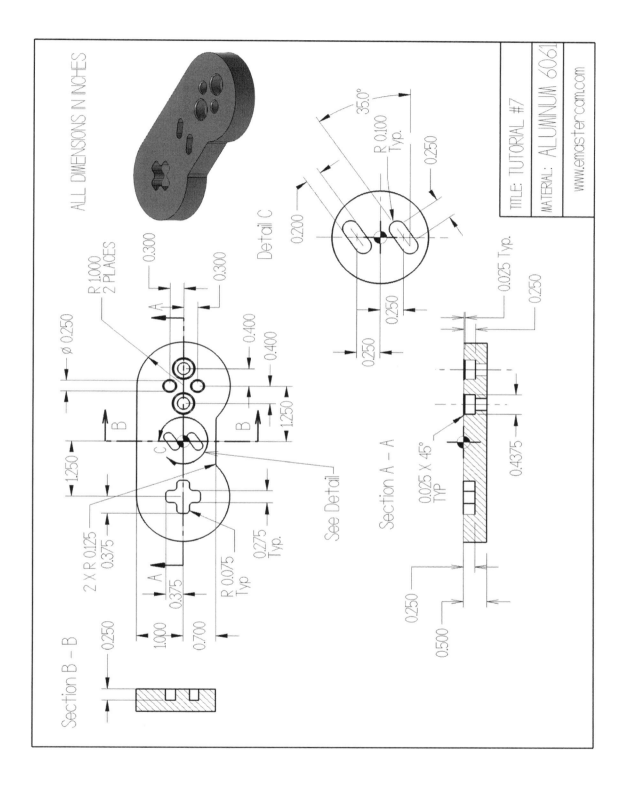

ALL DIMENSIONS IN INCHES

MATERIAL: ALUMINUM 6061

TITLE: TUTORIAL #7

www.emastercam.com

Detail C

35.0°

R 0.100
Typ.

0.250

0.200

0.250

0.250

Section A – A

0.025 x 45°
TYP

0.025 Typ.

0.250

0.4375

0.250

0.500

Section B – B

R 1.000
2 PLACES

0.300

0.300

Ø 0.250

0.400

0.400

1.250

1.250

See Detail

2 X R 0.125

0.375

R 0.075
Typ

0.275
Typ.

0.375

1.000

0.700

0.250

A

A

B

B

C

STEP 1: SETTING UP THE GRAPHICAL USER INTERFACE

Please refer to the **Getting Started** section to set up the graphical user interface.

STEP 2: CREATE CIRCLE CENTER POINT

Circle Center Point lets you create circles knowing the center point and the radius or the diameter.

Step Preview:

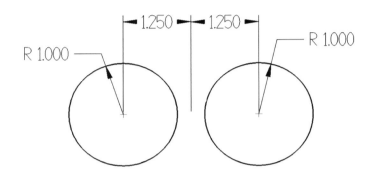

Wireframe

♦ From the **Arcs** group, select **Circle Center Point** as shown.

♦ In the **Ribbon Bar**, enter the **Radius** value of **1.0** and click on the **Lock** icon to lock it as shown.

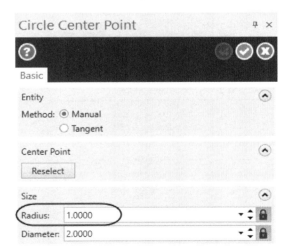

♦ Select the **AutoCursor Fast Point** icon from the **General Selection** toolbar and the field where you can type the coordinates will open at the upper left side of the graphics window as shown.

♦ Enter the coordinates for the center point as shown.

```
-1.25,0
```

♦ Press **Enter** to position the circle.
♦ Press Enter again to finish the circle.
♦ Press **Alt + F1** to fit the circle into the graphics window.
♦ Select the **AutoCursor Fast Point** icon again to enter coordinates for the center point as shown.

```
1.25,0
```

♦ Press **Enter** to position the circle.

♦ Choose the **OK** button to exit the command.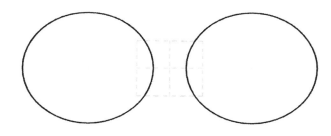
♦ Press **Alt + F1** to fit the geometry into the graphics window.
♦ The geometry should look as shown.

> Note: While creating geometry for this tutorial, if you make a mistake, you can undo the last step using the **Undo** icon. You can undo as many steps as needed. If you delete or undo a step by mistake, just use the **Redo** icon. To delete unwanted geometry, select the geometry first and then press **Delete** from the keyboard.

STEP 3: CREATE LINE TANGENT

You will create a line tangent to two arcs. You will use the **Line Endpoints** command with the **Tangent** option enabled.

Step Preview:

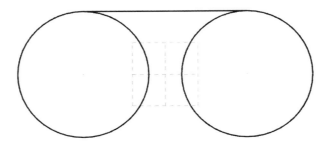

Wireframe

♦ From the **Lines** group, select **Line Endpoints** as shown.

♦ In the **Line Endpoints** panel, make sure that **Freeform** and **Tangent** are enabled as shown

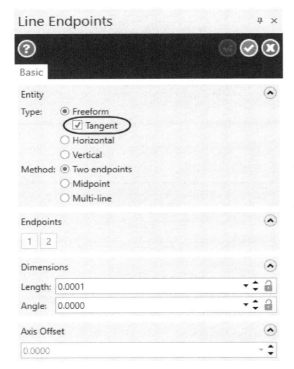

Note: Make sure that you do not select the quadrant points while selecting the circles.

- ◆ [Specify the first endpoint]: Select Entity A as shown in Figure: 3.0.1.
- ◆ [Specify the second endpoint]: Select Entity B as shown in Figure: 3.0.1.

Figure: 3.0.1

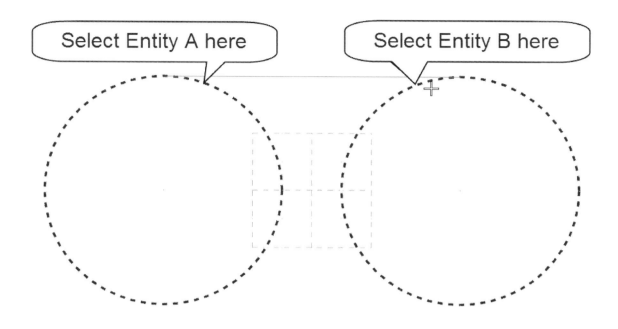

- ◆ Choose the **OK** button to exit the command.

- ◆ The geometry should look as shown.

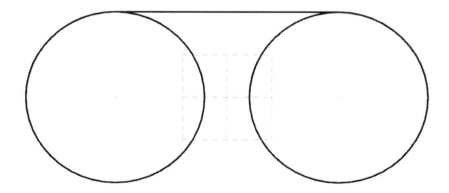

STEP 4: CREATE A LINE PARALLEL

Create a **Line Parallel** command knowing the distance between the lines.

Step Preview:

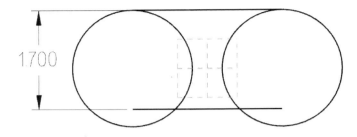

Wireframe

- ◆ From the **Lines** group, select **Line Parallel** as shown.

- ◆ [Select a line]: Select the line as shown in Figure: 4.0.1.
- ◆ [Select the point to place a parallel line through]: Click somewhere below the line as shown in Figure: 4.0.1.

Figure: 4.0.1

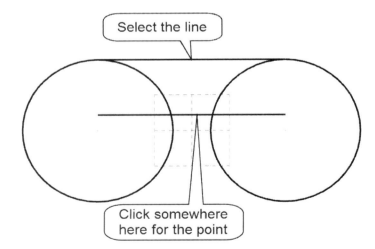

♦ In the **Line Parallel** panel, change the **Offset Distance** to **1.7**.

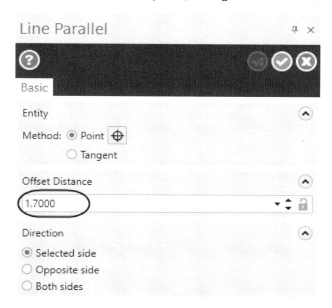

♦ Press **Enter** to position the line at the proper distance.

♦ Select the **OK** button to exit the command.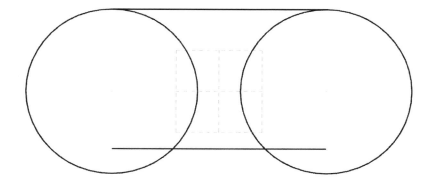

♦ The geometry should look as shown.

STEP 5: TRIM THE ENTITIES

You will trim the entities using the **Trim 3 entities** command. The first two entities that you select are trimmed to the third, which acts as a trimming curve. The third entity is then trimmed to the first two.

Step Preview:

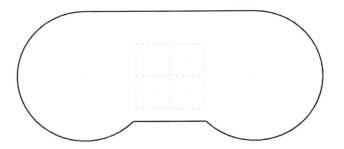

Wireframe

♦ From the **Modify** group, select **Trim to Entities** icon as shown.

♦ In the **Trim to Entities** panel, make sure that the **Trim Mode** and **Trim 3 entities** are enabled as shown.

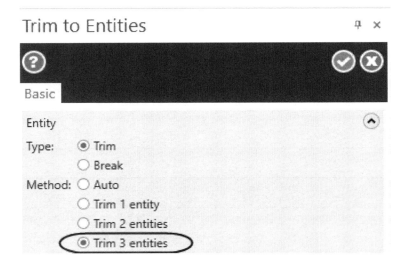

- ◆ [Select the first entity to trim/extend]: Select Entity A as shown in Figure: 5.0.1.
- ◆ [Select the second entity to trim/extend]: Select Entity B as shown in Figure: 5.0.1.
- ◆ [Select the entity to trim/extend to]: Select Entity C as shown in Figure: 5.0.1.

*Note: Make sure to follow the orders from **A to C**.*

Figure: 5.0.1

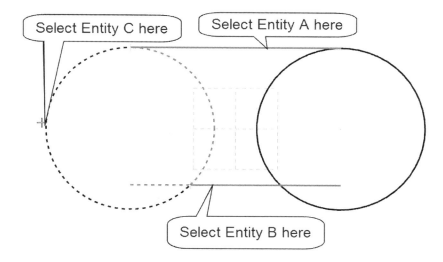

- ◆ [Select the first entity to trim/extend]: Select Entity A as shown in Figure: 5.0.2.
- ◆ [Select the second entity to trim/extend]: Select Entity B as shown in Figure: 5.0.2.
- ◆ [Select the entity to trim/extend to]: Select Entity C as shown in Figure: 5.0.2.

Figure: 5.0.2

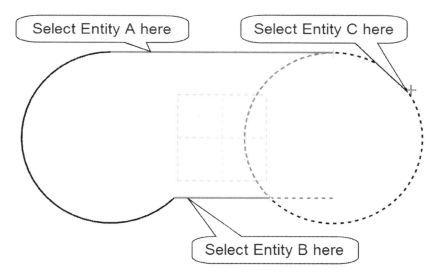

♦ Select the **OK** button to exit the command.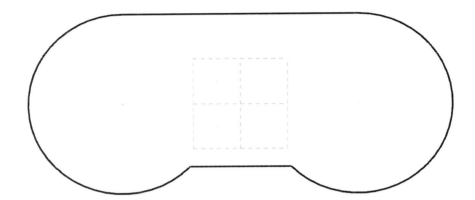

♦ The geometry should look as shown.

STEP 6: CREATE RECTANGULAR SHAPE

In this step you will create two rectangles using **Rectangular Shapes**.

Step Preview:

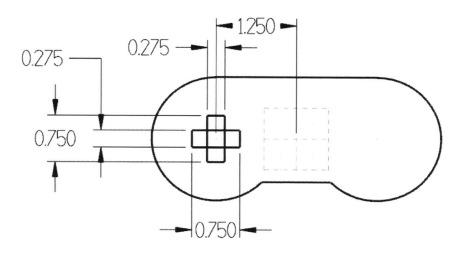

Wireframe

♦ From the **Shapes** group, select the drop down below **Rectangle** and select **Rectangular Shapes** as shown.

♦ Enter the **Width**, the **Height** and enable the **Anchor** location as shown.

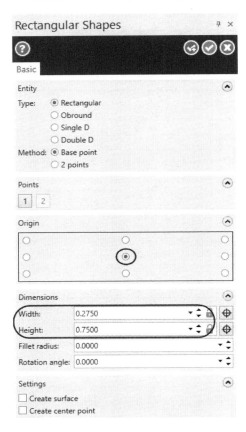

♦ Press **Enter** to see a preview of the rectangle while positioning it.
♦ [Select position of base point]: Select the circle center point as shown.

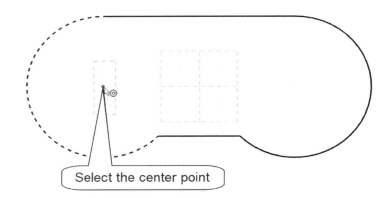

Select the center point

Note: Make sure that the center point icon appears while selecting the point.

♦ Select the **OK and Create New Operation** button or presse **Enter** to continue in the same command.

♦ In the **Rectangular Shapes** panel, click on the **Lock** icons to lock the rectangle values as **Width 0.275** and **Height 0.75** and enter **90** in the **Rotation Angle** field as shown.

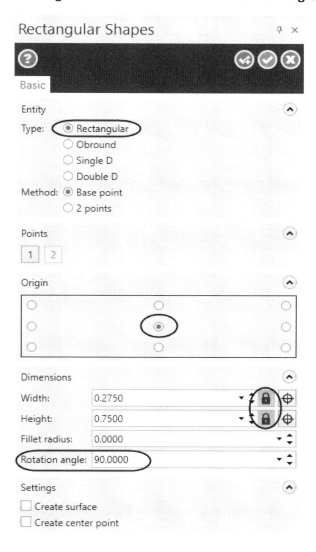

♦ [Select position of base point]: Select the same center point as shown.

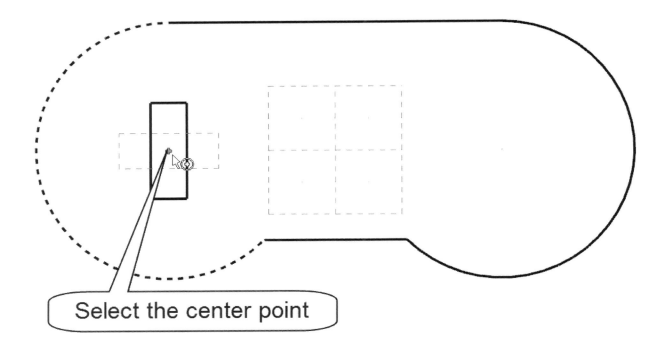

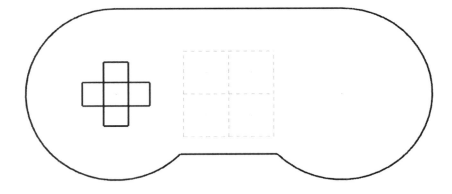

Select the center point

♦ Selected the **OK** button to exit the command.

♦ The geometry should look as shown.

STEP 7: TRIM DIVIDE

In this step you will trim the entities using **Divide** which trims a line, arc, or spline into two disjointed segments by removing the segment that lies between two dividing intersections. When you choose the Divide function and select an entity in the graphics window, Mastercam uses the nearest two intersections on each end to divide the entity. If only one intersection exists, the selected entity is trimmed to the single intersection. If no intersection is found on the selected entity, or the point of intersection is an endpoint of the selected entity, the entity is deleted.

Step Preview:

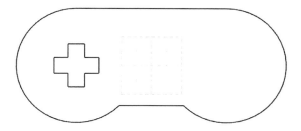

Wireframe

♦ From the **Modify** group, select **Divide** as shown.

♦ In the **Divide** panel, enable **Trim** as shown.

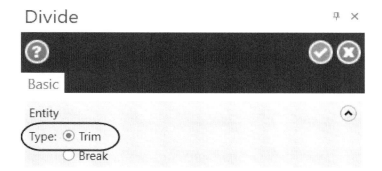

♦ [Select the curve to divide/delete]: Select the line as shown.

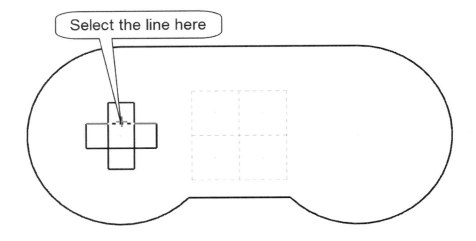

♦ Select the rest of the lines as shown.

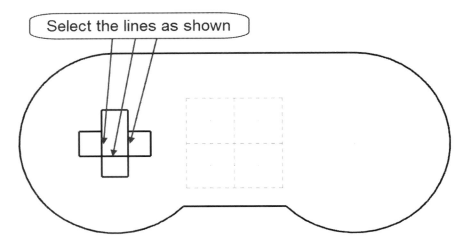

♦ Choose the **OK** button to exit the command.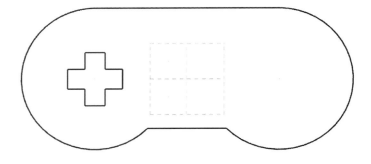

♦ The geometry should look as shown.

STEP 8: FILLET CHAINS

In this step we will fillet all the sharp edges of the shape using the **Fillet Chains** command.

Step Preview:

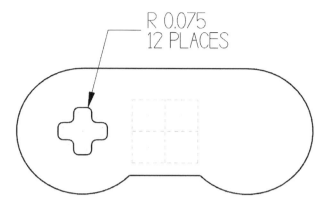

R 0.075
12 PLACES

Wireframe

◆ From the **Modify** group, click on the drop down arrow next to **Fillet Entities** and select **Fillet Chains** as shown.

◆ Leave the **Chain** button enabled in the **Chaining** dialog box as shown.

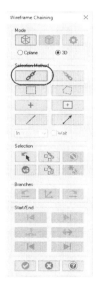

♦ Select the chain as shown.

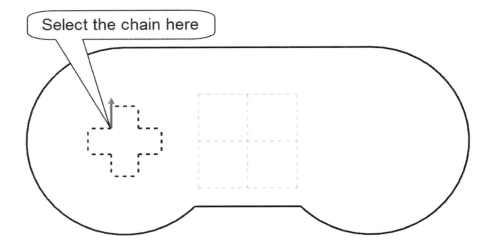

Select the chain here

♦ Select the **OK** button to exit the Chaining dialog box.
♦ In the **Fillet Chains** panel, change the **Radius** and make sure **Trim entities** is enabled as shown.
♦ Press **Enter** to apply the radius.

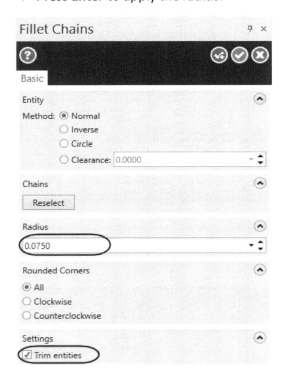

♦ Select the **OK** button to exit the **Fillet Chain** command.

◆ The geometry should look as shown.

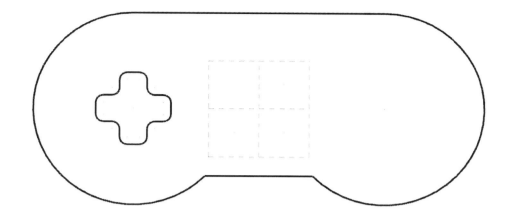

STEP 9: CREATE THE OBROUND SHAPES

In this step you will create the two **Obround** shapes using the **Rectangular Shapes** command.

Step Preview:

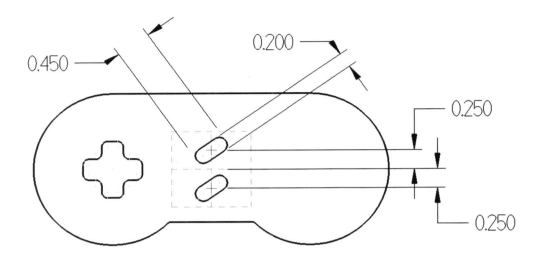

Wireframe

♦ From the **Shapes** group, select the drop down arrow below **Rectangle** and select **Rectangular Shapes** as shown.

♦ In the **Rectangular Shapes**, enter a **Width 0.45**, a **Height** of **0.2**, Angle 35 and enable the **Obround shape**.Lock the values by clicking on the **Lock** icons at the back of the value fields. Make sure that the **Anchor** location is in the center as shown.

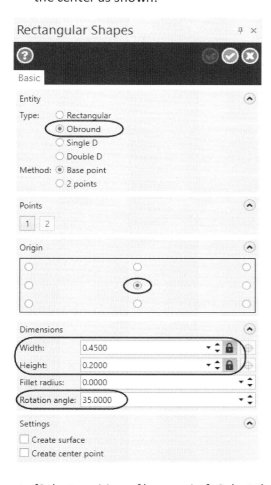

♦ [Select position of base point]: Select the **AutoCursor Fast Point** icon from the **General Selection** toolbar and the field where you can type the coordinates will open at the upper left side of the graphics window as shown.

♦ Enter the coordinate as shown.

```
0,0.25
```

♦ Press **Enter**.
♦ Select the **OK and Create New Operation** button or press **Enter** to continue in the same command.

♦ [Select position of base point]: Select the **AutoCursor Fast Point** and enter the coordinates as shown.

0,-0.25

♦ Press **Enter**.

♦ Select the **OK** button to exit the **Rectangular Shapes** command.

♦ The geometry should look as shown.

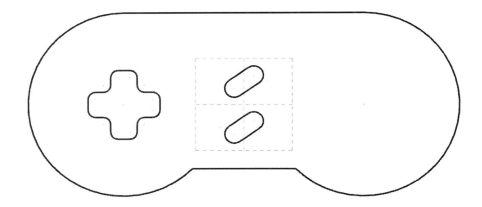

STEP 10: CREATE CIRCLE CENTER POINT

In this step you will create the four 0.25" diameter holes knowing the diameter and the center points.

Step Preview:

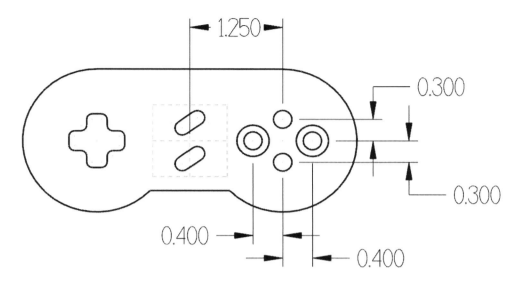

10.1 Create the 1/4" diameter circles

Wireframe

◆ From the **Arcs** group, select **Circle Center Point** as shown.

♦ In the **Circle Center Point**, enter the **Diameter** value of **0.25**, press **Enter** and make sure that the value is locked as shown.

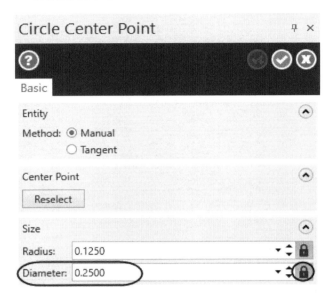

♦ Select the **AutoCursor Fast Point** icon from the **General Selection** toolbar to enter coordinates for the center point **1.25-0.4, 0** as shown.

♦ Press **Enter** to position the circle.

Note: Mastercam lets you perform basic mathematical operations such as addition, subtraction, multiplication or division.

♦ Press **Enter** to continue in the same command.
♦ Select the **AutoCursor Fast Point** icon to enter coordinates for the center point **1.25+0.4, 0** as shown.

1.25+0.4,0

♦ Press **Enter** to position the circle.
♦ Press **Enter** to continue in the same command.
♦ Select the **AutoCursor Fast Point** icon to enter coordinates for the center point **1.25, 0.3** as shown.

1.25,0.3

♦ Press **Enter** to position the circle.
♦ Press **Enter** to continue in the same command.

♦ Select the **AutoCursor Fast Point** icon to enter coordinates for the center point **1.25, -0.3** as shown.

> 1.25,-0.3

♦ Press **Enter** to position the circle.
♦ Press **Enter** to continue in the same command.
♦ The geometry should look as shown.

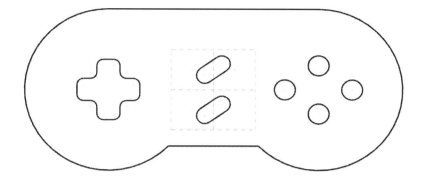

10.2 Create the 0.4375" diameter circles

♦ In the **Circle Center Point** panel, enter a **Diameter** value of **0.4375**, press **Enter** and make sure that the value is locked as shown.

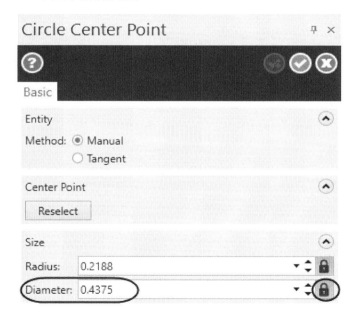

◆ [Enter the center point]: Select the center point of the circle as shown.

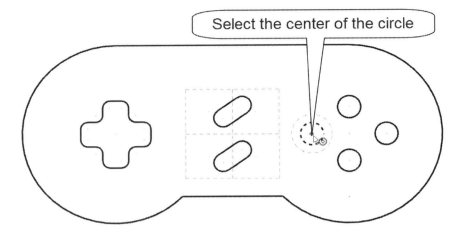

Select the center of the circle

◆ Press **Enter** to continue in the same command.
◆ [Enter the center point]: Select the center point of the circle as shown.

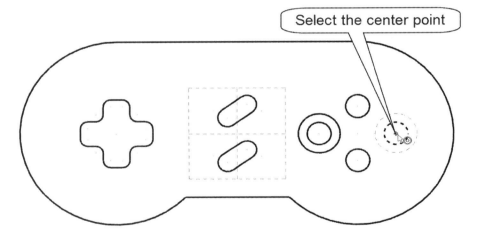

Select the center point

◆ Choose the **OK** button to exit the command.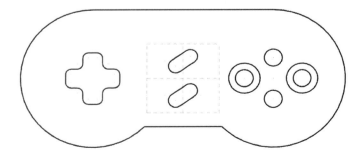
◆ The geometry should look as shown.

STEP 11: SET THE LEVEL

In this step you will change the solid color and the level on which the solid will be created on. This will be done to allow us to view our part easier.

♦ From the left side of the graphics window, click on the **Levels** tab as shown.

♦ When the **Levels Manager** appears, enter in the **Name** field "**Wireframe**" as shown.

♦ In the **Number** field, input "**2**" and enter the name "**Solid**" as shown.

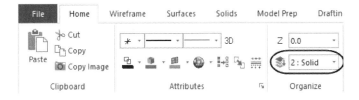

♦ In the **Home** tab you should see the **Level** will be set to **2**.

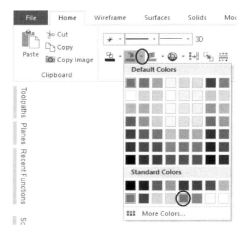

♦ To set the solid color, in the **Attributes** group, select the drop down next to **Solid Color** and select the red color as shown.

STEP 12: EXTRUDE THE BASE OF THE SOLID

Extrude function lets you extrude geometry to create one or more solid bodies, create cuts on an existing body or create bosses on an existing body.

Step Preview:

12.1 Create the body and the four holes

Solids

♦ From the **Create** group, select **Extrude** as shown.

♦ When the **Chaining** dialog box appears, leave the default settings as shown.

♦ Right mouse click in the graphics window and select Isometric.

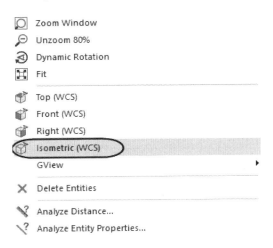

♦ Start selecting the outside profile of the part and then select the four holes in a clockwise direction as shown.

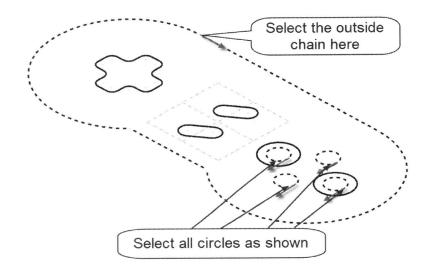

Select the outside chain here

Select all circles as shown

Note: The arrows will disappear as you select the next chain.

♦ Once the geometry has been chained, select the **OK** button.

♦ From the **Solid Extrude** panel, select the **Reverse All** button 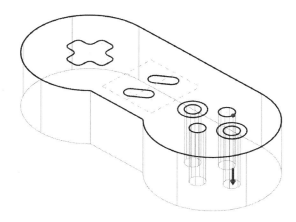 to ensure that the arrow is pointing in a negative or downward direction as shown. Press **Alt + S** to see the solid in the unshaded mode.

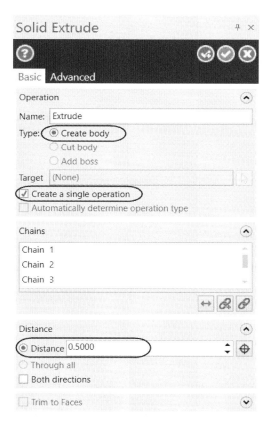

♦ In the **Solid Extrude** panel, ensure **Create Body** and **Create a single operation** are enabled and enter **0.5** into **Distance** as shown.

♦ Select the **OK** button to create the solid.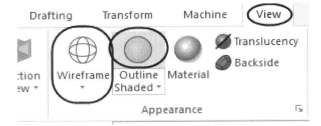

♦ From **View**, use the icons located in the **Appearance** group to **Shade** or **Unshade** (Wireframe) the solid, or press **Alt + S** on your keyboard.

♦ Your part will appear as shown.

♦ Unshade the solid.

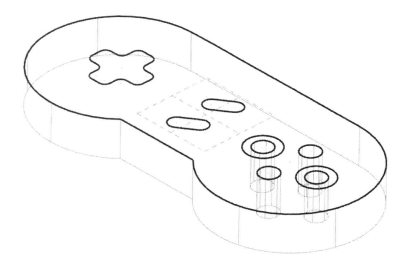

12.2 Cut the shapes

Solids

♦ From the **Create** group, select **Extrude** as shown.

♦ When the **Chaining** dialog box appears, leave the default settings.
♦ Right mouse click in the graphics area and select **Top**.

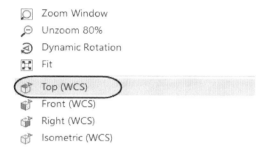

Zoom Window
Unzoom 80%
Dynamic Rotation
Fit
Top (WCS)
Front (WCS)
Right (WCS)
Isometric (WCS)

♦ Press **Alt + F1** to fit the geometry into the graphics window.
♦ Select the five chains in a clockwise direction as shown.

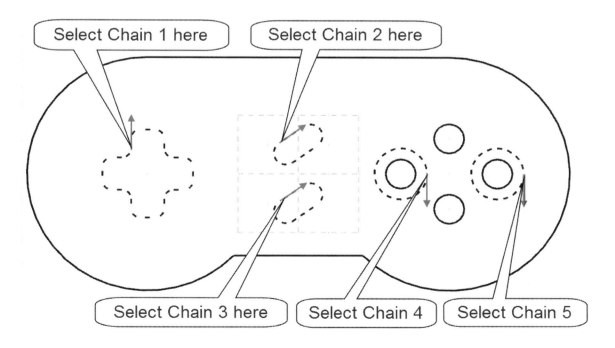

◆ Select the **OK** button in the **Chaining** dialog box.

◆ Right mouse click in the graphics window and select **Isometric**.

Zoom Window	
Unzoom 80%	
Dynamic Rotation	
Fit	
Top (WCS)	
Front (WCS)	
Right (WCS)	
Isometric (WCS)	
GView	▶
Delete Entities	
Analyze Distance...	
Analyze Entity Properties...	

◆ Make sure that the arrow is pointing downwards as shown.

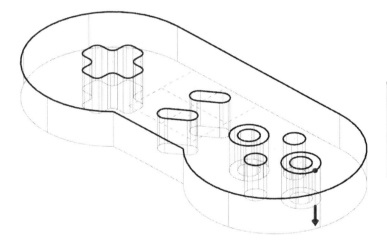

Note: To change the arrow direction, click on the chain closest to the respective arrow.

♦ In the **Solid Extrude** dialog box enable **Cut body** and input a **Distance** of **0.25** as shown.

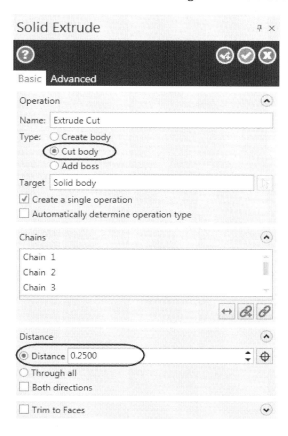

♦ Press **Enter** to preview the updated solid.

♦ Select the **OK** button to exit the **Solid Extrude** panel.

♦ Press **Alt + S** to shade the solid. The part will appear as shown.

12.3 Make Level 1 Invisible

This will hide the 2D wireframe on your screen.

View

♦ To have a better display of the solid, click on the **Outline Shaded**.

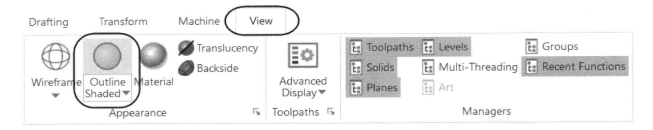

♦ From the left side of the graphics window, select the **Levels** tab.

♦ When the **Levels Manager** appears, left click in the **Visible** column and remove the "**X**" as shown.

Num... ∧	Visible	Name	Entities	Level Set
1		Wireframe	42	
2	X	Solid	1	

♦ The part will appear as shown.

♦ From the left corner of the graphics window, select the **Solids** tab to open the **Solids Manager** panel.

♦ In the **Solids Manager** you should see a **Solid** body as shown.

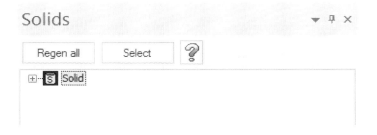

♦ To see the solid operations that you created, in the **Solids Manager**, click on the plus in front of the **Solid** to expand the solid tree with two operations as shown.

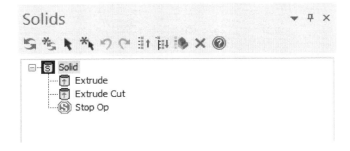

Note: To modify the solid, you can double click on the operation and the respective **Solid Extrude** panel will appear and you can change the parameters as needed. Once you select the **OK** button to exit the **Solid Extrude** panel, click on the **Regen all** button to regenerate the solid.

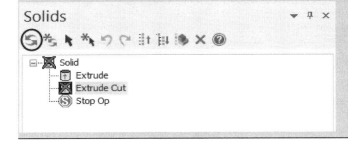

STEP 13: CHAMFER THE HOLES

One-Distance Chamfer uses edge blending to create a symmetrical beveled edge with the same chamfer distance for both edge faces.

In this step you will apply a 0.025" X 45°chamfer to the holes.

Step Preview:

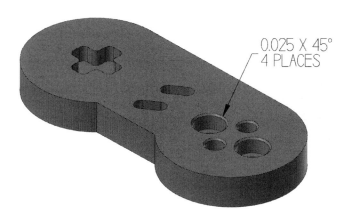

Solids

♦ From the **Modify** group, select **One Distance Chamfer**.

♦ In the **Solid Selection** panel, enable only the **Edge** button, and make sure that **Face**, **Body** and other buttons are disabled, as shown in the figure.

♦ [Select entities to chamfer]: Select all the edges of the holes as shown.

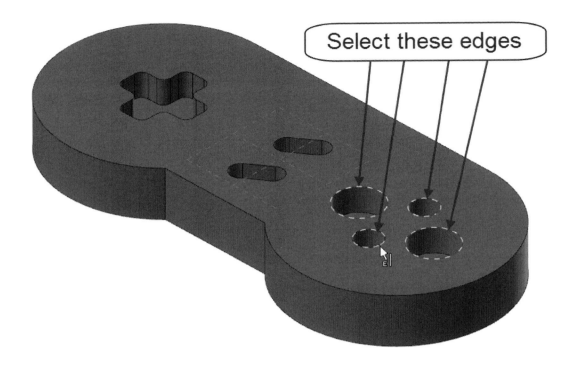

♦ Select the **OK** button to exit the **Solid Selection** dialog box.

♦ The **One-Distance Chamfer** panel will appear. Enable **Propagate along tangencies** and set the **Distance** as shown.

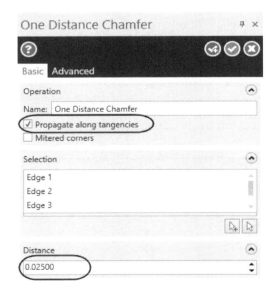

Distance sets the distance of the chamfer from the selected edge on the adjacent faces.

Mitered Corners will extend each chamfer to the extent of the edge. Use this feature where three or more chamfered edges meet at a vertex. With this option disabled, a smooth face at the vertex where the chamfers meet will be created.

Propagate Along Tangencies extends the chamfer along all tangent edges until a non-tangent edge is reached.

♦ Select the **OK** button to exit the command.

♦ The geometry should look as shown.

STEP 14: FILLET THE EDGES

Fillet - Constant Radius Fillet uses edge blending to produce a rounded edge.

In this step you will fillet the edges with a 1/8" radius.

Step Preview:

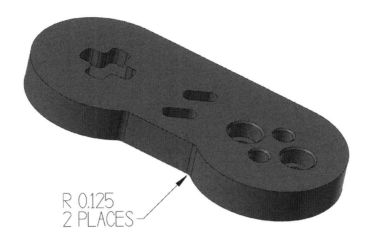

R 0.125
2 PLACES

Solids

♦ From the **Modify** group, select **Constant Fillet** as shown.

♦ In the **Solid Selection** dialog box, enable only the **Edge** button, and make sure that **Face**, **Body** and other buttons are disabled, as shown in the figure.

♦ [Select entities to fillet]: Click somewhere in the middle of the part, and holding down the mouse wheel slightly rotate the part as shown in Figure: 14.0.1.

♦ Select the two edges as shown in Figure: 14.0.1.

Figure: 14.0.1

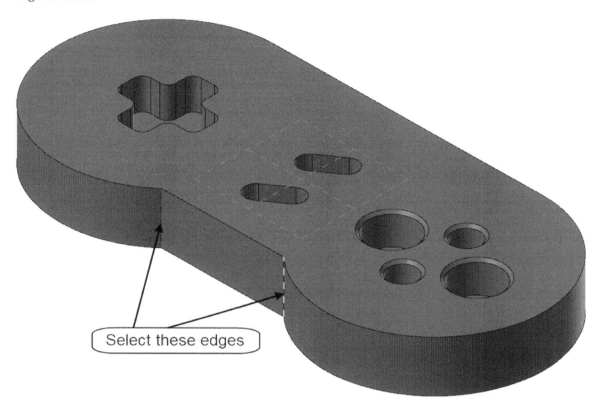

Select these edges

♦ Select the **OK** button to exit the **Solid Selection** dialog box.

♦ In the **Constant Radius Fillet** panel, change the **Radius** to **0.125** as shown.

Radius sets the radius of the fillet.

Propagate along tangencies extends the fillet along all tangent edges until a non-tangent edge is reached.

♦ Select the **OK** button to exit the command.
♦ The geometry should look as shown.

STEP 15: SAVE THE FILE

File

♦ **Save As.**

♦ Click on the **Browse** icon as shown. 
♦ Find a location on the computer to save your file.
♦ File name: "Your Name_7".

TUTORIAL #7 REVIEW EXERCISE

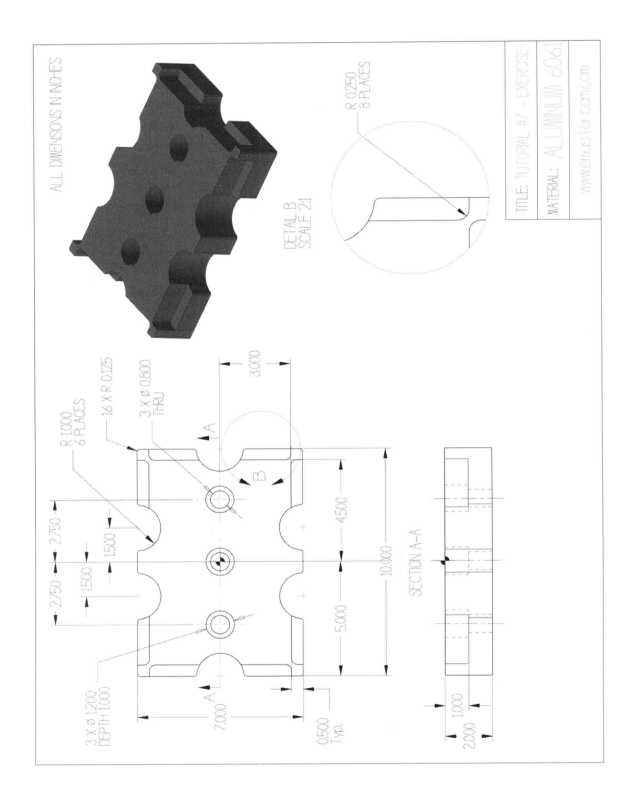

Mastercam 2020

CREATE THE GEOMETRY FOR TUTORIAL #7 EXERCISE

Use these commands to create the geometry.

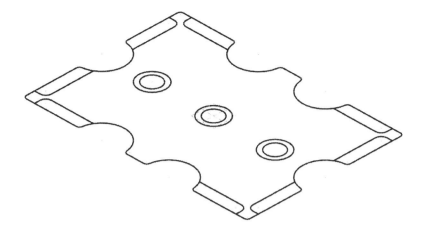

- ♦ Rectangle.
- ♦ Arc Polar.
- ♦ Break Two Pieces.
- ♦ Mirror.
- ♦ Translate.
- ♦ Join.
- ♦ Circle Center Point.
- ♦ Trim Break Extend.

CREATE THE SOLID GEOMETRY FOR TUTORIAL #7 EXERCISE

Change the Main Level to Level 2.
Use these commands to create the geometry.

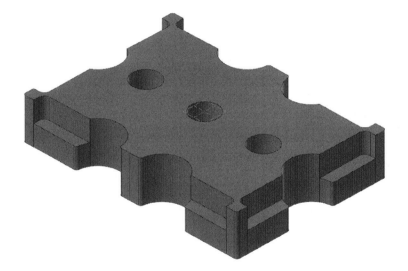

- ♦ Solid Extrude Create body.
- ♦ Solid Extrude Cut body.

TUTORIAL #7 GEOMETRY CREATION QUIZ

♦ How do you modify a solid that you previously extruded?

♦ What does the Constant Radius Fillet command do?

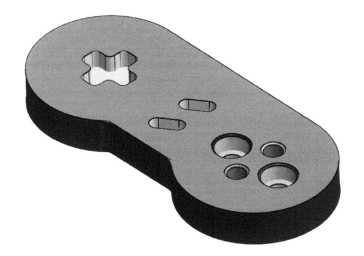

OVERVIEW OF STEPS TAKEN TO CREATE THE FINAL PART:

Create the necessary Toolpaths to machine the part:

♦ The student will set up the stock size and the clamping method to be used.
♦ The 2D HS Dynamic Mill toolpath will be used to machine the pockets.
♦ The Feature Based Drill toolpath will be used to machine the four holes.
♦ The 2D HS Dynamic Mill toolpath will be used to machine the outside profile.
♦ The Pocket toolpath will be used to finish the pocket walls.
♦ The Contour toolpath will be used to finish the outside profile.

Backplot and Verify the file:

♦ Backplot will be used to simulate a step-by-step process of the tool's movements.
♦ Verify will be used to watch a tool machine the part out of a solid model.

Post Process the file to generate the G-code:

♦ The student will then post process the file to obtain an NC file containing the necessary code for the machine.

SUGGESTED FIXTURE

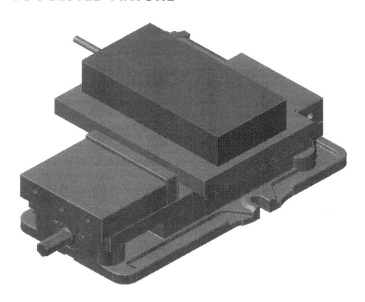

SETUP SHEET

TOOL LIST

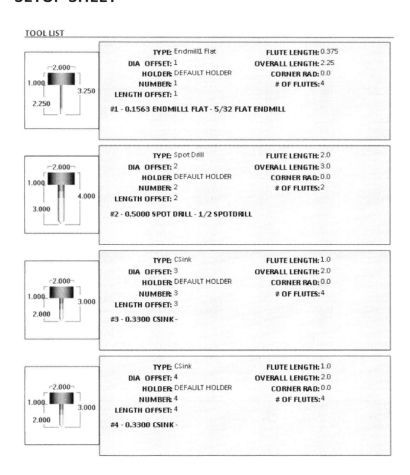

TYPE: Endmill1 Flat	**FLUTE LENGTH:** 0.375
DIA OFFSET: 1	**OVERALL LENGTH:** 2.25
HOLDER: DEFAULT HOLDER	**CORNER RAD:** 0.0
NUMBER: 1	**# OF FLUTES:** 4
LENGTH OFFSET: 1	

#1 - 0.1563 ENDMILL1 FLAT - 5/32 FLAT ENDMILL

TYPE: Spot Drill	**FLUTE LENGTH:** 2.0
DIA OFFSET: 2	**OVERALL LENGTH:** 3.0
HOLDER: DEFAULT HOLDER	**CORNER RAD:** 0.0
NUMBER: 2	**# OF FLUTES:** 2
LENGTH OFFSET: 2	

#2 - 0.5000 SPOT DRILL - 1/2 SPOTDRILL

TYPE: CSink	**FLUTE LENGTH:** 1.0
DIA OFFSET: 3	**OVERALL LENGTH:** 2.0
HOLDER: DEFAULT HOLDER	**CORNER RAD:** 0.0
NUMBER: 3	**# OF FLUTES:** 4
LENGTH OFFSET: 3	

#3 - 0.3300 CSINK -

TYPE: CSink	**FLUTE LENGTH:** 1.0
DIA OFFSET: 4	**OVERALL LENGTH:** 2.0
HOLDER: DEFAULT HOLDER	**CORNER RAD:** 0.0
NUMBER: 4	**# OF FLUTES:** 4
LENGTH OFFSET: 4	

#4 - 0.3300 CSINK -

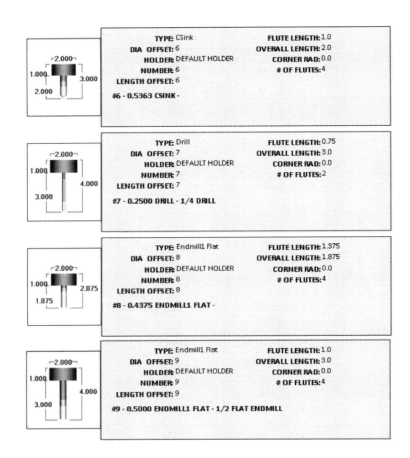

TYPE: CSink	**FLUTE LENGTH:** 1.0
DIA OFFSET: 6	**OVERALL LENGTH:** 2.0
HOLDER: DEFAULT HOLDER	**CORNER RAD:** 0.0
NUMBER: 6	**# OF FLUTES:** 4
LENGTH OFFSET: 6	

#6 - 0.5363 CSINK -

TYPE: Drill	**FLUTE LENGTH:** 0.75
DIA OFFSET: 7	**OVERALL LENGTH:** 3.0
HOLDER: DEFAULT HOLDER	**CORNER RAD:** 0.0
NUMBER: 7	**# OF FLUTES:** 2
LENGTH OFFSET: 7	

#7 - 0.2500 DRILL - 1/4 DRILL

TYPE: Endmill1 Flat	**FLUTE LENGTH:** 1.375
DIA OFFSET: 8	**OVERALL LENGTH:** 1.875
HOLDER: DEFAULT HOLDER	**CORNER RAD:** 0.0
NUMBER: 8	**# OF FLUTES:** 4
LENGTH OFFSET: 8	

#8 - 0.4375 ENDMILL1 FLAT -

TYPE: Endmill1 Flat	**FLUTE LENGTH:** 1.0
DIA OFFSET: 9	**OVERALL LENGTH:** 3.0
HOLDER: DEFAULT HOLDER	**CORNER RAD:** 0.0
NUMBER: 9	**# OF FLUTES:** 4
LENGTH OFFSET: 9	

#9 - 0.5000 ENDMILL1 FLAT - 1/2 FLAT ENDMILL

STEP 1: SELECT THE MACHINE AND SET UP THE STOCK

In Mastercam, you select a **Machine Definition** before creating any toolpath. The **Machine Definition** is a model of your machine's capabilities and features. It acts like a template for setting up your machine. The machine definition ties together three main components: the schematic model of your machine's components, the control definition that models your control capabilities, and the post processor that will generate the required machine code (G-code). For a Mill Essentials exercise (2D toolpaths), we need just a basic machine definition.

*Note: For the purpose of this tutorial, we will be using the **Default Mill** machine.*

- ♦ To make sure that **3D** construction mode is enabled, right mouse click on the screen and check the mode as shown.
- ♦ If not, click on the **2D** button to switch to **3D** mode.

- ♦ Press **Alt + F1** to fit the drawing to the screen.
- ♦ From the left side of the graphics window, click on the **Toolpaths** tab as shown.

- ♦ Pin the **Toolpaths Manager** by clicking on the **Auto Hide** icon as shown.

1.1 Select the machine

Machine

♦ From the **Machine Type** group, select the drop down arrow below **Mill**. Select the **Default**.

*Note: Once you select the **Mill Default**, the **Ribbon bar** changes to reflect the toolpaths that could be used with **Mill Default**.*

♦ Select the plus sign (**+**) in front of **Properties** in the **Toolpaths Manager** to expand the **Toolpaths GroupProperties**.

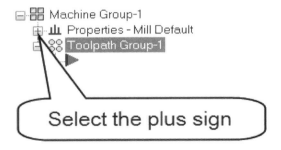

♦ Select **Tool settings** to set the tool parameters.

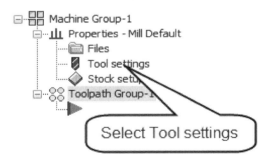

♦ Change the parameters to match the screen shot as shown.

Default program number is used to enter a number if your machine requires a number for a program name.

Assign tool numbers sequentially allows you to overwrite the tool number from the library with the next available tool number. (First operation tool number 1; second operation tool number 2, etc.).

Warn of duplicate tool numbers allows you to get a warning if you enter two tools with the same number.

Override defaults with modal values enables the system to keep the values that you enter.

Feed Calculation set to **From tool** uses feed rate, plunge rate, retract rate, and spindle speed from the tool definition.

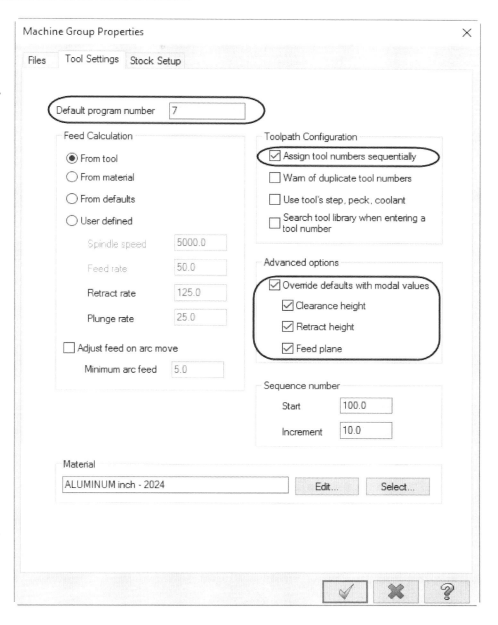

- ◆ Select the **Stock Setup** tab to define the stock.
- ◆ Select the **Rectangular** shape option.
- ◆ Select the **All Entities** button and the stock size will be input as shown.

The **Stock Origin** values adjust the positioning of the stock, ensuring that you have an equal amount of extra stock around the finished part.

Display options allow you to set the stock as Wireframe and to fit the stock to the screen. (Fit Screen)

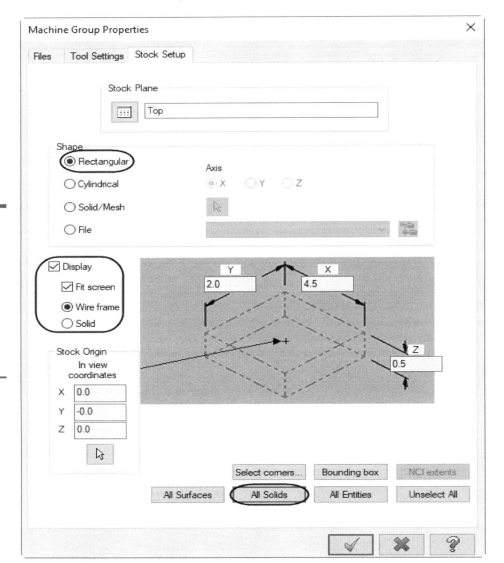

Note: The **stock** model that you create can be displayed with the part geometry when viewing the file or the toolpaths, during backplot, or while verifying toolpaths. In the graphics window, the plus sign (+) shows you where the stock origin is. The default position is the middle of the stock.

- ◆ Select the **OK** button to exit **Machine Group Properties**.

◆ Right mouse click in the graphics window and select the **Isometric** view to see the stock.

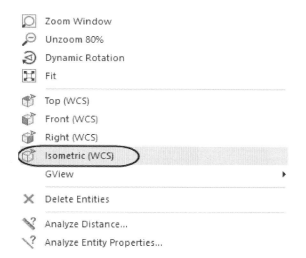

◆ The stock model will appear as shown.

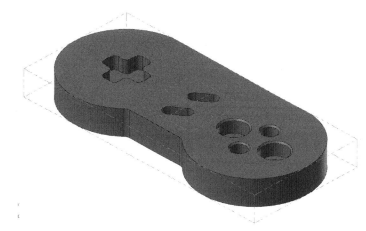

Note: The stock is not geometry and cannot be selected.

STEP 2: 2D HIGH SPEED DYNAMIC MILL

2D High Speed Dynamic Mill utilizes the entire flute length of cutting tools to produce the smoothest, most efficient tool motion for high speed pocketing. The toolpath supports a custom entry method and many others. **Micro lifts** further refine the dynamic milling motion and avoid excessive heat build up. Custom feeds and speeds optimize and generate safe tool motion.

Dynamic Mill machines pockets, material that other toolpaths left behind, and standing bosses or cores. The toolpath depends on the **Machining strategy** that you choose in the **Chain Options**. The outside chain contains the toolpath; all inside chains are considered islands.

Toolpath Preview:

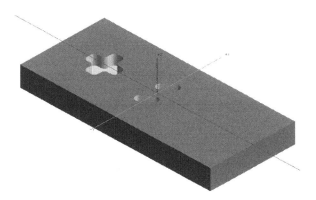

Toolpaths

♦ From the **2D** group, select the **Dynamic Mill** icon.

♦ From the **Chain Options** dialog box, click on the **Select machining chains** button in the **Machining regions** as shown.

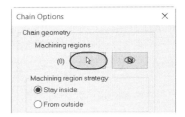

◆ In the **Chaining** dialog box, enable **Solids** selection as shown.

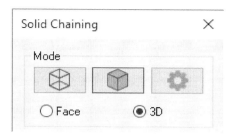

◆ In the **Chaining** dialog box, enable only the **Face** button and make sure that no other button is enabled as shown.

◆ Right mouse click in the graphics window and select the **Top** view as shown.

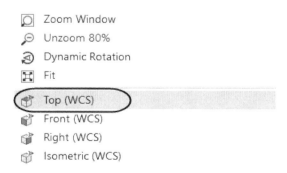

◆ Press **Alt + S** if needed to display the solid in shaded mode.

◆ Select the bottom of the pockets as shown.

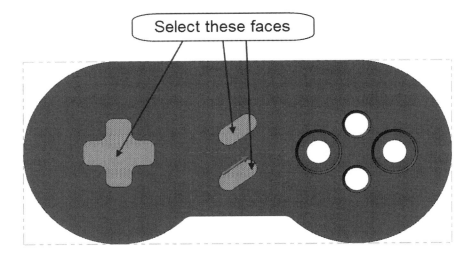

◆ Select the **OK** button to exit the **Chaining** dialog box.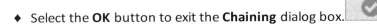

◆ In the **Chain Options** dialog box, **Machining regions** will have 1 chain (solid selection displays one chain although all three chains are currently selected).

◆ Make sure that **Stay inside** is enabled as shown.

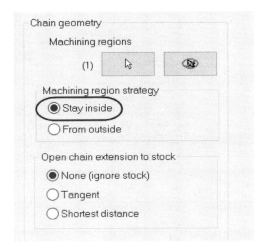

◆ Select the **OK** button to exit the **Chain Options** dialog box.

◆ In the **Toolpath Type** page, **Dynamic Mill** will be already selected as shown.

Dynamic Mill　　Area Mill　　Dynamic Contour　　Peel Mill　　Blend Mill

2.1 Preview Chains

The **Preview Chains** function is intended to give the user a quick visual representation of how Mastercam sees the various pieces of geometry that have been selected, how they interact with one another and a general overview of how the toolpath will be calculated with the selections presently made.

♦ Click on the **Color** icon to see the legend for **Preview chains** as shown.

♦ The **Preview Chains Colors** dialog box should look as shown.

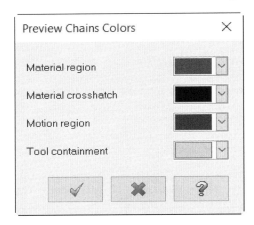

The **Material region** and **Material crosshatch** are the two colors that are used to define the material to be cut. The default colors are red for the background and black for the crosshatch.

The **Motion region** displays the area that Mastercam is making available to the toolpath for motion if it needs it. The color to represent it is dark blue. The primary reason for the display of the entire available (but not necessarily used) **Motion region** is to help the user visualize how the tool may move near or interact with any adjacent geometry.

The **Tool containment** is what you have selected as the containment region in the chain geometry. If you have not selected a containment region, it will default to the outside of the **Motion region** since that is currently the default area the toolpath is being contained to. The color used to represent the **Tool containment** is yellow.

♦ Select the **OK** button to exit **Preview Chains Colors**.

♦ Select the **Preview chains** button as shown.

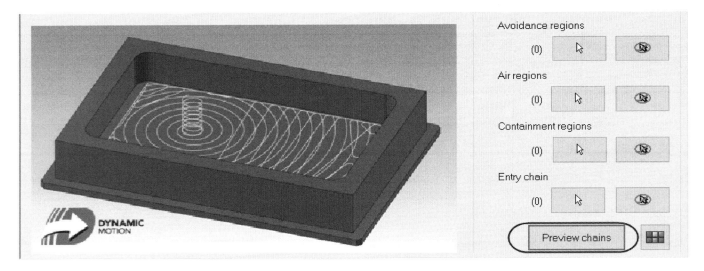

- ◆ Select the **Hide dialog** button to see the preview in the graphics window.
- ◆ The **Preview chains** should look as shown.

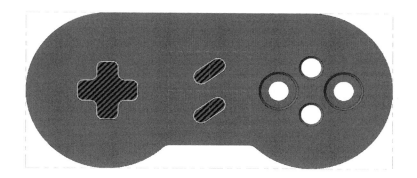

- ◆ Press **Esc** key to return to the toolpath parameters.

- ◆ Click on the **Preview chains** button again to clear the Preview chains display.

2.2 Select a 5/32" Flat Endmill from the library and set the Tool Parameters

- ◆ Select **Tool** from the **Tree View list**.

- ◆ Click on the **Select library tool** button.

- ◆ Select the **Filter** button.

- ◆ Select the **None** button and then under **Tool Types**, choose the **Flat Endmill** icon.
- ◆ Under **Tool Diameter**, pick **Equal** and input a value of **5/32"** as shown.

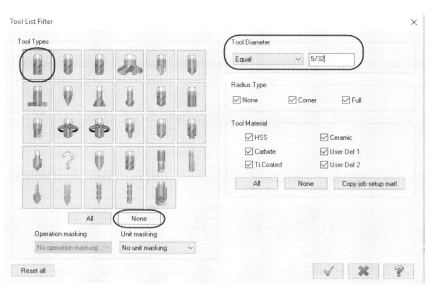

♦ Select the **OK** button to exit the **Tool List Filter**.

♦ In the **Tool Selection** dialog box you should only see a **5/32" Flat Endmill**.

#	Assembly Na...	Tool Name	Holder Name	Dia.	Cor. rad.	Length	# Flutes	Type	Rad. ...
283	--	5/32 FLAT ENDMILL	--	0.156...	0.0	0.375	4	Endmi...	None

♦ Select the **5/32" Flat Endmill** in the **Tool Selection** dialog box and then select the **OK** button to exit.

♦ Make all the necessary changes as shown.

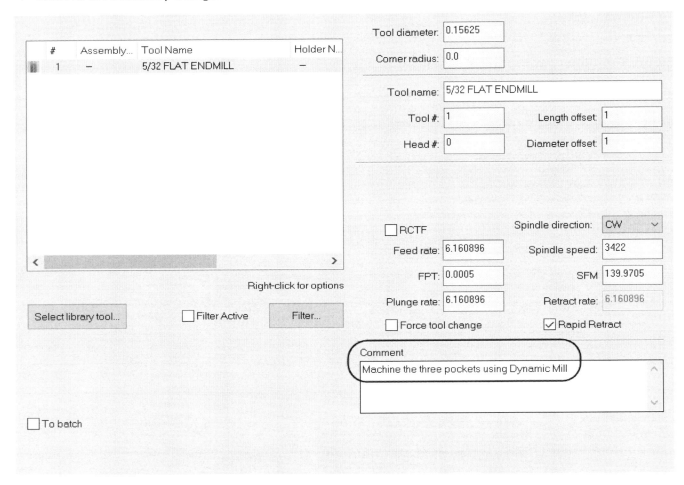

2.3 Set the Cut Parameters

◆ From the **Tree View list**, select **Cut Parameters**.
◆ Change the settings for this first toolpath as shown.

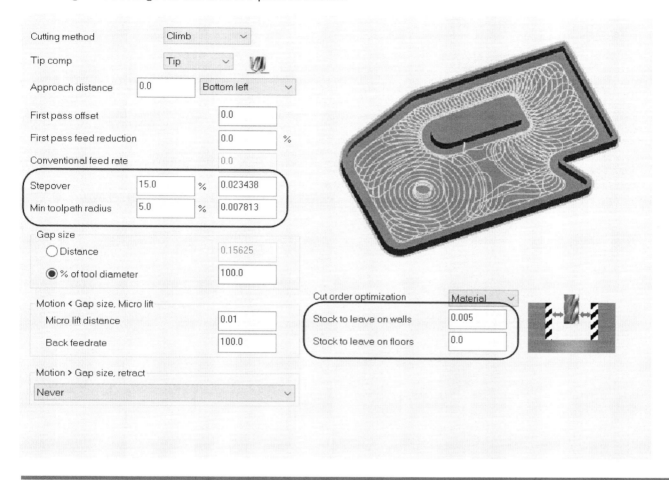

Stepover sets the distance between cutting passes in the X and Y axes.

Toolpath radius reduces sharp corner motion between cut passes.

Micro lift distance enters the distance the tool lifts off the part on the back moves. **Micro lifts** are slight lifts that help clear chips and minimize excessive tool heating.

Back feedrate controls the speed of the backfeed movement of the tool.

Motion > Gap Size, retract controls retracts in the toolpath when making a non-cutting move within an area where the tool can be kept down or microlifted.

Cut order optimization defines the cut order Mastercam applies to different cutting passes in the Dynamic Mill toolpath.

2.4 Set the Entry Motion

♦ From the **Tree View list**, select **Entry Motion**
♦ **Entry Motion** configures an entry method for the **Dynamic Mill** toolpath which determines not only how and where the tool enters the part, but also the cutting method/machining strategy used by the toolpath. The previous settings will be saved.
♦ Change the **Entry method** to **Profile** as shown.

Entry method set to **Profile** creates a boundary based on the shape of the selected chain and uses the tool to ramp into the part. The slot is cleared by taking lighter cuts in the Z axis until the tool reaches the full depth.

Z clearance adds extra height used in the ramping motion down from a top profile. It ensures that the tool has fully slowed down from rapid speeds before touching the material.

Plunge angle sets the angle of descent for the entry move and determines the pitch.

2.5 Set the Linking Parameters

♦ Select **Linking Parameters** and enable **Clearance**, input a value of **Absolute 1.0.** Change the **Top of stock** value to **Absolute 0.0** and the **Depth** to **Incremental 0.0** as shown.

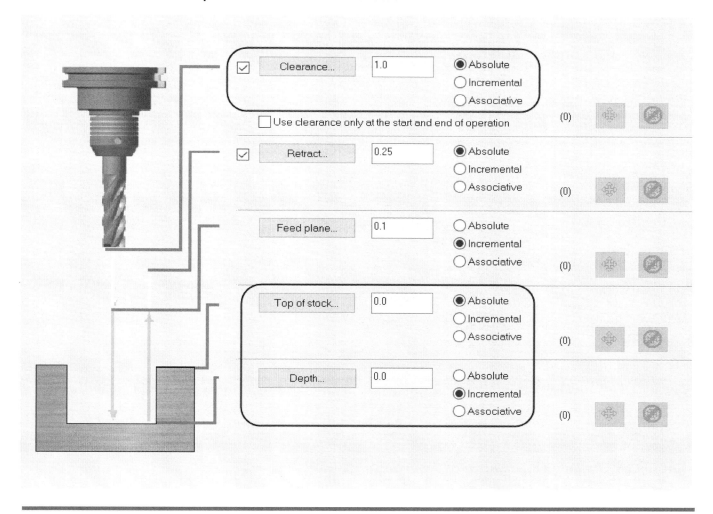

Incremental value for the **Depth** is measured at the chained geometry. In this tutorial, the pocket chains were selected at the bottom, which is their final depth.

2.6 Preview the Toolpath

◆ To quickly check how the toolpath will be generated, select the **Preview toolpath** icon as shown.

◆ To hide the dialog box, click on the **Hide dialog** icon as shown.

◆ To see the part from an **Isometric** view, right mouse click in the graphics window and select **Isometric** as shown.

◆ The toolpath should look as shown.

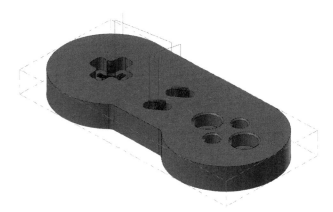

◆ Press **Esc** key to exit the preview.

Note: If the toolpath does not look as shown in the preview, check your parameters again.

◆ Select the **OK** button to generate the toolpath.

STEP 3: BACKPLOT THE TOOLPATHS

Backplotting shows the path the tools take to cut the part. This display lets you spot errors in the program before you machine the part. As you backplot toolpaths, Mastercam displays additional information such as the X, Y, and Z coordinates, the path length, the minimum and maximum coordinates, and the cycle time.

♦ Select the **Backplot selected operations** button.

♦ Right mouse click in the graphics window and select **Isometric** as shown.

View

♦ From the **Appearance** group, select **Translucency** as shown.

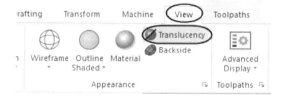

♦ Select the **Play** button to run **Backplot**.

♦ The toolpath should look as shown.

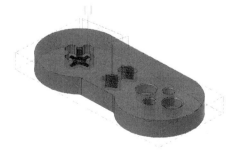

♦ Select the **OK** button to exit **Backplot** dialog box.

STEP 4: SIMULATE THE TOOLPATH IN VERIFY

Verify Mode shows the path the tools take to cut the part with material removal. This display lets you spot errors in the program before you machine the part. As you verify toolpaths, Mastercam displays additional information such as the X, Y, and Z coordinates, the path length, the minimum and maximum coordinates and the cycle time. It also shows any collisions between the workpiece and the tool.

♦ From the **Toolpaths Manager**, select **Verify selected operations** icon as shown.

Note: Mastercam launches a new window that allows you to check the part using **Backplot** or **Verify**.

♦ Select the **Play** button to run **Verify**.

♦ The part should appear as shown.

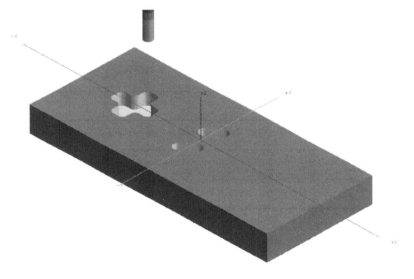

♦ To go back to the Mastercam window, minimize the **Mastercam Simulator** window as shown. ⊖ ⬜ ✕
♦ Press **Alt + T** to remove the toolpath display.

STEP 5: DRILL THE HOLES USING FBM DRILL

FBM Drill automatically detects holes in a solid based on your specific criteria and generates a complete series of drilling and chamfering. **FBM Drill** also generates circle mill or helix bore operations for large-hole features when you activate these settings.

Toolpath Preview:

Toolpaths

♦ From the **2D** group, click on the **Expand gallery** icon.

♦ From the **Toolpaths Gallery**, select the **FBM Drill**.

- ◆ When the **FBM Toolpaths - Drill** page appears, enable **Automatic initial hole detection**.
- ◆ Change the **Grouping** to **Plane** as shown to group the operations by the plane in which the holes lie.

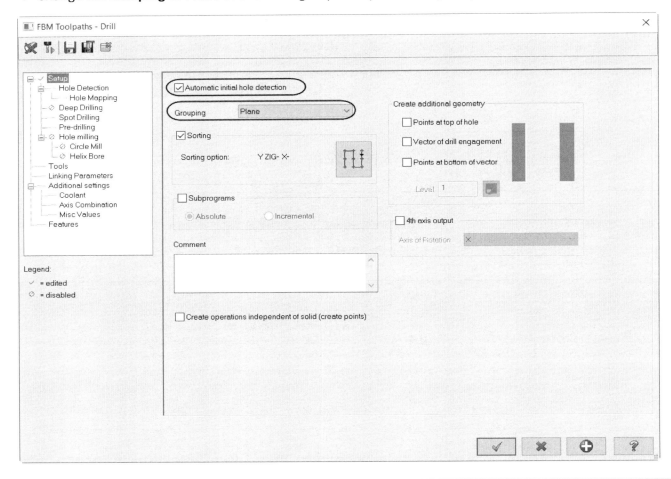

Automatic initial hole/feature detection when selected, Mastercam automatically detects the solid.

Grouping controls how the drill cycles that **FBM Drill** creates are organized in the **Toolpaths Manager**. Mastercam orders operations within groups into subgroups by operation type.

Plane groups all operations based on the plane of the hole.

Create additional geometry selects one or more options to create geometry for detected hole features without generating toolpaths. The geometry is saved to a level you choose in this section and is non-associative.

5.1 Hole Detection

♦ Choose Hole Detection to control the types of holes FBM Drill detects. Enable/disable the options as shown.

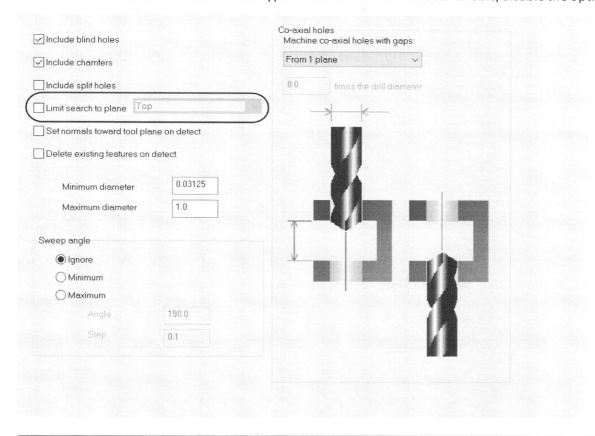

Include blind holes will search your part for blind holes (holes that do not go through the entire solid).

Include chamfers searches for holes with chamfers.

Include split holes searches the part for holes that are incomplete.

Limit search to plane detects features that can only be machined in the selected plane.

Minimum diameter finds holes which are equal to or greater than this value.

Maximum diameter finds holes which are equal to or less than this value.

Sweep angle lets you set a tolerance for how complete holes need to be in terms of their included angle to be detected by and included in the **FBM Drill** operation.

Machine co-axial holes with gaps determines whether Mastercam treats multiple holes that share a common axis as a single hole, or as multiple holes from different planes.

5.2 Spot Drilling

♦ Select **Spot Drilling** to activate and define the spot drilling toolpaths for the **FBM Drill** operation.
♦ Enable the option **Use this tool for all spot drill operations** as shown.

Note: It takes a couple of minutes to enable Use this tool for all spot drill operations.

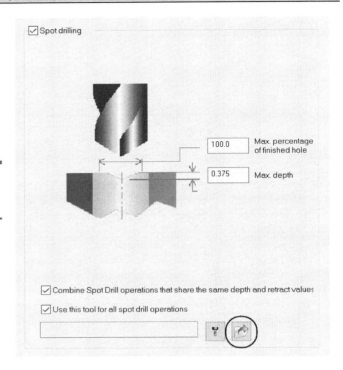

Use this tool for all spot drill operations allows you to choose a specific spot drill cycle generated by the **FBM Drill** operation.

♦ Pick the button **Select tool from library**.
♦ This will let you choose a tool from the current tool library.
♦ Find and select the **1/2" Spot Drill** from the list.

	#	Assembly Na...	Tool Name	Holder Name	Dia.	Cor. rad.	Length	# Flutes	Type	Rad. .
	22	--	1/4 SPOTDRILL	--	0.25	0.0	2.0	2	Spot ...	None
	23	--	3/8 SPOTDRILL	--	0.375	0.0	2.0	4	Spot ...	None
	24	--	1/2 SPOTDRILL	--	0.5	0.0	2.0	2	Spot ...	None
	25	--	3/4 SPOTDRILL	--	0.75	0.0	2.0	4	Spot ...	None
	26	--	1. SPOTDRILL	--	1.0	0.0	2.0	4	Spot ...	None
	27	--	1/64 DRILL	--	0.015...	0.0	1.0	2	Drill	None

♦ Select the **OK** button and the **Spot Drill** will appear in the box to the left of the buttons.

5.3 Pre-Drilling

This page defines pre-drilling cycles that rough out the drilled holes before the finish drill cycle.

◆ Select **Pre-drilling** from the **Tree View list**. Leave **Pre-drilling** settings as shown.

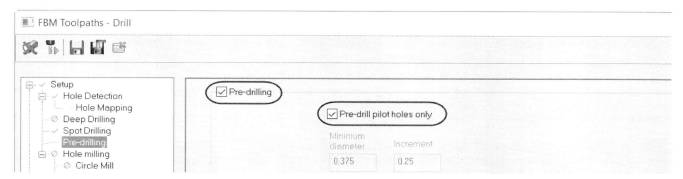

Pre-drilling creates pre-drilling operations that rough out the detected holes before creating any finished drill and chamfer operation.

Pre-drill pilot holes only deactivates all pre-drill roughing cycles except for assigned pilot holes cycles. This also deactivates the parameters for minimum diameter, increment and stock to leave on the page because they are not applicable.

FBM Drill generates only pilot holes on pre-drill cycles followed by finish hole cycles.

5.4 Tools

This page controls the tools Mastercam selects for the drill cycles that the **FBM Drill** operation creates.

♦ Select **Tools** from the **Tree View list**. Enable/disable the parameters as shown.

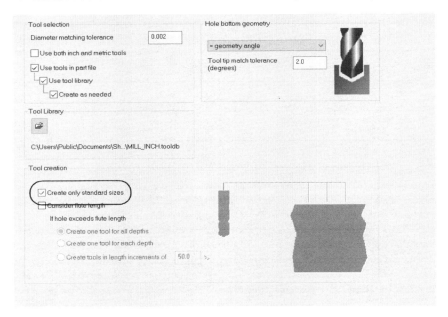

Tool selection lets you pick one or more of the following options to tell Mastercam where to locate tools for the FBM-generated toolpaths.

Diameter matching tolerance uses this value to determine how closely the diameter of the tool and the hole must match before selecting an appropriate tool.

Use tools in part file looks in the current Mastercam file for an appropriate tool. The tools do not have to be used in previous operations to be available to the FBM operations.

Use tool library searches the selected tool library for the necessary tools.

Create as needed creates the necessary tools using the tool creation parameters you define.

Hole bottom geometry defines the relationship of the bottom hole geometry to the tool tip geometry.

= geometry angle the tool tip angle must match the hole bottom geometry within the specified tool tip match tolerance.

> geometry angle the tool tip must be greater than the floor angle geometry.

< geometry angle the tool tip must be less than the floor angle geometry.

5.5 Linking Parameters

This page defines how **FBM Drill** calculates clearance height and retract height for the drilling cycles.

♦ Select **Linking Parameters** from the **Tree View list**. Set the parameters as shown.

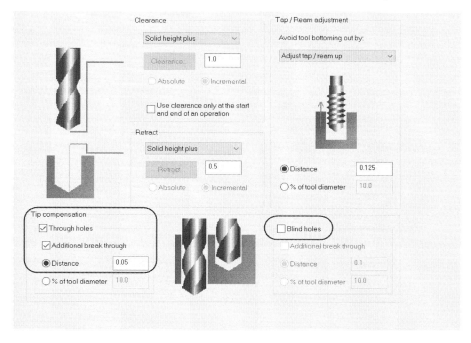

Clearance is the height at which the tool moves to and from the part. There are several options available from where the height is measured:

Solid height plus adds a fixed height above the highest point of the solid model.

Stock model plus adds a specified height above the stock model.

Top of hole plus adds clearance distance above the top of each hole.

Top of coaxial holes plus sets the clearance above the highest hole on the shared axis for holes that share the same axis

Manual allows you to set the clearance using all options in any combination.

Retract is the height at which the tool moves before the next tool pass. The same options are available as the Clearance height.

Tap/Ream adjustment determines whether tapped and reamed holes are fully finished.

Tip compensation compensates for the tool tip.

5.6 Features

This page allows you to manage the list of hole features that **FBM Drill** detects in the solid model.

- Select **Features** from the **Tree View list**.
- Choose the button to **Detect the Features** on the top left corner of the dialog box for Mastercam to detect the holes as shown.

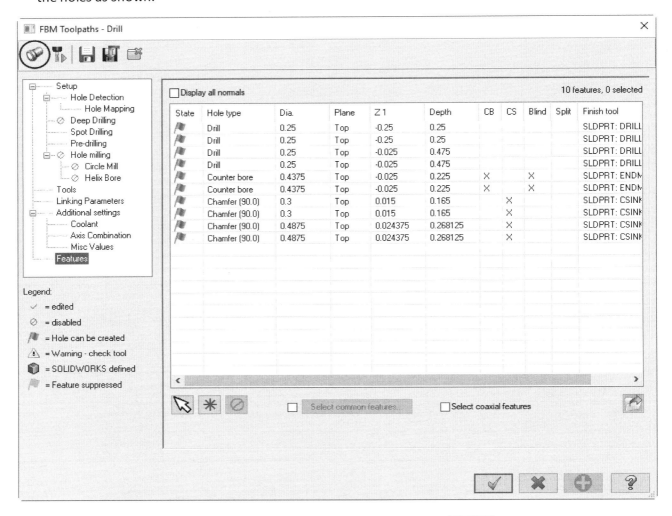

- Choose the **OK** button to exit the **FBM Toolpaths - Drill** parameters.

*Note: If a **Warning** message error appears on the screen: " Drilling point data from a solid is not editable" select the OK button untill it disappears. The toolpath will not be affected.*

5.7 Backplot the toolpath

♦ Click on the **Select all operations** icon in the **Operations Manager**.

♦ **Backplot** the toolpaths. See **"Backplot The Toolpaths" on page 825** to review the procedure.

♦ The toolpaths should look as shown.

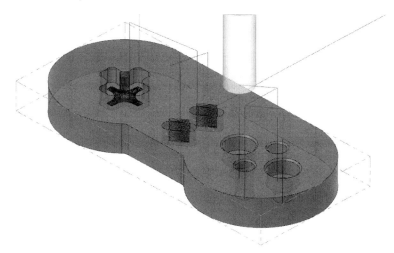

♦ Select the **OK** button to exit **Backplot**.

5.8 Verify the toolpaths

♦ **Verify** the toolpaths. See **"Simulate the toolpath in Verify" on page 826** to review the procedure.

♦ The part should look as shown.

♦ To go back to the Mastercam window, minimize the **Mastercam Simulator** window as shown.

STEP 6: MACHINE THE OUTSIDE OF THE PART USING DYNAMIC MILLING

2D High Speed Dynamic Mill utilizes the entire flute length of their cutting tools to produce the smoothest, most efficient tool motion for high speed pocketing and core milling.

The **Dynamic Mill** toolpath machines pockets, material that other toolpaths left behind, and standing bosses or cores. The toolpath depends on the **Machining strategy** that you choose in the **Chain Options**. If the strategy chosen is **From outside**, the toolpath starts at the outmost chain and moves freely outside of this area; the inner chain defines the limit of the toolpath. You can also machine pockets, in which case the strategy selected is **Start inside**, which keeps the tool inside the machining regions.

Toolpath Preview:

♦ Click on the **Move insert arrow down one item** icon to move the arrow at the end of the toolpaths as shown.

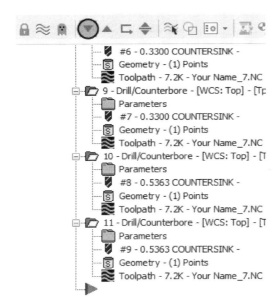

♦ In the **Toolpaths Manager**, click **Select all operations**.
♦ Press **Alt + T** until you remove the toolpath display.

Toolpaths

♦ From the **2D** group, select the **Expand gallery** arrow and then from the **Toolpath Gallery** select **Dynamic Mill**.

♦ In the **Chain Options, Machining regions**, enable From outside and in the **Open chain extension to stock**, enable **Shortest distance** as shown in Figure: 6.0.1.
♦ Click on the **Select avoidance chains** button in the **Avoidance regions** as shown in Figure: 6.0.1.

Figure: 6.0.1

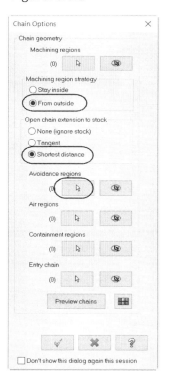

♦ Enable **Loop** in the **Chaining** dialog box and make sure that all the other buttons are not selected as shown.

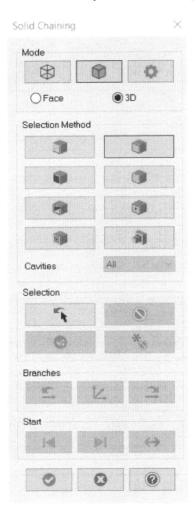

♦ Right mouse click in the graphics window and select the **Isometric** view as shown.

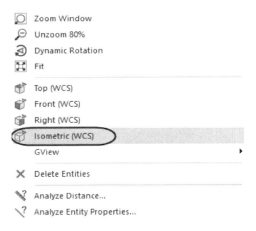

♦ [Solid Toolpath Chain: Select faces, edges, and/or loops]: Select the edge as shown.

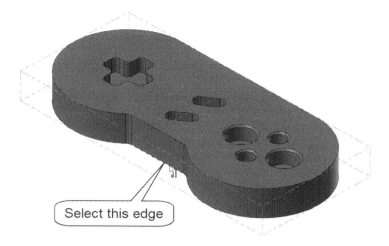

Select this edge

♦ The entire profile will be selected as shown.

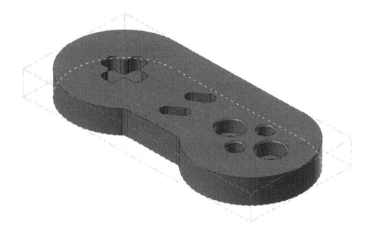

♦ In the **Pick Reference Face** dialog box, select the **OK** button to accept this face.

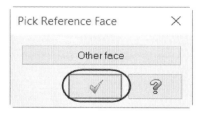

♦ Select the **OK** button to exit the **Chaining** dialog box.

♦ The **Chain Options** dialog box should look as shown.

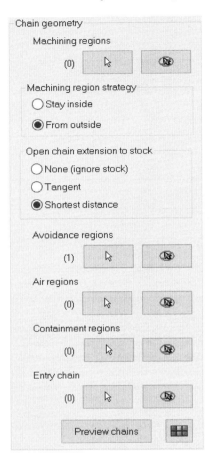

From outside enabled ensures that the tool will approach the part from the outside.

Open chain extension to stock set to the Shortest distance sets how the system calculates the amount of the material that has to be removed based on the shortest distance from the chain to the edge of the stock.

Avoidance regions allows you to select the profile that describes the shape up to where the material will be removed.

♦ Select the **OK** button to exit the Chain Options dialog box.

♦ In the **Toolpath Type** page, **Dynamic Mill** with **From outside** option should be already selected.

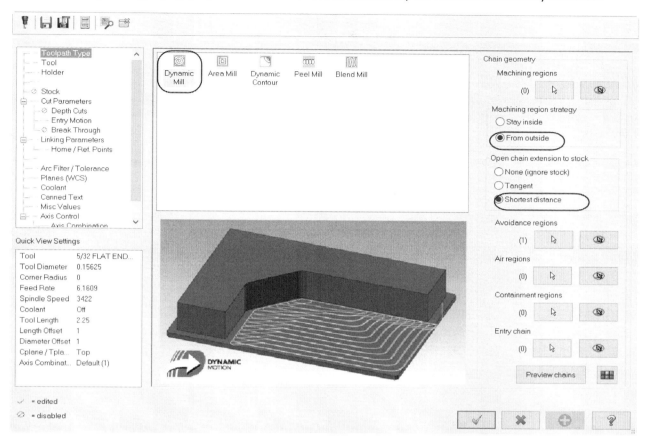

6.1 Preview Chains

♦ Select the Preview chains button as shown.

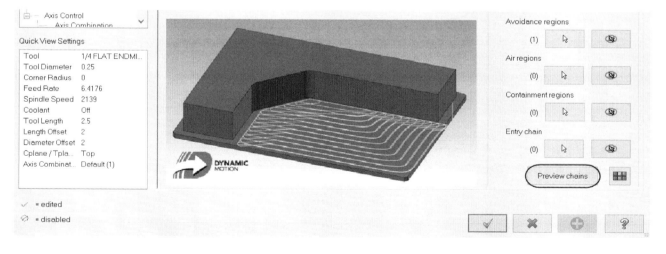

♦ See **"Preview Chains" on page 817** to review the procedure.

◆ The Preview chains should look as shown.

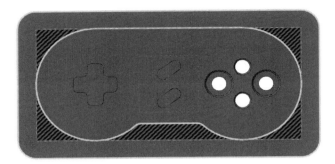

◆ Press **Esc** key to exit the preview.

◆ Click on the **Preview chains** button again to clear the **Preview** chains display.

6.2 Select a 0.5" Flat Endmill from the library and set the Tool Parameters

◆ Select **Tool** from the **Tree View list**.

◆ Click on the **Select library tool** button.

◆ Select the **Filter** button.

◆ Select the **None** button and then under **Tool Types**, choose the **Flat Endmill** icon.
◆ Under **Tool Diameter**, pick **Equal** and input a value of **0.5** as shown.

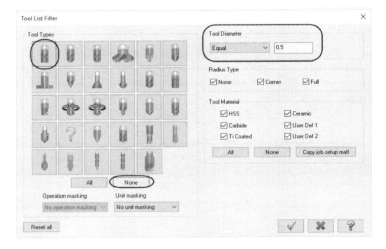

◆ Select the **OK** button to exit the **Tool List Filter**.

♦ In the **Tool Selection** panel you should only see a **1/2" Flat Endmill**.

#	Assembly...	Tool Name	Holder N...	Dia.	Cor. r...	Length	# Flut...	Type	Rad....
290	–	1/2 FLAT ...	–	0.5	0.0	1.0	4	End...	None

♦ Select the **1/2" Flat Endmill** in the **Tool Selection** page and then select the **OK** button to exit.

♦ Make all the necessary changes as shown.

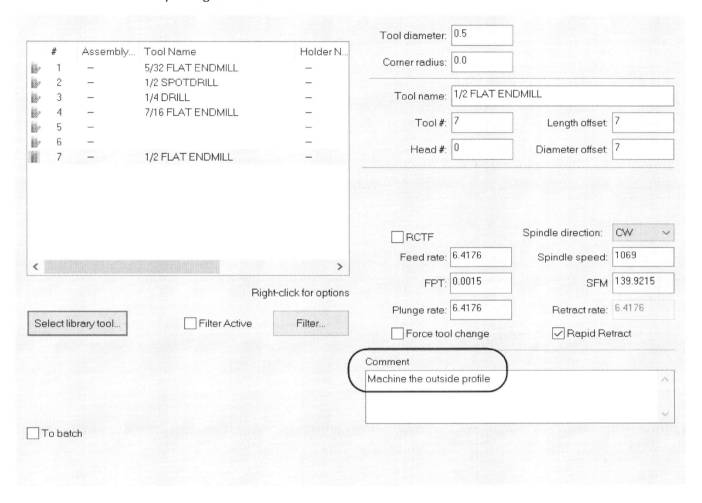

6.3 Set the Cut Parameters

♦ From the **Tree View list**, select **Cut Parameters** and ensure the parameters appear the same as shown.

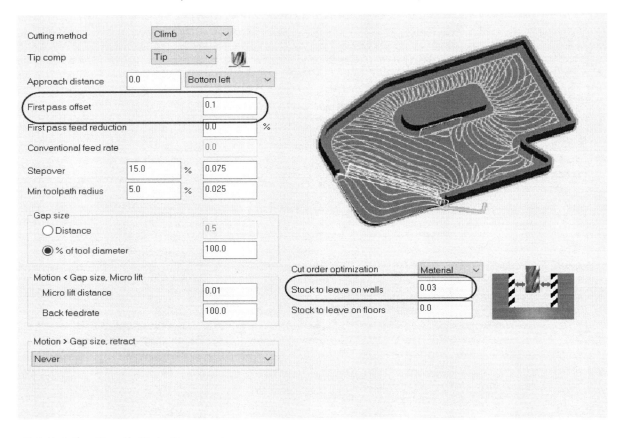

6.4 Set the Depth Cuts Parameters

♦ From the **Tree View list**, select **Depth Cuts** and ensure **Depth cuts** are disabled as shown.

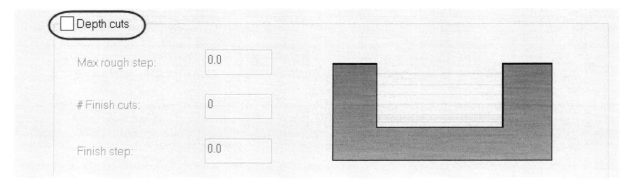

6.5 Set the Linking Parameters

♦ Select **Linking Parameters**, ensure **Clearance** is enabled and has a value of **1.0** and input a **Depth** value of **-0.5** as shown.

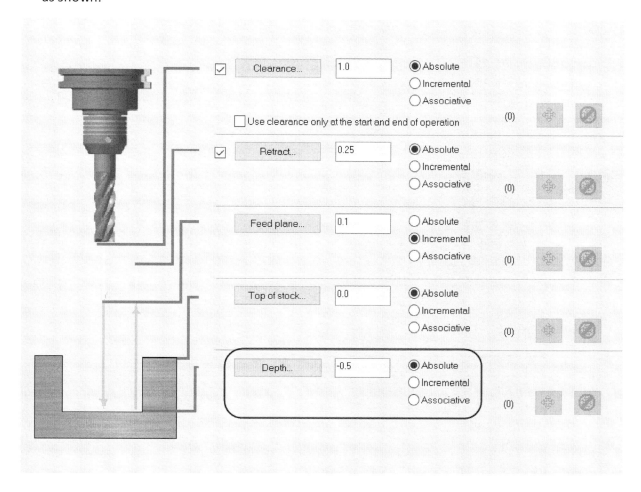

6.6 Preview the Toolpath

♦ To quickly check how the toolpath will be generated, select the **Preview toolpath** icon as shown.

♦ See **"Preview the Toolpath" on page 824** to review the procedure.
♦ The toolpath should look as shown.

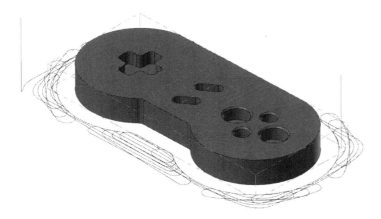

♦ Press **Esc** key to exit the preview.

Note: If the toolpath does not look as shown in the preview, check your parameters again.

♦ Select the **OK** button to generate the toolpath.

6.7 Backplot the toolpath

♦ **Backplot** the toolpath. See **"Backplot The Toolpaths" on page 825** for more information.

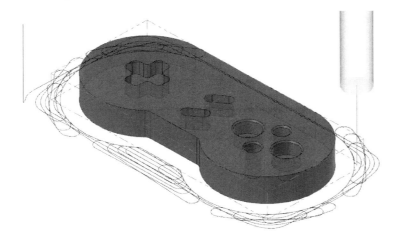

♦ Select the **OK** button to exit **Backplot**.

6.8 Verify the toolpaths

♦ **Verify** the toolpaths. See **"Simulate the toolpath in Verify" on page 826** for more information.

♦ To **Verify** all toolpaths, from the **Toolpaths Manager**, choose the **Select all operations** icon.

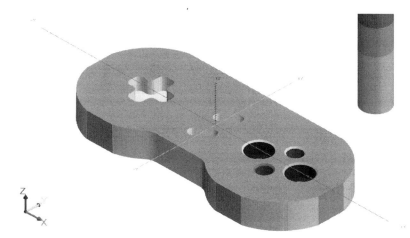

♦ To go back to the Mastercam window, minimize the **Mastercam Simulator** window as shown.

STEP 7: FINISH THE POCKETS USING A POCKET TOOLPATH

In this step you will use a pocket toolpath to finish the walls of all pockets since the high speed toolpaths do not have a finish wall option inside of their parameters. You will use the solid selections.

Toolpath Preview:

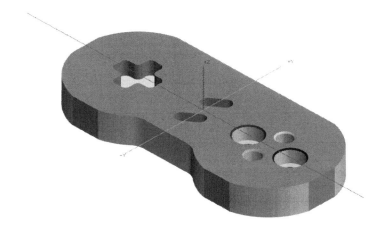

Toolpaths

♦ From the **2D** group, click on the **Expand gallery** arrow and in the **Toolpath Gallery** select **Pocket** as shown.

7.1 Select the pocket floors using Solid Face selections

◆ From the **Chaining** dialog box, enable the **Face** button and make sure all the other buttons are unselected as shown.

◆ Right mouse click in the graphics window and select the **Top** graphics view.

 Zoom Window

 Unzoom 80%

Dynamic Rotation

Fit

 Top (WCS)

Front (WCS)

Right (WCS)

Isometric (WCS)

♦ Select the bottom of the pockets as shown.

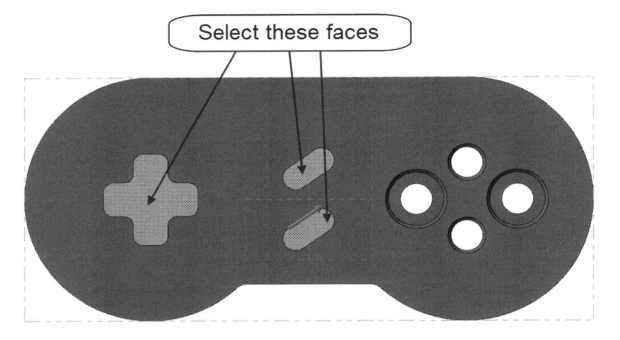

Select these faces

♦ Select the **OK** button to exit the **Chaining** dialog box.
♦ In the **Toolpath Type**, **Pocket** should already be selected as shown.

Contour   Pocket   Facing   Slot mill   Model Chamfer

7.2 Select the tool and set the Tool parameters

♦ From the **Tree View list**, select **Tool**.

♦ From the **Tool display window**, select the **5/32" Flat Endmill**. Make all the necessary changes as shown.

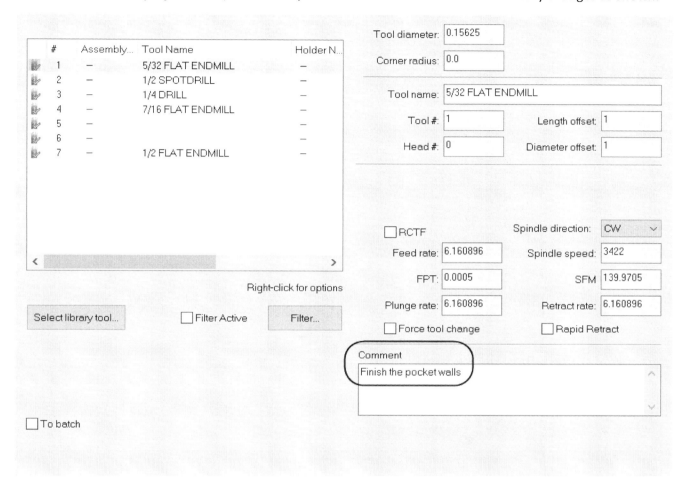

7.3 Set the Cut Parameters page

♦ From the **Tree View list**, select **Cut Parameters** and make the changes as shown.

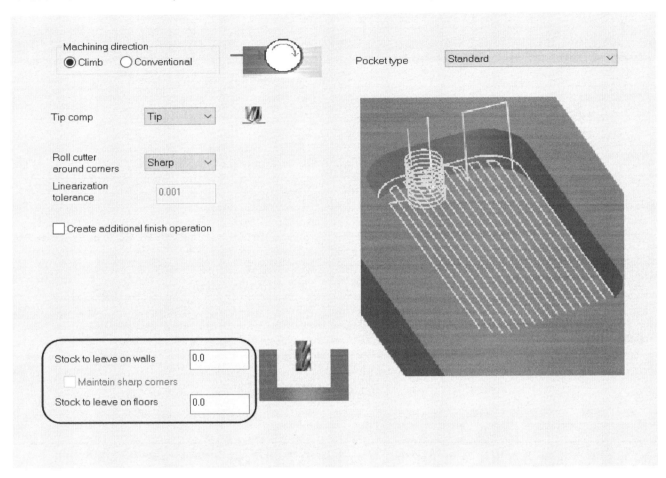

7.4 Disable Roughing page

♦ From the **Tree View list**, select **Roughing** and disable **Rough** as shown.

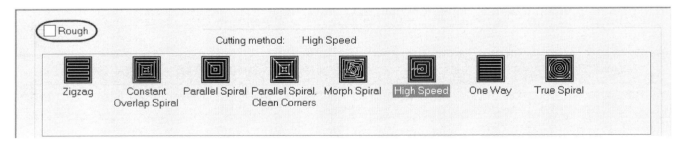

*Note: The **Roughing** option should be disabled as in this case you only want to finish the walls and not to machine the pocket floors again. For the same reason, you will turn the **Entry Motion** off.*

7.5 Set the Finishing page

♦ From the **Tree View list**, select **Finishing** and set the parameters as shown.

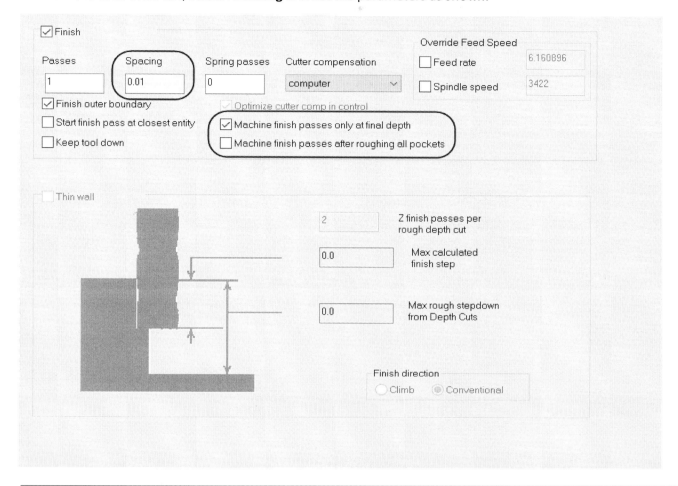

Passes sets the number of finish passes for the toolpath.

Spacing sets the amount of material to be removed with each cut.

7.6 Set the Lead In/Out page

♦ From the **Tree View list**, select **Lead In/Out** and make the changes to ensure smooth entry and exit moves to and from the part as shown.

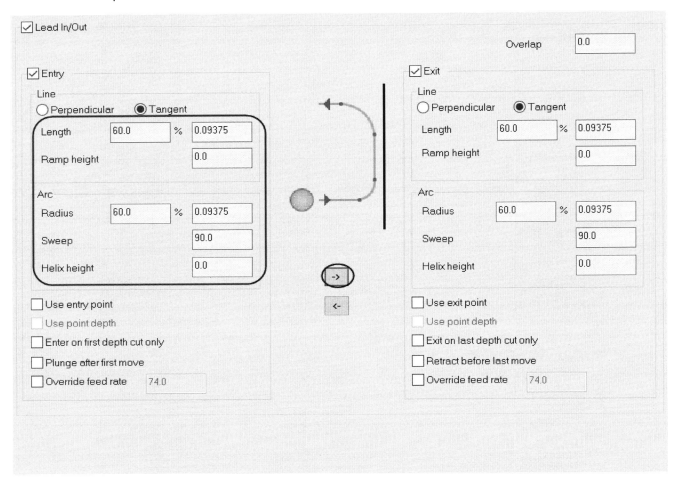

7.7 Set the Depth Cuts Parameters

♦ From the **Tree View list**, select **Depth Cuts** and ensure **Depth cuts** are disabled as shown.

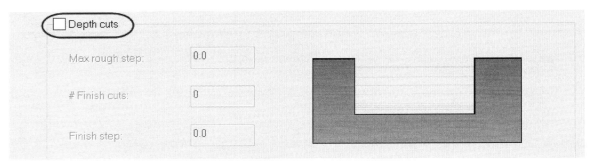

7.8 Set the Linking Parameters page

♦ From the **Tree View list**, select **Linking Parameters** and make sure the parameters are set as shown.

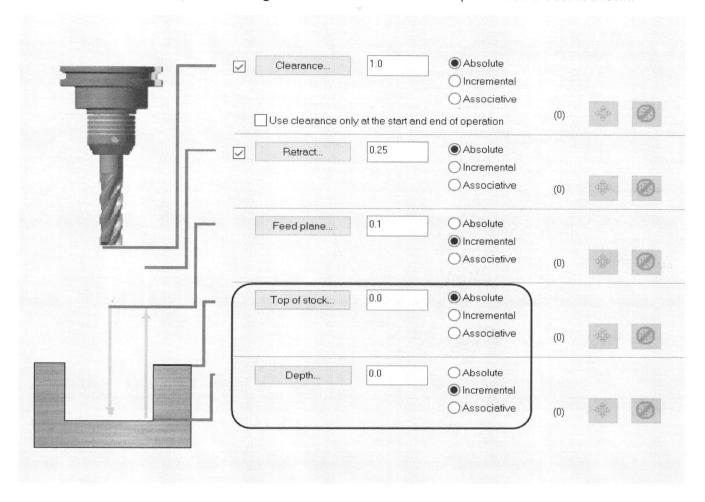

7.9 Preview the Toolpath

♦ To quickly check how the toolpath will be generated, select the **Preview toolpath** icon as shown.

♦ See **"Preview the Toolpath" on page 824** to review the procedure.
♦ The toolpath should look as shown.

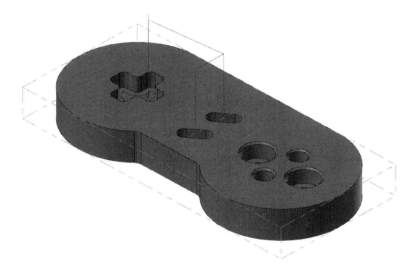

♦ Press **Esc** key to exit the preview.

Note: If the toolpath does not look as shown in the preview, check your parameters again.

♦ Select the **OK** button to exit the **2D Toolpaths - Pocket** parameters.
♦ Right mouse click in the graphics window and change the graphics view back to **Isometric**.

7.10 Verify the toolpath using both Backplot and Verify

♦ Select the last toolpath only and run **Backplot**.
♦ The toolpath should look as shown.

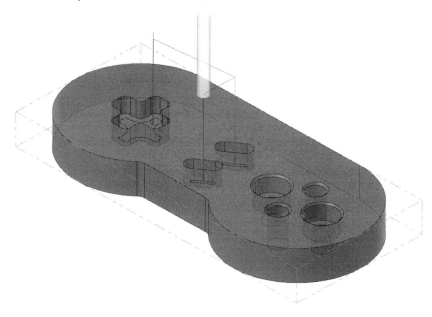

♦ Select the **OK** button to exit **Backplot**.
♦ Select all toolpaths to **Verify** them as shown on **"Backplot The Toolpaths" on page 825**.

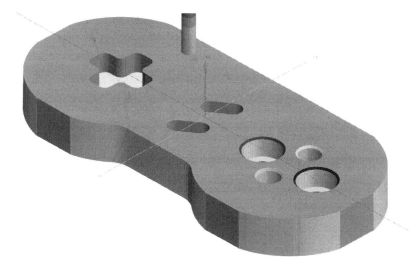

♦ To go back to the Mastercam window, minimize the **Mastercam Simulator** window as shown.

STEP 8: CONTOUR TOOLPATH

A **Contour** toolpath removes material along a path defined by a chain of curves. A **Contour** toolpath only follows a chain; it does not clean out an enclosed area. You will use this toolpath to finish the outside profile.

Toolpath Preview:

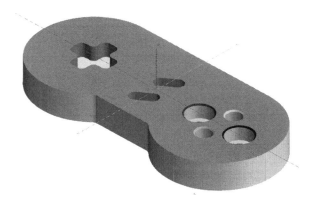

♦ Hover the cursor in the **Toolpaths Manager** and press **T** or press **Alt + T** to remove the toolpath display if needed.

Toolpaths

♦ From the **2D** group, select the **Expand gallery** arrow and from the **Toolpath Gallery** select **Contour** as shown.

♦ First enable **Solids** selection. Then check only the **Loop** button in the **Chaining** dialog box as shown.

♦ Click on somewhere along the edge of the lower outside profile and the entire profile will be highlighted as shown.

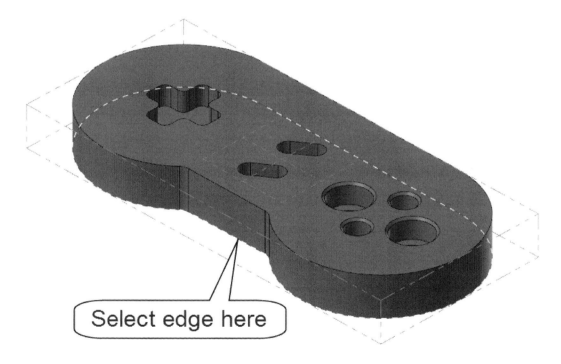

Select edge here

♦ In the **Pick Reference Face** dialog box, select the **OK** button to accept this face.

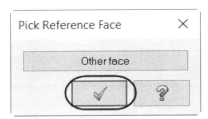

♦ Make sure the chaining direction is **Clockwise** as shown. Otherwise, from the **Chaining** dialog box, select the **Reverse** button.

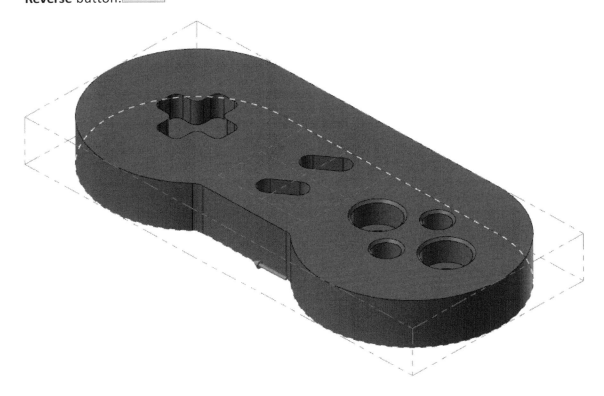

♦ Select the **OK** button to exit the **Chaining** dialog box.
♦ In the **Toolpath Type** page, the **Contour** toolpath will be selected.

Contour   Pocket   Facing   Slot Mill

8.1 Select the 1/4" Flat Endmill from the library and set the Tool Parameters

♦ Select Tool from Tree View list.

♦ Select a **1/4" Flat Endmill**. You will need to use the tool library to select this tool.

♦ Make all the necessary changes as shown.

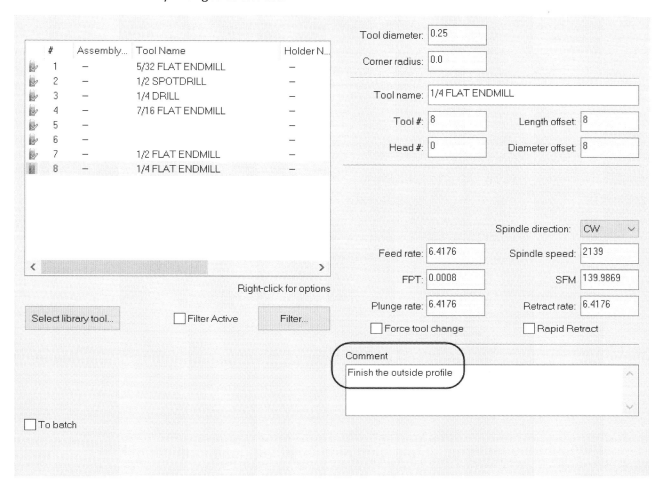

8.2 Cut Parameters

♦ Select the **Cut Parameters** and make the necessary changes as shown.

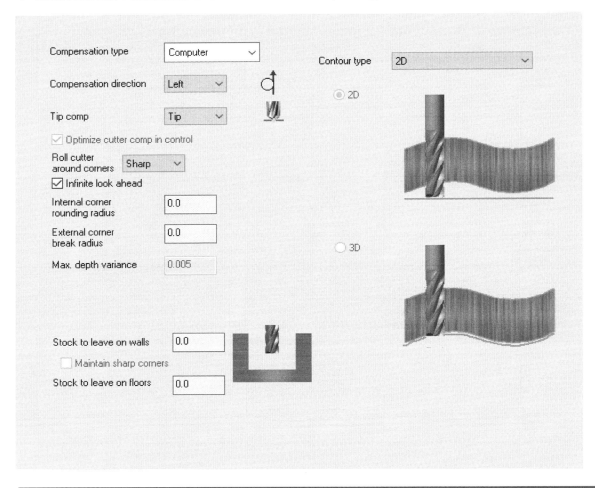

Roll cutter around corners inserts arc moves around corners in the toolpath.

None guarantees all sharp corners.

Sharp rolls the tool around sharp corners (135 degrees or less).

All rolls the tool around all corners and creates smooth tool movement.

8.3 Depth Cuts

♦ Select **Depth Cuts** and make sure it is disabled as shown.

8.4 Lead In/Out

◆ Navigate to the **Lead In/Out** page and input an **Overlap** value of **0.0**2. Make any other necessary changes as shown.

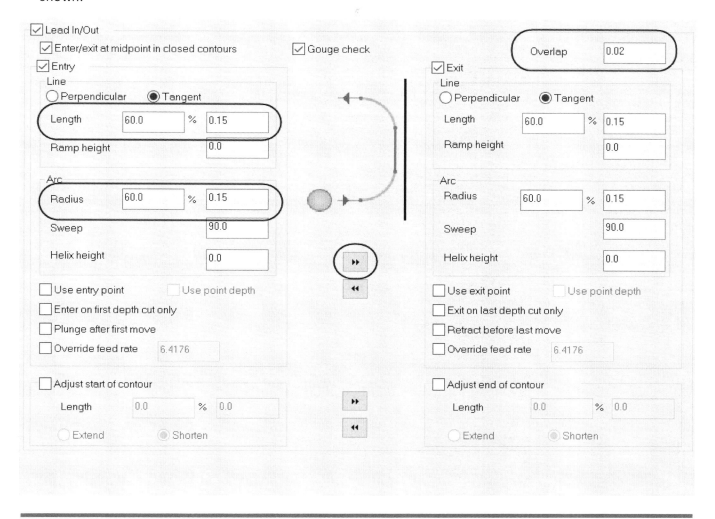

Lead In/Out allows you to select a combination of a Line and an Arc at the beginning and/or end of the contour toolpath for a smooth entry/exit while cutting the part.

Length set to 60% of the tool diameter ensures that the linear movement is bigger than the tool radius in case **Cutter Compensation** in **Control** was used.

Radius set to 60% of the tool diameter ensures that the arc movement is bigger than the tool radius to generate an arc output.

Overlap sets how far the tool goes past the end of the toolpath before exiting for a cleaner finish.

8.5 Linking Parameters

♦ Select **Linking Parameters** from the **Tree View list**. Set the **Top of stock** to **0.0** and the **Depth** to **Incremental** and **0.0** as shown.

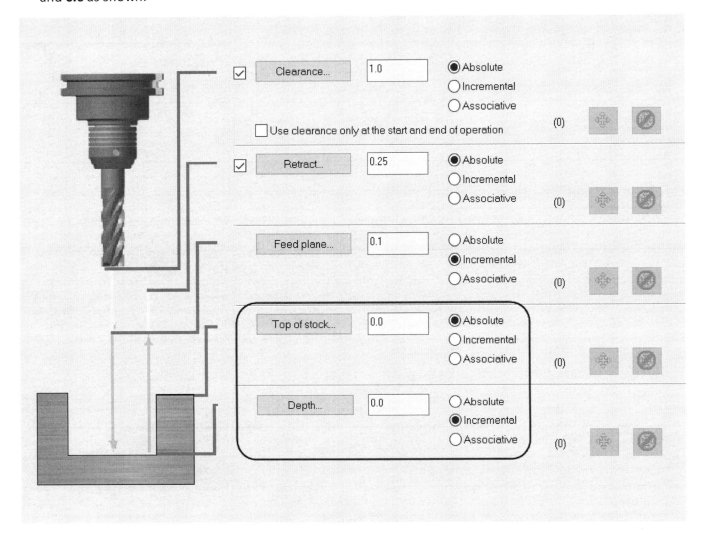

8.6 Preview the Toolpath

◆ To quickly check how the toolpath will be generated, select the **Preview toolpath** icon as shown.

◆ See **"Preview the Toolpath" on page 824** to review the procedure.
◆ The toolpath should look as shown.

◆ Press **Esc** key to exit the preview.

Note: If the toolpath does not look as shown in the preview, check your parameters again.

◆ Select the **OK** button to exit the **2D Toolpaths - Contour** parameters.

8.7 Verify the toolpaths

◆ **Select all operations.**

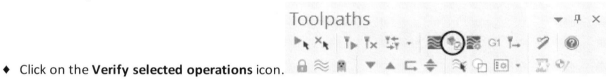

◆ Click on the **Verify selected operations** icon.
◆ For information on how to set the verify parameters and to simulate the toolpath, check **"Simulate the toolpath in Verify" on page 826**.
◆ The finished part will appear as shown.

◆ To go back to the Mastercam window, close **Mastercam Simulator** window as shown.

STEP 9: POST THE FILE

♦ Ensure all operations are selected. If they are not, use the button **Select all operations** in the **Toolpaths Manager**.

♦ Select the **Post selected operations** icon from the **Toolpaths Manager** as shown. G1

♦ In the **Post processing** window, make necessary changes as shown.

NC file enabled allows you to keep the NC file and to assign the same name as the MCAM file.

Edit enabled allows you to automatically launch the default.

♦ Select the **OK** button to continue.

♦ Save "Your Name_7.NC" file.

♦ A window with **Mastercam Code Expert** will be launched and the **NC** program will appear as shown.

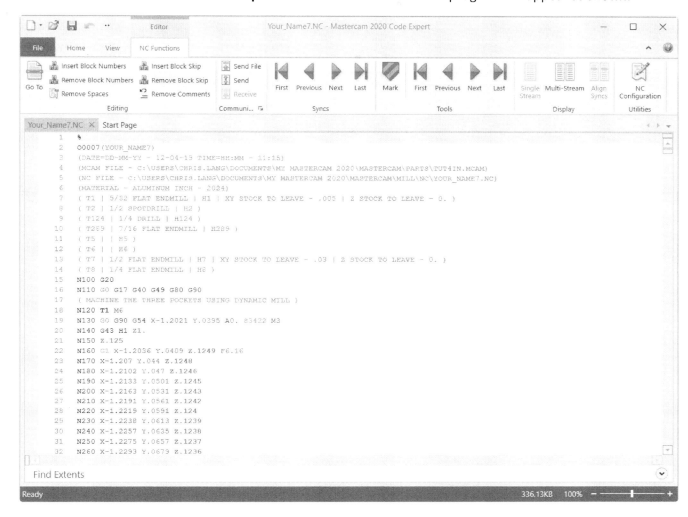

♦ Select the "**X**" box at the upper right corner to exit the editor.

STEP 10: SAVE THE UPDATED MCAM FILE

CREATE THE TOOLPATHS FOR TUTORIAL #7 EXERCISE

Create the Toolpaths for Tutorial #7 Exercise as per the instructions below.

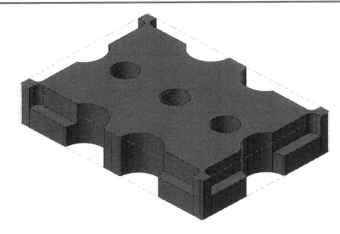

Set the machine properties including the stock.

FBM Drill.

- ◆ Enable **Automatic initial hole detection**.
- ◆ **Grouping** set to **Plane**.
- ◆ Under **Hole Detection** enable **Include blind holes**.
- ◆ Enable **Include chamfers**.
- ◆ **Maximum diameter** set to **1.625**.
- ◆ **Spot drilling** and **Combine Spot Drill operations** that share the same depth and retract values enabled.
- ◆ **Max percentage of finished hole** set to **100%** and **Max depth** set to **0.375**.
- ◆ **Pre-drilling** and **Pre-drill pilot holes only** enabled.
- ◆ In **Tool selection**, have **Use tools in part file**, **Use tool library** and **Create as needed** enabled.
- ◆ In **Tool creation**, disable **Create only standard sizes**, enable **Consider flute length** and **Create one tool for all depths**.
- ◆ In the **Linking Parameters**, have **Clearance** set to **Solid height** plus **1.0** and **Retract** set to **Solid height** plus **0.5**.
- ◆ Enable **Through holes**.
- ◆ Click on **Detect the features**.

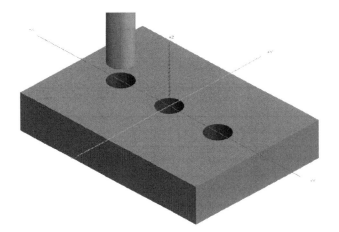

Machine the outside profile using 2D HS Dynamic Mill.

♦ In the **Chain Options**, enable **From outside**, **Shortest distance** for **open chain extension to stock**.

♦ Click on the **Select avoidance chains** button in the **Avoidance regions**. In the **Chaining** dialog box, enable **Solids** mode and select **Loop**. Then select the bottom edge of the solid.

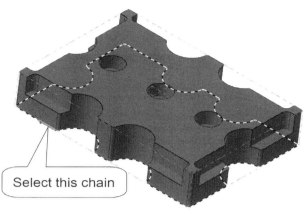

Select this chain

♦ Select the **1/2" Flat Endmill**.
♦ **First pass offset** = **0.1**.
♦ **Stepover** = **25%**.
♦ **Min toolpath radius** = **10%**.
♦ **Micro lift distance** = **0.01**.
♦ **Stock to leave on walls** = **0.03**.
♦ **Stock to leave on floors** = **0.0**.
♦ **Entry motion Helix only**; **Radius** = **0.25**.
♦ **Clearance** = **1.0** (Absolute).
♦ **Retract** = **0.25** (Absolute).
♦ **Feed plane** = **0.1** (Incremental).
♦ **Depth** = **-2.0** (Absolute).

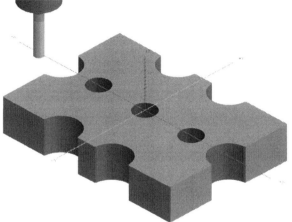

*Note: Change the **Cutting length** and **Overall length** as needed. To change the default tool properties, in the tool list, right mouse click on the tool and select **Edit tool** to set tool parameters.*

Machine the steps using 2D HS Dynamic Mill.

♦ In the **Chain Options**, enable **From outside**, **None** for **Open chain extension to stock**.

♦ Click on the **Select machining chains** button in the **Machining regions**. In the **Chaining** dialog box, enable **Solids** mode and select only **Loop**. Select the bottom edges as a contour.

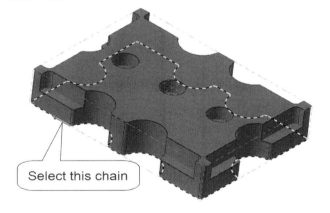

Select this chain

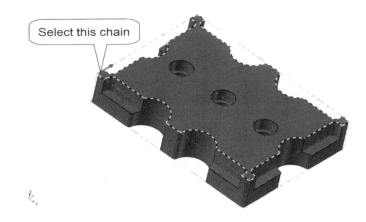

Select this chain

- Click on the **Select avoidance chains** button in the **Avoidance regions** and stay in the **Solids** mode. Enable **Loop** and select the top edges as a contour.

- Select the same **1/2" Flat Endmill**.
- **First pass offset** = **0.1**.
- **Stepover** = **25%**.
- **Min toolpath radius** = **10%**.
- **Micro lift distance** = **0.01**.
- **Stock to leave on walls** = **0.03**.
- **Stock to leave on floors** = **0.0**.
- **Entry motion Helix only**; **Radius** = **0.25**.
- **Clearance** = **1.0** (Absolute).
- **Retract** = **0.25** (Absolute).
- **Feed plane** = **0.1** (Incremental).
- **Top of stock** = **0.0** (Absolute).
- **Depth** = **-1.0** (Absolute).

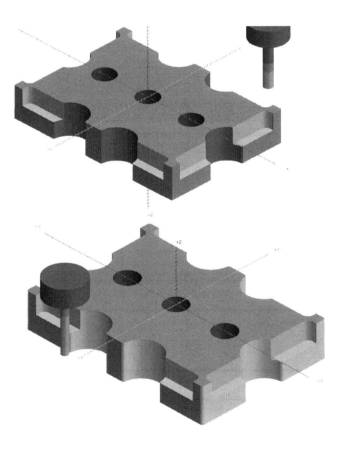

Finish the bottom profile using Contour toolpath.

- Enable **Solids** selection, then check **Loop** button and select the bottom profile as shown before in the **Clockwise** direction.
- Select a **3/8" Flat Endmill**.
- **Contour type 2D**.
- **Compensation type** as **Computer**.
- **Compensation direction** set to **Left**.
- **Stock to leave on walls** and **floors** = **0.0**.
- **Lead In/Out** set to defaults.
- **Clearance** = **1.0** (Absolute).
- **Retract** = **0.25** (Absolute).
- **Feed plane** = **0.1** (Incremental).
- **Top of stock** = **0.0** (Absolute).
- **Depth** = **0.0** (Incremental).

*Note: Change the **Cutting length** and **Overall length** as needed. To change the default tool properties, in the tool list, right mouse click on the tool and select **Edit tool** to set tool parameters.*

Finish the step profile using Contour toolpath.

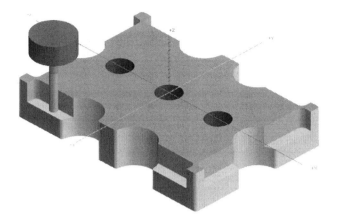

- ◆ Enable **Solids** selection, then check **Partial loop** button and select the bottom profiles of the 8 steps in the **Counter-clockwise** direction.
- ◆ Use the same **3/8" Flat Endmill**.
- ◆ **Contour type 2D**.
- ◆ **Compensation type** in **Computer**.
- ◆ **Compensation direction** set to **Left**.
- ◆ **Stock to leave on walls** and **floors** = **0.0**.
- ◆ **Lead In/Out** set to defaults.
- ◆ **Clearance** = **1.0** (Absolute).
- ◆ **Retract** = **0.25** (Absolute).
- ◆ **Feed plane** = **0.1** (Incremental).
- ◆ **Top of stock** = **0.0** (Absolute).
- ◆ **Depth** = **-1.0** (Absolute).

TUTORIAL #7 TOOLPATH CREATION QUIZ

◆ What does FBM Drill allow you to do?

◆ What does Open chain extension to stock set to Shortest distance do?

◆ What does Avoidance regions selection do?

Creating/Editing A Mill Tool Library

CREATE AND EDITING A MILL TOOL LIBRARY

Objectives: The Student Will Learn How To Create And Modify Tools.

> *Note: The purpose of tool libraries is to hold the tool data. The libraries can be edited or added to by following the directions below. Each time the **Tool Type** or **Cutter diameter** is changed in the Toolpath parameters, the tool library recalculates the feed rate and spindle speed. The following menu selections will allow you to create a new tool.*

CREATE A NEW TOOL

Machine

> *Note: Once you select the **Mill Default**, the **Ribbon bar** changes to reflect the toolpaths that could be used with **Mill Default**.*

Option 1: Create A New Tool Using Mill Tool Manager

Toolpaths

♦ From the **Utilities** group, select **Tool Manager** as shown.

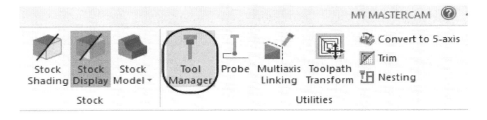

◆ Right click in the tool display area.
◆ Select **Create tool** as shown.

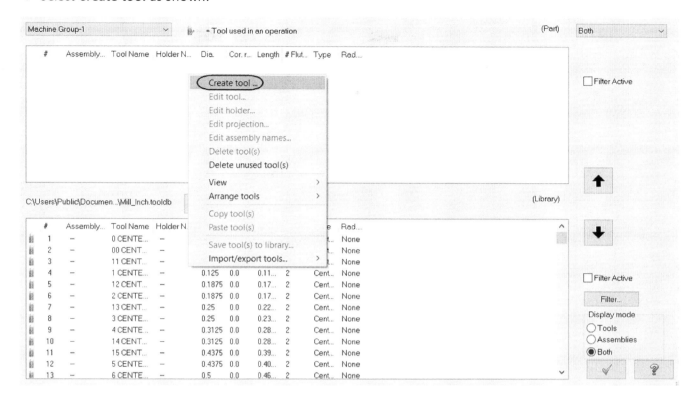

Option 2: Create A New Tool Inside Of The Toolpath Parameters

Close the Tool Manager.
Create a rectangle.

Toolpaths

- From the **2D** area, select **Contour**.
- Chain the rectangle.
- From the **Tree View list**, select **Tool**.
- Right click in the tool display area.
- Select **Create tool** as shown.

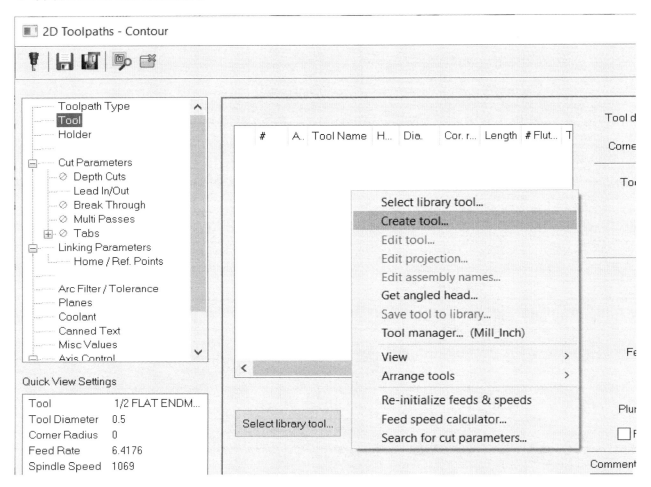

1. What Type Of Tool Would You Like To Create?

The **Create New Tool** dialog box displays all the default tool type options in Mastercam.

♦ The **Define Tool** screen will appear as shown.

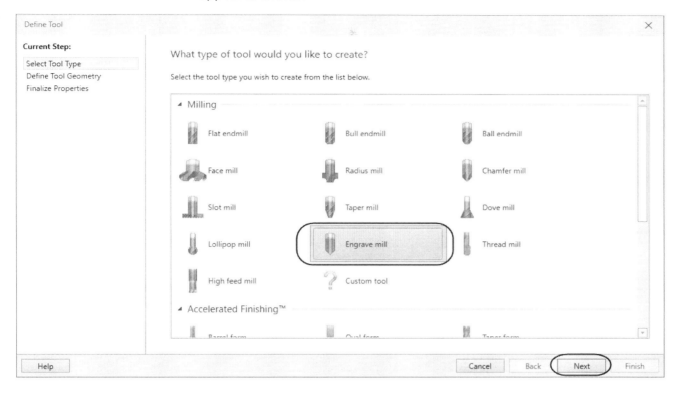

♦ Choose the tool type you wish to modify and then select the **Next** button.

2. Define Geometric Tool Parameters.

Define geometric tool parameters lets you enter new parameters or edit current parameters of Mill tools. A description of each parameter in the **Define geometric tool parameters** is listed below.

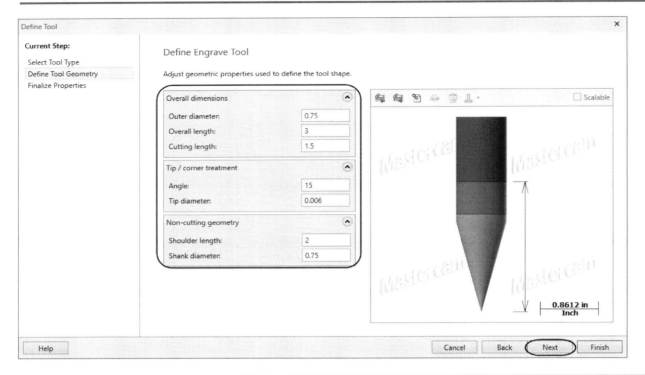

Note: The fields on the tabs change depending on the type of tool you are creating.

Overall Dimensions

Outer Diameter - sets the diameter of the tool.

Overall Length - sets the length of the tool.

Cutting Length - sets the length from the top of the flutes to the tip of the tool.

Tip/Corner Treatment

Corner Type - allows you to choose between None, Chamfer, Corner radius and Full radius.

Angle - measures the angle from the center line of the tool to the outer angle of the tool.

Tip Diameter - sets the tool tip diameter.

Non-Cutting Geometry

Shoulder Length - sets the distance from the top of the shoulder to the tip of the tool.

Shank Diameter - sets the diameter of the tool shank.

◆ Set the dimension values and then select the **Next** button.

3. Finalize Miscellaneous Properties.

This area allows you to type information such as Name, Manufacturer Name and Manufacturer's tool code. It also allows you to enter the tool offset numbers, the feeds and speeds, the material, coolant settings and other settings.

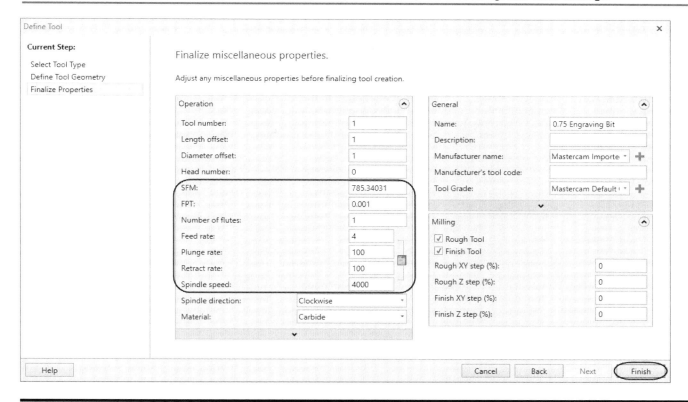

Note: To set up the coolant, click on the drop down arrow.

♦ Make any necessary changes as shown and select the **Finish** button to complete the tool creation.

Operation

Tool Number - sets the default tool assembly number.

Length Offset - sets the number that corresponds to a register in the machine that compensates for the tool length.

Diameter Offset - sets the number that corresponds to a register in the machine that offsets the diameter.

Number of Flutes - specifies the number of flutes on the tool which is used to calculate the feed rate.

Feed Rate - sets the default feed rate.

Plunge Rate - sets the default plunge rate.

Retract Rate - sets the default retract rate.

Spindle Speed - sets the spindle speed in RPM.

Spindle Direction - allows you to choose the spindle direction between Clockwise, Counterclockwise and Static.

Material - displays the tool material.

Coolant - allows you to set the canned text coolant options.

Metric - allows you to enable metric tools.

General

Name - allows you to type the name of the tool.

Description - displays additional info.

Manufacturer Name - allows you to type the name of the Manufacturer.

Manufacturer's Tool Code - allows you to type the tool code.

Milling

Rough XY step (%) - allows you to set the size of a roughing step in the X and Y axes for the tool. The system measures this distance as a percentage of the tool diameter.

Rough Z step (%) - allows you to set the size of a roughing step in the Z axis for the tool. The system measures this distance as a percentage of the tool diameter.

Finish XY step (%) - allows you to set the size of a finish step in the X and Y axes for the tool. The system measures this distance as a percentage of the tool diameter.

Finish Z step (%) - allows you to set the size of a finish step in the Z axis for the tool. The system measures this distance as a percentage of the tool diameter.

EDITING AN EXISTING TOOL

Option 1: Edit An Existing Tool Using The Tool Manager

Machine

Option 1: Create A New Tool Using Mill Tool Manager

Toolpaths

♦ From the **Utilities** group, select **Tool Manager** as shown.

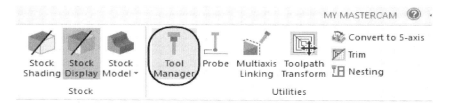

♦ Find the **3/8" Ball Endmill (#309)** from the library list and click on the upward arrow to move it in the current tool list as shown.

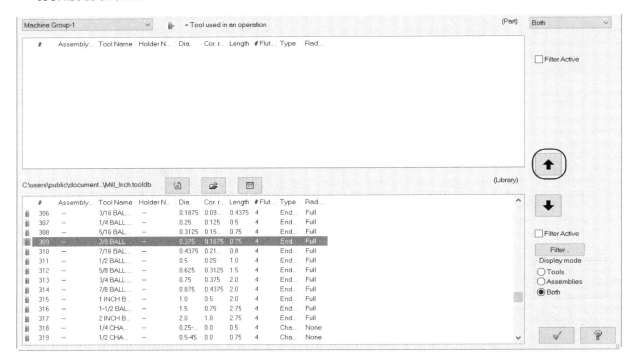

♦ Right click on the existing tool.
♦ Select **Edit tool** as shown.

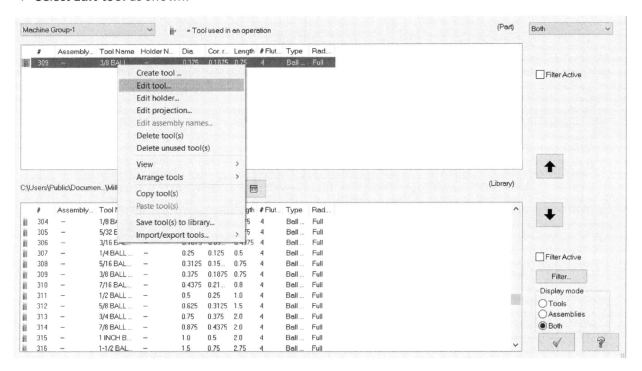

♦ Once the **Tool Wizard** opens, you can change any of the dimensions or properties of the tool that you want.

Option 2: Editing An Existing Tool Inside Of The Toolpath Parameters

♦ In the **Tool** dialog box, right click on the existing tool and then select **Edit tool** as shown.

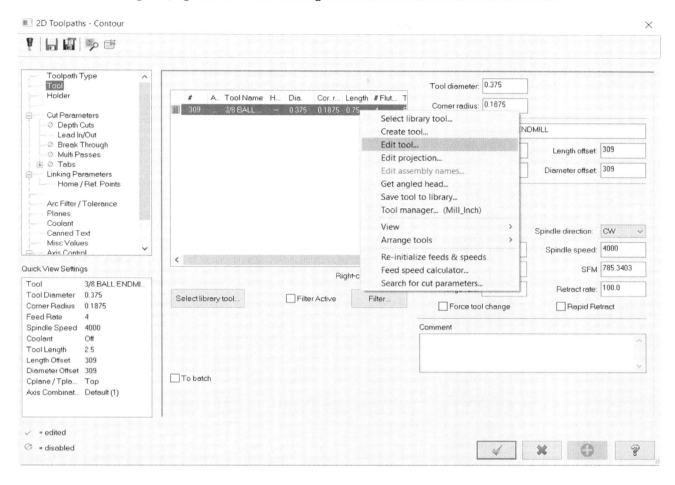

♦ Make the changes to the tool.
♦ Once you select the **OK** button, the tool will be automatically saved with the new changes.

EXERCISES:

◆ Create a finish turn tool with a 35 Deg. Insert.

◆ Create a boring bar with a 55 Deg. Insert.

Quiz Answers

MILL ESSENTIALS TUTORIAL QUIZ ANSWERS

Tutorial #1 Answers

♦ **When creating wireframe geometry, what does the cyan color mean?**

♦ The color of the geometry is cyan which means that the entity is "live" and you can still change the dimension or postion if needed.

♦ **If you make a mistake while creating geometry or delete some geometry by accident, what can you do?**

♦ While creating geometry for this tutorial, if you make a mistake, you can undo the last step using the Undo icon ↺ or by pressing Ctrl + Z.

♦ **What is the Cartesian Coordinate System?**

♦ The Cartesian Coordinate System is a coordinate system that specifies each point uniquely in a plane using a pair of numerical coordinates.

♦ **What is a Contour Toolpath used for?**

♦ **Contour toolpath** removes the material along a path defined by a chain of curves. Contour toolpaths only follow a chain; they do not clean out an enclosed area.

♦ **What is a Facing Toolpath used for?**

♦ **Facing toolpath** quickly removes material from the top of the part to create an even surface for future operations.

♦ **What does a Circle Mill toolpath allow you to do?**

♦ **Circle Mill toolpath** is used to mill circular pockets based on a single point. Mastercam will pocket out a circular area of the diameter and to the depth that you specify.

♦ **What does Backplot do?**

♦ **Backplotting** shows the path the tools take to cut the part. This display lets you spot errors in the program before you machine the part. As you backplot toolpaths, Mastercam displays the current X, Y, and Z coordinates in the lower left corner of the screen.

♦ **What does Verify allow you to do?**

♦ **Verify** allows you to use a solid model to simulate the machining of a part. The model created by verification represents the surface finish, and shows collisions, if any exist.

Tutorial #2 Answers

♦ **What do you need to know to create a rectangle?**

♦ The width, the height, and the anchor position of the rectangle are required to create a rectangle.

♦ **What command do you need to use to create an obround shape?**

♦ Using the **Rectangular shapes** command under **Rectangular** drop down to create an obround shape.

♦ **What does Divide command allow you to do?**

♦ When you choose the **Divide** command and select an entity in the graphics window, Mastercam uses the nearest two intersections on each end to divide the entity. Trimming mode will remove the segment that lies between two dividing intersections.

♦ **What does Slot Mill toolpath do?**

♦ **Slot Mill** toolpath allows Mastercam to efficiently machine oblong slots. These are slots that consist of 2 straight lines and two 180-degree arcs at the ends.

♦ **What does 2D HS Dynamic Mill do?**

♦ **2D HS Dynamic** machines, utilizing the entire flute length of their cutting tools, open pocket shapes, standing core shapes or pockets. To machine standing cores the toolpath uses the outmost chain as the stock boundary. The tool moves freely outside of this area; the inner chain defines the limit of the toolpath.

♦ **What does 2D HS Dynamic Contour Mill do?**

♦ **2D HS Dynamic Contour** toolpath utilizes the entire flute length of the cutting tools and is used to mill material off walls. It does support both closed or open chains.

♦ **What is the process used to be able to post different operations as different programs?**

♦ Create a new toolpath group and then rename it.

Tutorial #3 Answers

- **What does Break at intersection command do?**
- **Break at Intersection** allows you to select entities and automatically break them at each intersection.

- **What does Mirror command do?**
- **Mirror** command can move, copy, or join selected entities by reflecting them symmetrically with respect to a defined axis or point.

- **What does Area Mill do?**
- **Area Mill** takes small cuts to machine open pocket shapes, standing core shapes or pockets based on the machining region strategies.

- **What does smoothing do?**
- **Smoothing** replaces sharp corners with arcs for faster and smoother transitions in tool direction.

- **What does Pocket Remachining do?**
- **Pocket Remachining** calculates areas where the pocket roughing tool could not machine the stock and creates a remachining pocket toolpath to clear the remaining material.

Tutorial #4 Answers

- **What are levels and why do we need to change the main level to 2?**
- **Levels** are a primary organizational tool in Mastercam. A Mastercam file can contain separate levels for wireframe, surfaces, drafting entities, solids, and toolpaths. By organizing your files into levels, you can easily control which areas of the drawing are visible at any time and which parts are selectable. By doing so, you will not inadvertently make changes to areas of the drawing you do not want to change.

- **What does translate do?**
- **Translate** command can move, copy, or join entities winthin the same plane, without altering their orientation or shape.

- **What does the Solid Extrude command do?**
- translate entities to a different Z depth.

♦ **What does a Dwell before cut spindle speed do?**
♦ It adds a dwell after the entry ramp into the cut. This pause allows the spindle to ramp up to the desired spindle speed before starting the cutting passes.

♦ **What does a Transform toolpath operation do?**
♦ It allows you to run the same toolpath in different locations. You can transform a single toolpath or several at a time.

Tutorial #5 Answers

♦ **What function does Alt+F1 short cut perform?**
♦ To fit the geometry to the screen you can also press **Alt + F1**.

♦ **What function does Alt+S short cut perform?**
♦ To see the solid in a shaded or unshaded mode press **Alt + S**.

♦ **What does Translate To Plane command do?**
♦ Allows you to rotate the part and posion it for machining.

♦ **What settings do you need to use to remachine a pocket using High Speed Area Mill Toolpath?**
♦ **2D High Speed Area Mill** toolpath with the Rest Material enabled targets material left behind by previous toolpaths.

♦ **What is the use of WCS in Mastercam?**
♦ This tells Mastercam how your part is positioned or orientated in the machine.

♦ **After creating a new toolpath group, why do you rename the NC file?**
♦ You rename the NC file to create two separate programs.

Tutorial #6 Answers

♦ **What do you need to know to create an arc by using Arc Tangent One Entity?**
♦ **Arc Tangent One Entity** lets you create an arc given the radius, the entity to which it is tangent and the tangency point.

♦ **What do you need to know to create chamfers and what is 1 Distance chamfer method?**

♦ The width and angle of a chamfer are needed to create a chamfer. **1 Distance** method creates a chamfer where the endpoints are positioned an equal distance from the intersections.

♦ **What does the Translate 3D do?**

♦ **Translate 3D** allows you to move the geometry between views (from one plane to another).

♦ **How does a Blend Mill toolpath work?**

♦ 2D High Speed Blend Mill toolpath morphs smoothly between two open chains.

♦ **What does Peel Mill toolpath do?**

♦ **2D High Speed Peel Mill** toolpath allows for efficient constant climb milling between two selected contours or along a single contour. It uses a trochodial style of motion to cut the slot.

Tutorial #7 Answers

♦ **How do you modify a solid that you previously extruded?**

♦ To modify the solid, you can double click on the operation and the respective **Solid Extrude** panel will appear and you can change the parameters as needed. Once you select the OK button to exit the **Solid Extrude** panel, click on the **Regen all** button to regenerate the solid.

♦ **What does the Constant Radius Fillet command do?**

♦ **Constant Radius Fillet** uses edge blending to produce a rounded edge.

♦ **What does FBM Drill allow you to do?**

♦ **FBM Drill** automatically detects holes in a solid based on your specific criteria and to generate a complete series of drilling and chamfering. FBM drill also generates circle mill or helix bore operations for large-hole features when you activate these settings.

♦ **What does Open chain extension to stock set to Shortest distance do?**

♦ **Open chain extension to stock** set to **Shortest distance** sets how the system calculates the amount of the material that has to be removed based on the defined stock.

- **What does Avoidance regions selection do?**
- **Avoidance regions** selection allows you to select the profile that describes the shape up to where the material will be removed.